# AS / Year 1
# Chemistry

## Exam Board: Edexcel

Revising for Chemistry exams is stressful, that's for sure — even just getting your notes sorted out can leave you needing a lie down.  But help is at hand...

This brilliant CGP book explains **everything you'll need to learn** (and nothing you won't), all in a straightforward style that's easy to get your head around. We've also included **exam questions** to test how ready you are for the real thing.

There's even a free Online Edition you can read on your computer or tablet!

---
### How to get your free Online Edition

Go to **cgpbooks.co.uk/extras** and enter this code...

4083 8619 2428 6873

This code only works for one person.  If somebody else has used
this book before you, they might have already claimed the Online Edition.

---

# A-Level revision?  It has to be CGP!

# Contents

## Topic 8 — Energetics I

## Topic 9 — Kinetics I

## Topic 10 — Equilibrium I

## Practical Skills

Published by CGP

Editors:
Katherine Faudemer, Emily Howe, Paul Jordin, Sophie Scott and Ben Train.

Contributors:
John Duffy, Ian Davis, Chris Workman, Lucy Muncaster, Paul Warren, Emma Grimwood and Derek Swain.

ISBN: 978 1 78294 288 7

With thanks to Katie Braid and Jamie Sinclair for the proofreading.
With thanks to Jan Greenway for the copyright research.

Cover Photo **Laguna Design**/Science Photo Library.

Clipart from Corel®
Printed by Elanders Ltd, Newcastle upon Tyne.

Based on the classic CGP style created by Richard Parsons.

# The Scientific Process

*These pages are all about the scientific process — how we develop and test scientific ideas.*
*It's what scientists do all day, every day (well except at coffee time — never come between scientists and their coffee).*

## Scientists Come Up with **Theories** — Then **Test Them**...

Science tries to explain **how** and **why** things happen. It's all about seeking and gaining
**knowledge** about the world around us. Scientists do this by **asking** questions and **suggesting**
answers and then **testing** them, to see if they're correct — this is the **scientific process**.

1) **Ask** a question — make an **observation** and ask **why or how** whatever you've observed happens.
   *E.g. Why does sodium chloride dissolve in water?*

2) **Suggest** an answer, or part of an answer, by forming a **theory** or a **model**
   (a possible **explanation** of the observations or a description of
   what you think is happening actually happening).
   *E.g. Sodium chloride is made up of charged particles*
   *which are pulled apart by the polar water molecules.*

   > A theory is only scientific if it can be tested.

3) Make a **prediction** or hypothesis — a **specific testable statement**,
   based on the theory, about what will happen in a test situation.
   *E.g. A solution of sodium chloride will conduct electricity much better than water does.*

4) Carry out **tests** — to provide **evidence** that will support the prediction or refute it.
   *E.g. Measure the conductivity of water and of sodium chloride solution.*

## ...Then They **Tell** Everyone About Their **Results**...

The results are **published** — scientists need to let others know about their work. Scientists publish their results
in **scientific journals**. These are just like normal magazines, only they contain **scientific reports** (called papers)
instead of the latest celebrity gossip.

1) Scientific reports are similar to the **lab write-ups** you do in school. And just as a lab write-up is **reviewed**
   (marked) by your teacher, reports in scientific journals undergo **peer review** before they're published.

   Scientists use standard terminology when writing their reports. This way they know that other scientists will
   understand them. For instance, there are internationally agreed rules for naming organic compounds, so that
   scientists across the world will know exactly what substance is being referred to. See page 70.

2) The report is sent out to **peers** — other scientists who are experts in the **same area**. They go through it
   bit by bit, examining the methods and data, and checking it's all clear and logical. When the report is
   approved, it's **published**. This makes sure that work published in scientific journals is of a **good standard**.

3) But peer review **can't guarantee** the science is **correct** — other scientists still need to **reproduce** it.

4) Sometimes **mistakes** are made and bad work is published. Peer review **isn't perfect** but it's
   probably the best way for scientists to self-regulate their work and to publish **quality reports**.

## ...Then **Other Scientists** Will **Test** the Theory Too

1) Other scientists read the published theories and results, and try to **test the theory** themselves. This involves:
   - Repeating the **exact same experiments**.
   - Using the theory to make **new predictions** and then testing them with **new experiments**.

2) If all the experiments in the world provide evidence to back it up, the theory is thought of as **scientific 'fact'**.

3) If **new evidence** comes to light that **conflicts** with the current evidence the theory is questioned all over again.
   More rounds of **testing** will be carried out to try to find out where the theory **falls down**.

> This is how the scientific process works — evidence supports a theory, loads of other scientists
> read it and test it for themselves, eventually all the scientists in the world agree with it and then
> bingo, you get to learn it. When looking at experiments that give conflicting results, it's important
> to look at all the evidence to work out whether a theory is supported or not — this includes
> looking at the methodology (the techniques) used in the experiments and the data collected.

This is how scientists arrived at the structure of the atom (see page 4) — and how they came to the conclusion that electrons are
arranged in shells and orbitals. As is often the case, it took years and years for these models to be developed and accepted.

# The Scientific Process

## If the **Evidence** Supports a Theory, It's **Accepted** — for Now

Our currently accepted theories have survived this '**trial by evidence**'. They've been tested **over and over again** and each time the results have backed them up. **BUT**, and this is a big but (teehee), they never become totally indisputable fact. Scientific **breakthroughs** or **advances** could provide new ways to question and test the theory, which could lead to **changes and challenges** to it. Then the testing starts all over again...

And this, my friend, is the **tentative nature of scientific knowledge** — it's always **changing** and **evolving**.

## **Evidence** Comes From **Lab Experiments**...

1) Results from **controlled experiments** in **laboratories** are **great**.
2) A lab is the easiest place to **control variables** so that they're all **kept constant** (except for the one you're investigating).
3) This means you can draw meaningful **conclusions**.

> For example, if you're investigating how temperature affects the rate of a reaction, you need to keep everything but the temperature constant, e.g. the pH of the solution, the concentration of the solution, etc.

## ...But You **Can't** Always do a Lab Experiment

There are things you **can't** study in a lab. And outside the lab, controlling the variables is tricky, if not impossible.

- *Are increasing $CO_2$ emissions causing climate change?*
  There are other variables which may have an effect, such as changes in solar activity. You can't easily rule out every possibility. Also, climate change is a very **gradual process**. Scientists won't be able to tell if their predictions are correct for donkey's years.

- *Does drinking chlorinated tap water increase the risk of developing certain cancers?*
  There are always differences between groups of people. The best you can do is to have a **well-designed study** using **matched groups** — **choose two groups** of people (those who drink tap water and those who don't) which are **as similar as possible** (same mix of ages, same mix of diets, etc). But you still can't rule out every possibility. Taking newborn identical twins and treating them identically, except for making one drink gallons of tap water and the other only pure water, might be a fairer test, but it would present huge **ethical problems**.

Samantha thought her study was very well designed — especially the fitted bookshelf.

## Science Helps to Inform **Decision-Making**

Lots of scientific work eventually leads to **important discoveries** that **could** benefit humankind — but there are often **risks** attached (and almost always **financial costs**). **Society** (that's you, me and everyone else) must weigh up the information in order to **make decisions** — about the way we live, what we eat, what we drive, and so on. Information is also used by **politicians** to devise policies and laws.

- **Chlorine** is added to water in **small quantities** to disinfect it (see page 49).
  Some studies link drinking chlorinated water with certain types of cancer.
  But the risks from drinking water contaminated by nasty bacteria are far, far greater.
  There are other ways to get rid of bacteria in water, but they're heaps **more expensive**.

- Scientific advances mean that **non-polluting hydrogen-fuelled cars** can be made. They're better for the environment, but are really expensive. And it'd cost a lot to adapt filling stations to store hydrogen.

- Pharmaceutical drugs are really expensive to develop, and drug companies want to make money. So they put most of their efforts into developing drugs that they can sell for a good price. Society has to consider the **cost** of buying new drugs — the **NHS** can't afford the most expensive drugs without **sacrificing** something else.

---

## So there you have it — how science works...

*Hopefully these pages have given you a nice intro to how science works. You need to understand it for the exam, and for life. Once you've got it sussed it's time to move on to the really good stuff — the chemistry. Bet you can't wait...*

# The Atom

*This stuff about atoms and elements should be ingrained in your brain from GCSE. You do need to know it perfectly though if you are to negotiate your way through the field of man-eating tigers and pesky atoms...*

## Atoms are made up of **Protons**, **Neutrons** and **Electrons**

**Atoms** are the stuff **all** elements and compounds are made of.
They're made up of 3 types of **subatomic** particle — **protons**, **neutrons** and **electrons**.

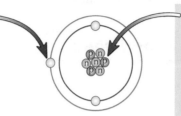

**Electrons**
1) Electrons have **–1** charge.
2) They whizz around the nucleus in **orbitals**. The orbitals take up most of the **volume** of the atom.

**Nucleus**
1) Most of the **mass** of the atom is concentrated in the nucleus.
2) The **diameter** of the nucleus is rather titchy compared to the whole atom.
3) The nucleus is where you find the **protons** and **neutrons**.

The mass and charge of these subatomic particles are **tiny**, so **relative mass** and **relative charge** are used instead.

| Subatomic particle | Relative mass | Relative charge |
|---|---|---|
| Proton | 1 | +1 |
| Neutron | 1 | 0 |
| Electron, e⁻ | 0.0005 | –1 |

*The mass of an electron is negligible compared to a proton or a neutron — this means you can usually ignore it.*

## **Nuclear Symbols** Show Numbers of **Subatomic Particles**

You can figure out the **number** of protons, neutrons and electrons from the **nuclear symbol**, which is found in the periodic table.

**Mass number**
This tells you the **total** number of **protons** and **neutrons** in the nucleus.

$$_Z^A X$$

**Element symbol**

*Sometimes the atomic number is left out of the nuclear symbol, e.g. $^7Li$. You don't really need it because the element's symbol tells you its value.*

**Atomic (proton) number**
1) This is the number of **protons** in the nucleus — it identifies the element.
2) **All** atoms of the same element have the **same** number of protons.

1) For **neutral** atoms, which have no overall charge, the number of electrons is **the same as** the number of protons.
2) The number of neutrons is just **mass number minus atomic number**, i.e. 'top minus bottom' in the nuclear symbol.

*To work out the number of each subatomic particle present in a molecule, just work out how many there are in each atom and then add them all up.*

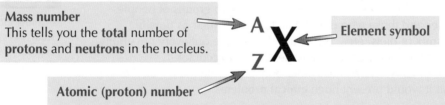

| Nuclear symbol | Atomic number, Z | Mass number, A | Protons | Electrons | Neutrons |
|---|---|---|---|---|---|
| $_3^7 Li$ | 3 | 7 | 3 | 3 | 7 – 3 = 4 |
| $_9^{19} F$ | 9 | 19 | 9 | 9 | 19 – 9 = 10 |
| $_{12}^{24} Mg$ | 12 | 24 | 12 | 12 | 24 – 12 = 12 |

"Hello, I'm Newt Ron..."

## Ions have **Different** Numbers of **Protons** and **Electrons**

**Negative** ions have **more electrons** than protons...

$F^-$
The **negative charge** means that there's **1 more electron** than there are protons. F has **9 protons** (see table above), so F⁻ must have **10 electrons**. The overall charge = +9 – 10 = –1.

...and **positive** ions have **fewer electrons** than protons.

$Mg^{2+}$
The **2+ charge** means that there are **2 fewer electrons** than there are protons. Mg has **12 protons** (see table above), so Mg²⁺ must have **10 electrons**. The overall charge = +12 – 10 = +2.

# The Atom

## Isotopes are Atoms of the Same Element with Different Numbers of Neutrons

**Isotopes** of an element are atoms with the **same number of protons** but **different numbers of neutrons**. Chlorine-35 and chlorine-37 are examples of isotopes:

35 – 17 = 18 neutrons ⟵ **Different** mass numbers mean different ⟶ 37 – 17 = 20 neutrons
masses and different numbers of neutrons.

$^{35}_{17}\text{Cl}$

The **atomic numbers** are the same.
**Both** isotopes have 17 protons and 17 electrons.

$^{37}_{17}\text{Cl}$

1) It's the **number** and **arrangement** of electrons that decides the **chemical properties** of an element. Isotopes have the **same configuration of electrons** (see pages 10-11), so they've got the **same** chemical properties.

2) Isotopes of an element do have slightly different **physical properties** though, such as different densities, rates of diffusion, etc. This is because **physical properties** tend to depend more on the **mass** of the atom.

Here's another example — naturally occurring **magnesium** consists of 3 isotopes.

| $^{24}\text{Mg}$ (79%) | $^{25}\text{Mg}$ (10%) | $^{26}\text{Mg}$ (11%) |
|---|---|---|
| 12 protons | 12 protons | 12 protons |
| **12** neutrons | **13** neutrons | **14** neutrons |
| 12 electrons | 12 electrons | 12 electrons |

*The periodic table gives the atomic number for each element. The other number isn't the mass number — it's the relative atomic mass (see page 6). They're a bit different, but you can often assume they're equal — it doesn't matter unless you're doing really accurate work.*

## Practice Questions

Q1 Draw a diagram showing the structure of an atom, labelling each part.

Q2 Where is the mass concentrated in an atom, and what makes up most of the volume of an atom?

Q3 Draw a table showing the relative charge and relative mass of the three subatomic particles found in atoms.

Q4 Using an example, explain the terms 'atomic number' and 'mass number'.

### Exam Questions

Q1 Hydrogen, deuterium and tritium are all isotopes of each other.

   a) Identify one similarity and one difference between these isotopes. [2 marks]

   b) Deuterium can be written as $^2_1\text{H}$. Determine the number of protons, neutrons and electrons in a deuterium atom. [1 mark]

   c) Write the nuclear symbol for tritium, given that it has 2 neutrons. [1 mark]

Q2 This question relates to the atoms or ions A to D:   **A** $^{32}_{16}\text{S}^{2-}$    **B** $^{40}_{18}\text{Ar}$    **C** $^{30}_{16}\text{S}$    **D** $^{42}_{20}\text{Ca}$

   a) Identify the similarity for each of the following pairs, justifying your answer in each case.

      i)   A and B. [1 mark]

      ii)   A and C. [1 mark]

      iii)   B and D. [1 mark]

   b) Which two of the atoms or ions are isotopes of each other? Explain your reasoning. [2 marks]

Q3 A molecule of propanol, $C_3H_7OH$, is made up of $^1_1\text{H}$, $^{16}_8\text{O}$ and $^{12}_6\text{C}$ atoms. Calculate the number of electrons, protons and neutrons in one molecule of propanol. [2 marks]

## Got it learned yet? — Isotope so...

*This is a nice page to ease you into things. Remember that positive ions have fewer electrons than protons, and negative ions have more electrons than protons. Get that straight in your mind or you'll end up in a right mess.*

# Relative Mass

*Relative mass... What? Eh?... Read on...*

## Relative Masses are Masses of Atoms Compared to Carbon-12

The actual mass of an atom is **very**, **very tiny**. Don't worry about exactly how tiny for now, but it's far **too small** to weigh with a normal pair of scales in your classroom. So, the mass of one atom is compared to the mass of a different atom. This is its **relative mass**. Here are some **definitions** for you to learn:

The **relative atomic mass**, $A_r$, is the weighted **mean mass** of an atom of an element, compared to 1/12$^{th}$ of the mass of an atom of **carbon-12**.

Relative **isotopic mass** is the mass of an atom of an **isotope**, compared with 1/12$^{th}$ of the mass of an atom of **carbon-12**.

1)  Relative atomic mass is an **average** of all the relative isotopic masses, so it's not usually a whole number.
2)  Relative isotopic mass is usually a **whole number**.

E.g. a natural sample of chlorine contains a mixture of $^{35}Cl$ (75%) and $^{37}Cl$ (25%), so the relative isotopic masses are **35** and **37**. But its relative atomic mass is **35.5**.

*Jason's shirt was isotropical...*

## Relative Molecular Masses are Masses of Molecules

The **relative molecular mass** (or **relative formula mass**), $M_r$, is the average mass of a **molecule** or **formula unit**, compared to 1/12$^{th}$ of the mass of an atom of **carbon-12**.

Don't worry, this is one definition that you **don't** need to know for the exam.
But... you **do** need to know how to **work out** the relative molecular mass, and the **relative formula mass**, so it's probably best if you **learn** what they mean anyway.

1)  **Relative molecular mass** is used when referring to **simple molecules**.
2)  To find the relative molecular mass, just **add up** the **relative atomic mass values** of all the atoms in the molecule.

E.g. $M_r(C_2H_6O) = (2 \times 12.0) + (6 \times 1.0) + 16.0 = \textbf{46.0}$

See page 22 for more on simple molecules, and pages 20 and 26-27 for more on giant structures.

1)  **Relative formula mass** is used for compounds that are **ionic** (or **giant covalent**, such as $SiO_2$).
2)  To find the relative formula mass, **add up** the **relative atomic masses** ($A_r$) of all the ions or atoms in the formula unit. ($A_r$ of ion = $A_r$ of atom. The electrons make no difference to the mass.)

E.g. $M_r(CaF_2) = 40.1 + (2 \times 19.0) = \textbf{78.1}$

## $A_r$ Can Be Worked Out from Isotopic Abundances

You need to know how to calculate the **relative atomic mass** ($A_r$) of an element from its **isotopic abundances**.

1)  Different isotopes of an element occur in different quantities, or isotopic abundances.
2)  To work out the relative atomic mass of an element, you need to work out the **average** mass of all its atoms.
3)  If you're given the isotopic abundances in **percentages**, all you need to do is follow these two easy steps:

**Step 1: Multiply** each **relative isotopic mass** by its % **relative isotopic abundance**, and **add up** the results.
**Step 2: Divide** by **100**.

**Example:** Find the relative atomic mass of boron, given that 20.0% of the boron atoms found on Earth have a relative isotopic mass of 10.0, while 80.0% have a relative isotopic mass of 11.0.

Step 1: $(20.0 \times 10) + (80.0 \times 11) = 1080$
Step 2: $1080 \div 100 = \textbf{10.8}$

*TOPIC 1 — ATOMIC STRUCTURE AND THE PERIODIC TABLE*

# Relative Mass

## Mass Spectrometry Can Tell Us About Isotopes

**Mass spectra** are produced by mass spectrometers — devices which are used to find out what samples are made up of by measuring the masses of their components. Mass spectra can tell us dead useful things, e.g. the **relative isotopic masses** and **abundances** of different elements.

**Mass spectra** can be used to work out the relative atomic masses of different elements.

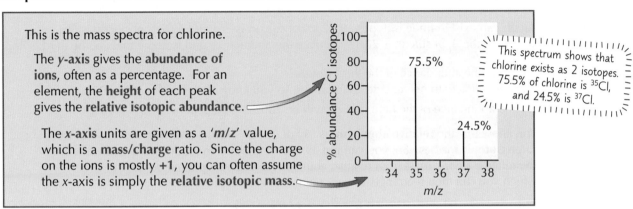

This is the mass spectra for chlorine.

The *y*-axis gives the **abundance of ions**, often as a percentage. For an element, the **height** of each peak gives the **relative isotopic abundance**.

The *x*-axis units are given as a '*m/z*' value, which is a **mass/charge** ratio. Since the charge on the ions is mostly **+1**, you can often assume the *x*-axis is simply the **relative isotopic mass**.

*This spectrum shows that chlorine exists as 2 isotopes. 75.5% of chlorine is ³⁵Cl, and 24.5% is ³⁷Cl.*

The method for working out the relative atomic mass from a graph is a bit different to working it out from percentages (see previous page), but it starts off in the same way.

**Step 1: Multiply** each **relative isotopic mass** by its **relative isotopic abundance**, and **add up** the results.

**Step 2: Divide** by the **sum** of the isotopic abundances.

**Example:** Use the data from this mass spectrum to work out the relative atomic mass of neon. Give your answer to 1 decimal place.

**Step 1:** $(20 \times 114.0) + (21 \times 0.2) + (22 \times 11.2) = 2530.6$

**Step 2:** $(114.0 + 0.2 + 11.2 = 125.4)$
$2530.6 \div 125.4 = \mathbf{20.2}$

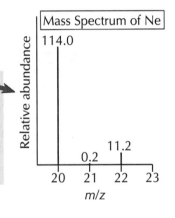

Mass Spectrum of Ne

## Practice Questions

Q1 Explain what relative atomic mass ($A_r$) and relative isotopic mass mean.

Q2 Explain the difference between relative molecular mass and relative formula mass.

Q3 Explain what relative isotopic abundance means.

**Exam Questions**

Q1 Copper exists in two main isotopic forms, ⁶³Cu and ⁶⁵Cu.

a) Calculate the relative atomic mass of copper using the information from the mass spectrum. [2 marks]

b) Explain why the relative atomic mass of copper is not a whole number. [2 marks]

Q2 The percentage make-up of naturally occurring potassium is: 93.1% ³⁹K, 0.120% ⁴⁰K and 6.77% ⁴¹K.
Use the information to determine the relative atomic mass of potassium. [2 marks]

Mass Spectrum of Cu

120.8

54.0

## *You can't pick your relatives, you just have to learn them...*

*Isotopic masses are a bit frustrating. Why can't all atoms of an element just be the same? But the fact is they're not, so you're going to have to learn how to use those spectra to work out the relative atomic masses of different elements. The actual maths is pretty simple. A pinch of multiplying, a dash of addition, some division to flavour and you're away.*

# More on Relative Mass

*"More relative mass?! How much more could there possibly be?" I hear you cry. Well, as you're about to see, there's plenty more. This is all dead useful to scientists and (more importantly) to you in your exams.*

## You Can Calculate *Isotopic Masses* from *Relative Atomic Mass*

If you know the **relative atomic mass** of an **element**, and you know all but one of the **abundances** and relative isotopic masses of its **isotopes**, you can work out the abundance and isotopic mass of the final isotope. Neat huh?

**Example:** Silicon can exist in three isotopes. 92.23% of silicon is $^{28}Si$ and 4.67% of silicon is $^{29}Si$. Given that the $A_r$ of silicon is 28.1, calculate the abundance and isotopic mass of the third isotope.

**Step 1:** First, find the **abundance** of the third isotope.
You're dealing with percentage abundances, so you know they need to total 100%.
So, the abundance of the final isotope will be 100% − 92.23% − 4.67% = **3.10%**

**Step 2:** You know that the **relative atomic mass** ($A_r$) of silicon is 28.1, and you know two of the three **isotopic masses**. So, you can put all of that into the equation you use to work out the relative atomic mass from relative abundances and isotopic masses (see page 6), which you can then rearrange to work out the **final isotopic mass**, $X$.

$$28.1 = ((28 \times 92.23) + (29 \times 4.67) + (X \times 3.10)) \div 100$$
$$28.1 = (2717.87 + (X \times 3.10)) \div 100$$
$$2810 - 2717.87 = X \times 3.10$$
$$29.719 = X \quad \text{So the isotopic mass of the third isotope is } 30 - ^{30}Si.$$

*Remember — isotopic masses are usually whole numbers, so you should round your answer to the nearest whole number.*

## You Can *Predict* the Mass Spectra for *Diatomic Molecules*

Now, this is where it gets even more mathsy and interesting (seriously — I love it). You can use your knowledge to **predict** what the **mass spectra** of diatomic molecules (i.e. molecules containing two atoms) look like.

**Example:** Chlorine has two isotopes. $^{35}Cl$ has an abundance of 75% and $^{37}Cl$ has an abundance of 25%. Predict the mass spectrum of $Cl_2$.

1) First, express each of the percentages as a decimal: 75% = 0.75 and 25% = 0.25.

*To convert a percentage to a decimal, just divide by 100.*

2) Make a **table** showing all the different $Cl_2$ molecules. For each molecule, **multiply** the abundances (as decimals) of the isotopes to get the relative abundance of each one.

|  | $^{35}Cl$ | $^{37}Cl$ |
|---|---|---|
| $^{35}Cl$ | $^{35}Cl - ^{35}Cl$: $0.75 \times 0.75$ = 0.5625 | $^{35}Cl - ^{37}Cl$: $0.25 \times 0.75$ = 0.1875 |
| $^{37}Cl$ | $^{37}Cl - ^{35}Cl$: $0.25 \times 0.75$ = 0.1875 | $^{37}Cl - ^{37}Cl$: $0.25 \times 0.25$ = 0.0625 |

3) Look for any molecules in the table that are the **same** and **add up** their abundances. In this case, $^{37}Cl-^{35}Cl$ and $^{35}Cl-^{37}Cl$ are the same, so the actual abundance for this molecule is:
0.1875 + 0.1875 = **0.375**.

4) **Divide** all the relative abundances by the smallest relative abundance to get the **smallest whole number ratio**. And by working out the relative molecular mass of each molecule, you can **predict** the mass spectrum for $Cl_2$:

| Molecule | Relative Molecular Mass | Relative abundance |
|---|---|---|
| $^{35}Cl - ^{35}Cl$ | 35 + 35 = 70 | 0.5625 ÷ 0.0625 = 9 |
| $^{35}Cl - ^{37}Cl$ | 35 + 37 = 72 | 0.375 ÷ 0.0625 = 6 |
| $^{37}Cl - ^{37}Cl$ | 37 + 37 = 74 | 0.0625 ÷ 0.0625 = 1 |

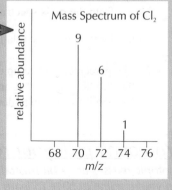
Mass Spectrum of $Cl_2$

# More on Relative Mass

## Mass Spectrometry Can Also Help to Identify Compounds

1) You've seen how you can use a mass spectrum showing the relative isotopic abundances of an element to work out its relative atomic mass. You need to make sure you can remember how to do this. You can also get mass spectra for **molecules** made up from more than one element.

2) When the molecules in a sample are bombarded with electrons, an electron is removed from the molecule to form a **molecular ion, $M^+_{(g)}$**.

*Assuming the ion has a 1+ charge, which it normally will have.*

3) To find the relative molecular mass of a compound, you look at the **molecular ion peak** (the **M peak**) on the mass spectrum. This is the peak with the highest $m/z$ value (ignoring any small M+1 peaks that occur due to the presence of any atoms of carbon-13). The mass/charge value of the molecular ion peak is the **molecular mass**.

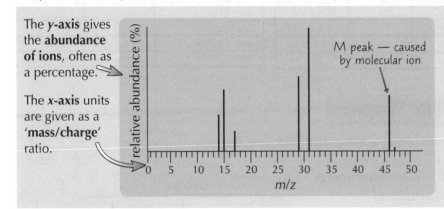

The **y-axis** gives the **abundance of ions**, often as a percentage.

The **x-axis** units are given as a 'mass/charge' ratio.

M peak — caused by molecular ion

This is the mass spectrum of an unknown alcohol.

1) The $m/z$ value of the molecular ion peak is 46, so the $M_r$ of the compound must be **46**.

2) If you calculate the molecular masses of the first few alcohols, you'll find that the one with a molecular mass of 46 is ethanol ($C_2H_5OH$).
$M_r$ of ethanol $= (2 \times 12.0) + (5 \times 1.0)$
$+ 16.0 + 1.0 = $ **46.0**

3) So the compound must be **ethanol**.

There's loads more on mass spectrometry on pages 100-101.

## Practice Questions

Q1 Explain why diatomic molecules can have different relative molecular masses.

Q2 What is the significance of the molecular ion peak on a mass spectrum?

**Exam Questions**

Q1 The table below shows the percentage abundances of isotopes of oxygen found in a sample of $O_2$.

| Isotopes | % Abundance |
|---|---|
| $^{16}O$ | 98 |
| $^{18}O$ | 2 |

a) Calculate the relative abundances of all the possible molecules of $O_2$. [3 marks]

b) Sketch a mass spectrum of $O_2$. [4 marks]

Q2 Potassium ($A_r = 39.1$) can exist in one of three isotopes. 94.20% exists as $^{39}K$ and 0.012% exists as $^{40}K$.

a) Calculate the abundance of the third isotope of potassium. [1 mark]

b) Calculate the isotopic mass of the third isotope of potassium. [2 marks]

Q3 A sample of an unknown straight-chain alkane is analysed using mass spectrometry. The molecular ion peak is seen at a $m/z$ value of 58.

The structures of alkanes are covered on page 76.

a) What is the $M_r$ of this compound? [1 mark]

b) Using your answer to part a), suggest a structure for this compound. [1 mark]

## How do you make a colourful early noughties girl group? Diatomic Kitten...

*Dye Atomic Kitten... Geddit...? Only nine pages into this revision guide and we already have a strong contender for world's worst joke. But don't be too dismayed, there are plenty more terrible puns on their way, I assure you. Before you go looking for them, make sure you know how to do all these relative mass calculations — they're pretty important.*

# Electronic Structure

*Those little electrons prancing about like mini bunnies decide what'll react with what — it's what chemistry's all about.*

## Electron Shells are Made Up of Subshells and Orbitals

1) Electrons move around the nucleus in **quantum shells** (sometimes called **energy levels**). These shells are all given numbers known as **principal quantum numbers**.

2) Shells **further** from the nucleus have a greater energy level than shells closer to the nucleus.

3) The shells contain different types of **subshell**. These subshells have different numbers of **orbitals**, which can each hold up to **2 electrons**.

*This table shows the number of electrons that fit in each type of subshell. You need to know how many electrons can fit into the s, p and d subshells for your exams.*

| Subshell | Number of orbitals | Maximum electrons |
|----------|-------------------|-------------------|
| s | 1 | $1 \times 2 = 2$ |
| p | 3 | $3 \times 2 = 6$ |
| d | 5 | $5 \times 2 = 10$ |
| 4 | 7 | $7 \times 2 = 14$ |

*And this one shows the subshells and electrons in the first four quantum shells.*

| Shell | Subshells | Total number or electrons | |
|-------|-----------|---------------------------|---|
| 1st | 1s | 2 | = 2 |
| 2nd | 2s 2p | $2 + (3 \times 2)$ | = 8 |
| 3rd | 3s 3p 3d | $2 + (3 \times 2) + (5 \times 2)$ | = 18 |
| 4th | 4s 4p 4d 4f | $2 + (3 \times 2) + (5 \times 2) + (7 \times 2)$ | = 32 |

## Orbitals Have Characteristic Shapes

There are a few things you need to know about orbitals... like what they are —

1) An orbital is the **bit of space** that an electron moves in. Orbitals within the same subshell have the **same energy**.

2) The electrons in each orbital have to 'spin' in **opposite** directions — this is called **spin-pairing**.

3) s-orbitals are **spherical** — p-orbitals have **dumbbell shapes**. There are 3 p-orbitals and they're at right angles to one another.

4) You can represent electrons in orbitals using arrows in boxes. Each of the boxes represents one orbital. Each of the arrows represents one electron.

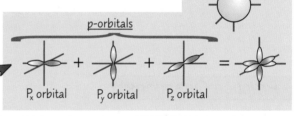

s-orbital

p-orbitals

$P_x$ orbital      $P_y$ orbital      $P_z$ orbital

1s   2s   2p

*The up and down arrows represent the electrons spinning in opposite directions.*

## Work Out Electronic Configurations by Filling the Lowest Energy Levels First

You can figure out most electronic configurations pretty easily, so long as you know a few simple rules —

1) Electrons fill up the **lowest** energy subshells first.

*There's always got to be an exception to mess things up. The 4s subshell has a lower energy level than the 3d subshell, even though its principal quantum number is bigger. This means the 4s subshell fills up first.*

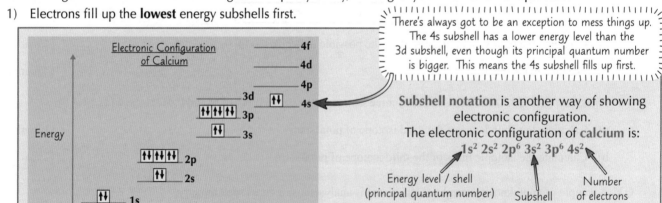

Electronic Configuration of Calcium

4f
4d
4p
3d
4s
3p
3s
2p
2s
1s

Energy

**Subshell notation** is another way of showing electronic configuration. The electronic configuration of **calcium** is:

$1s^2\ 2s^2\ 2p^6\ 3s^2\ 3p^6\ 4s^2$

Energy level / shell (principal quantum number)

Subshell

Number of electrons

2) Electrons fill orbitals **singly** before they start pairing up.

|  | 1s | 2s | 2p | | |
|---|----|----|----|---|---|
| Nitrogen | ⇅ | ⇅ | ↑ | ↑ | ↑ |

|  | 1s | 2s | 2p | | |
|---|----|----|----|---|---|
| Oxygen | ⇅ | ⇅ | ⇅ | ↑ | ↑ |

Watch out — **noble gas symbols**, like that of argon (Ar), are sometimes used in electronic configurations. For example, calcium ($1s^2\ 2s^2\ 2p^6\ 3s^2\ 3p^6\ 4s^2$) can be written as $[Ar]4s^2$, where $[Ar] = 1s^2\ 2s^2\ 2p^6\ 3s^2\ 3p^6$.

# Electronic Structure

## You can use the Periodic Table to work out *Electronic configurations*

The periodic table can be split into an **s-block**, **d-block** and **p-block**.

1) The **s-block** elements have an outer
shell electronic configuration of $s^1$ or $s^2$.
E.g. lithium ($1s^2\ 2s^1$) and magnesium ($1s^2\ 2s^2\ 2p^6\ 3s^2$).

2) The **p-block** elements have an outer
shell configuration of $s^2p^1$ to $s^2p^6$.
E.g. aluminium ($1s^2\ 2s^2\ 2p^6\ 3s^2\ 3p^1$) and
bromine ($1s^2\ 2s^2\ 2p^6\ 3s^2\ 3p^6\ 3d^{10}\ 4s^2\ 4p^5$).

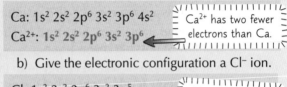

**Example:** Electronic configuration of phosphorus, P:

Period 1 — $1s^2$ ⟵ Complete subshells
Period 2 — $2s^2\ 2p^6$
Period 3 — $3s^2\ 3p^3$ ⟵ Incomplete outer subshell

So it's: $1s^2\ 2s^2\ 2p^6\ 3s^2\ 3p^3$

**Example:** a) Give the electronic configuration a $Ca^{2+}$ ion.

Ca: $1s^2\ 2s^2\ 2p^6\ 3s^2\ 3p^6\ 4s^2$
$Ca^{2+}$: $1s^2\ 2s^2\ 2p^6\ 3s^2\ 3p^6$ ⟵ $Ca^{2+}$ has two fewer electrons than Ca.

b) Give the electronic configuration a $Cl^-$ ion.

Cl: $1s^2\ 2s^2\ 2p^6\ 3s^2\ 3p^5$
$Cl^-$: $1s^2\ 2s^2\ 2p^6\ 3s^2\ 3p^6$ ⟵ $Cl^-$ has one more electron than Cl.

3) To work out the **configuration** of an **ion**, up to Ca,
you just write the **electronic structure** of the atom
and then **add** or **remove** electrons to or from
the **highest-energy occupied subshell**.

4) The **d-block** elements are a bit trickier to work out — the 4s sub-shell fills **before** the 3d subshell.
E.g. vanadium ($1s^2\ 2s^2\ 2p^6\ 3s^2\ 3p^6\ 3d^3\ 4s^2$) and nickel ($1s^2\ 2s^2\ 2p^6\ 3s^2\ 3p^6\ 3d^8\ 4s^2$).

5) **Chromium** (Cr) and **copper** (Cu) are badly behaved. They donate one of their **4s** electrons
to the **3d subshell**. It's because they're **more stable** with a full or half-full d-subshell.

Cr atom (24 e⁻): $1s^2\ 2s^2\ 2p^6\ 3s^2\ 3p^6\ 3d^5\ 4s^1$    Cu atom (29 e⁻): $1s^2\ 2s^2\ 2p^6\ 3s^2\ 3p^6\ 3d^{10}\ 4s^1$

6) Different elements form ions with different **charges**.
You can use the periodic table to **predict** what ion each element will form (see page 19 for more on this).

## Practice Questions

Q1 How many electrons do full s-, p- and d-subshells contain?

Q2 What does the term 'spin-pairing' mean?

Q3 Draw diagrams to show the shapes of a s- and a p-orbital.

Q4 Write down the subshells in order of increasing energy up to 4p.

**Exam Questions**

Q1 Potassium reacts with oxygen to form potassium oxide, $K_2O$.

a) Give the electronic configurations of the K atom and $K^+$ ion. [2 marks]

b) Give the electronic configuration of the oxygen atom. [1 mark]

Q2 This question concerns electronic configurations in atoms and ions.

a) Identify the element with the 4th shell configuration of $4s^2\ 4p^2$. [1 mark]

b) Suggest the identities of an atom, a positive ion and a negative ion
with the electronic configuration $1s^2\ 2s^2\ 2p^6\ 3s^2\ 3p^6$. [3 marks]

c) Give the electronic configuration of a Cu atom. [1 mark]

## *She shells sub-sells on the shesore...*

*The way electrons fill up the orbitals is kind of like how strangers fill up seats on a bus. Everyone tends to sit in their own seat till they're forced to share. Except for the scary man who comes and sits next to you. Make sure you learn the order that the subshells are filled up in, so you can write electronic configurations for any atom or ion they throw at you.*

# Atomic Emission Spectra

*Atomic emission spectra, which you're about to meet, provide evidence for quantum shells. Read on...*

## Electromagnetic Spectrum — the Range of Electromagnetic Radiation

1) Electromagnetic radiation is **energy** that's transmitted as waves, with a **spectrum** of different frequencies.

2) Along the electromagnetic spectrum, the radiation increases in **frequency** and decreases in **wavelength**:

| RADIO WAVES | MICRO- WAVES | INFRA- RED | VISIBLE LIGHT | ULTRA- VIOLET | X-RAYS | GAMMA RAYS |
|---|---|---|---|---|---|---|

INCREASING FREQUENCY / ENERGY & DECREASING WAVELENGTH

## Electrons Release Energy in Fixed Amounts

1) Electron shells are sometimes called **quantum shells**, or **energy levels** (see page 10).

2) In their **ground state**, atoms have their electrons in their **lowest** possible energy levels.

3) If an atom's electrons **take in energy** from their surroundings they can move to **higher energy levels**, further from the nucleus. At higher energy levels, electrons are said to be **excited**. (More excited than you right now, I'll bet.)

4) Electrons **release energy** by dropping from a higher energy level down to a **lower energy level**. The energy levels all have certain **fixed values** — they're **discrete**.

5) A **line spectrum** (called an **emission spectrum**) shows the frequencies of light emitted when electrons **drop down** from a higher energy level to a lower one. These frequencies appear as **coloured lines** on a dark background.

6) Each element has a **different** electron arrangement, so the frequencies of radiation absorbed and emitted are different. This means the **spectrum** for each element is unique.

emission spectrum

## Emission Spectra are Made Up of Sets of Lines

1) You get lots of **sets of lines** in emission spectra — each set represents electrons moving to **a different energy level**. So, in an emission spectrum, you get one **set of lines** produced when electrons fall to the **$n = 1$** level, and another set produced when they fall to the **$n = 2$** level, and so on.

2) Each set of lines on emission spectra get **closer together** as the frequency **increases**.

3) Here's the emission spectrum of hydrogen (it only has **one** electron that can move). It has three important sets of lines:

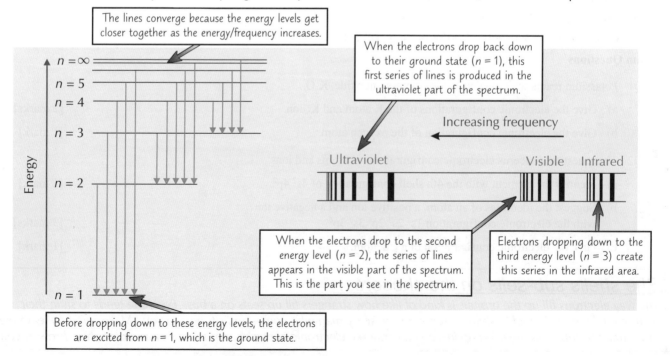

The lines converge because the energy levels get closer together as the energy/frequency increases.

When the electrons drop back down to their ground state ($n = 1$), this first series of lines is produced in the ultraviolet part of the spectrum.

Increasing frequency

When the electrons drop to the second energy level ($n = 2$), the series of lines appears in the visible part of the spectrum. This is the part you see in the spectrum.

Electrons dropping down to the third energy level ($n = 3$) create this series in the infrared area.

Before dropping down to these energy levels, the electrons are excited from $n = 1$, which is the ground state.

*TOPIC 1 — ATOMIC STRUCTURE AND THE PERIODIC TABLE*

# Atomic Emission Spectra

## Emission Spectra Support the Idea of Quantum Shells

1) Our current understanding of **electronic configuration** involves the idea that electrons exist in **quantum shells** around the **nucleus**.

2) When it comes to electron shells, there are **four basic principles**:

- Electrons can only exist in **fixed orbits**, or **shells**, and not anywhere in between.
- Each shell has a **fixed energy**.
- When an electron moves between shells **electromagnetic radiation** is **emitted** or **absorbed**.
- Because the energy of shells is fixed, the radiation will have a **fixed frequency**.

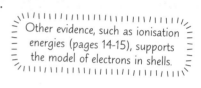

Herbert was a critically acclaimed expert in shells.

3) The emission spectrum of an atom has **clear lines** for different energy levels. This supports the idea that energy levels are discrete, i.e. **not continuous**. It means that an electron doesn't 'move' from one energy level to the next. It just **jumps**, with no in-between stage at all.

*Other evidence, such as ionisation energies (pages 14-15), supports the model of electrons in shells.*

4) This is a really weird and quite confusing idea, but emission spectra and other **evidence** back up the idea that electrons exist in quantum shells.

## Practice Questions

Q1 Is energy absorbed or released when electrons drop from a higher energy level to a lower one?

Q2 Are energy levels discrete or continuous?

**Exam Questions**

Q1 The diagram below shows part of an atomic emission spectrum of a single element. The lines in the spectrum are labelled A to E.

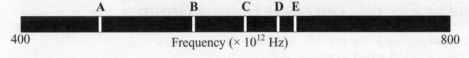

a) What happens in the atom when energy is emitted? [2 marks]

b) Which line in the spectrum represents the largest emission of energy? [1 mark]

c) Explain why the lines get closer together from A to E. [1 mark]

Q2 Many models of the atom have been presented in the past. One of the most widely used models currently relies on evidence provided by emission spectra, amongst other things.

a) What happens as an electron moves from a higher to a lower quantum shell? [1 mark]

b) Describe what the lines on an emission spectrum show. [1 mark]

c) Explain how emission spectra provide evidence that supports our current understanding of electrons existing in fixed energy levels. [2 marks]

d) Name one other factor that provides evidence that supports our current understanding of electrons existing in fixed energy levels. [1 mark]

## Spectra — aren't they the baddies in those James Bond films?

*All this stuff about fixed energy levels and electrons jumping up and down is a bit mind bending but it's actually pretty cool (if you're a Chemistry nerd like me). Emission spectra allow you to 'see' the gaps between these energy levels and show that the crazy idea of fixed energy levels dreamed up by an old, beardy chemist was actually spot on. Neat, huh?*

# Ionisation Energies

*This page gets a trifle brain-boggling, so I hope you've got a few aspirin handy...*

## Ionisation is the Removal of One or More Electrons

When electrons have been removed from an atom or molecule, it's been **ionised**.
The energy you need to remove the first electron is called the **first ionisation energy**.

*You might see 'ionisation energy' referred to as 'ionisation enthalpy' instead.*

> The **first ionisation energy** is the energy needed to remove 1 electron from **each atom** in **1 mole** of **gaseous** atoms to form 1 mole of gaseous 1+ ions.

You **must** use the gas state symbol, **(g)**, and always refer to **1 mole** of atoms, as stated in the definition.
Energy is put **in** to ionise an atom or molecule, so it's an **endothermic process** — there's more about this on page 104.

You can write **equations** for this process — here's
the equation for the **first ionisation of oxygen**:

$$O_{(g)} \rightarrow O^+_{(g)} + e^- \quad \text{1st ionisation energy} = +1314 \text{ kJ mol}^{-1}$$

## These Three Factors Affect Ionisation Energy

*Subshell structure also affects ionisation energy (see page 17).*

**Nuclear charge**  The **more protons** there are in the nucleus, the more positively charged the nucleus is and the **stronger the attraction** for the electrons.

**Electron shell**  Attraction falls off very **rapidly with distance**. An electron in an electron shell **close** to the nucleus will be **much more** strongly attracted than one in a shell further away.

**Shielding**  As the number of electrons **between** the outer electrons and the nucleus **increases**, the outer electrons feel less attraction towards the nuclear charge. This lessening of the pull of the nucleus by inner shells of electrons is called **shielding** (or **screening**).

> A **high ionisation energy** means there's a **strong attraction** between the **electron** and the **nucleus**, so **more energy** is needed to overcome the attraction and remove the electron.

## First Ionisation Energies Decrease Down a Group

*Ionisation energy also increases across a period (see page 17).*

1) As you **go down** a group in the periodic table, ionisation energies generally **fall**, i.e. it gets **easier** to remove outer electrons.

2) It happens because:

   - Elements further down a group have **extra electron shells** compared to ones above. The extra shells mean that the atomic radius is larger, so the outer electrons are **further away** from the nucleus, which greatly reduces their attraction to the nucleus.

   *The positive charge of the nucleus does increase as you go down a group (due to the extra protons), but this effect is overridden by the effect of the extra shells.*

   - The extra inner shells **shield** the outer electrons from the attraction of the nucleus.

3) A decrease in ionisation energy going down a group provides **evidence** that electron shells **really exist**.

## Successive Ionisation Energies Involve Removing Additional Electrons

1) You can remove **all** the electrons from an atom, leaving only the nucleus. Each time you remove an electron, there's a **successive ionisation energy**. For example, the definition for the **second ionisation energy** is:

> The **second ionisation energy** is the energy needed to remove 1 electron from **each ion** in **1 mole** of gaseous 1+ ions to form 1 mole of gaseous 2+ ions.

And here's the equation for
the **second ionisation of oxygen**:

$$O^+_{(g)} \rightarrow O^{2+}_{(g)} + e^- \quad \text{2nd ionisation energy} = +3388 \text{ kJ mol}^{-1}$$

2) You need to be able to write equations for **any** successive ionisation energy. The equation for the $n^{th}$ ionisation energy is....  $X^{(n-1)+}_{(g)} \rightarrow X^{n+}_{(g)} + e^-$

# Ionisation Energies

## Successive Ionisation Energies Show **Shell Structure**

A **graph** of successive ionisation energies (like this one for sodium) provides evidence for the **shell structure** of atoms.

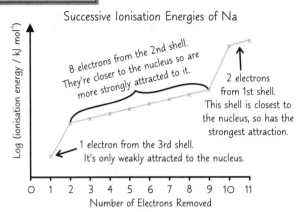

Successive Ionisation Energies of Na

8 electrons from the 2nd shell. They're closer to the nucleus so are more strongly attracted to it.

2 electrons from 1st shell. This shell is closest to the nucleus, so has the strongest attraction.

1 electron from the 3rd shell. It's only weakly attracted to the nucleus.

- **Within each shell**, successive ionisation energies **increase**. This is because electrons are being removed from an **increasingly positive ion** — there's **less repulsion** amongst the remaining electrons, so they're **held more strongly** by the nucleus.
- The **big jumps** in ionisation energy happen when a new shell is broken into — an electron is being removed from a shell **closer** to the nucleus.

1) Graphs like this can tell you which **group** of the periodic table an element belongs to. Just count **how many electrons are removed** before the first big jump to find the group number.

E.g. In the graph for sodium, **one electron** is removed before the first big jump — sodium is in **group 1**.

2) These graphs can be used to predict the **electronic structure** of elements. Working from **right to left**, count how many points there are before each big jump to find how many electrons are in each shell, starting with the first.

E.g. The graph for sodium has **2 points** on the right-hand side, then a jump, then **8 points**, a jump, and **1 final point**. Sodium has **2 electrons** in the first shell, **8** in the second and **1** in the third.

## Practice Questions

Q1 Define first ionisation energy and give an equation as an example.

Q2 Describe the three main factors that affect ionisation energies.

Q3 How is ionisation energy related to the force of attraction between an electron and the nucleus of an atom?

**Exam Questions**

Q1 This table shows the nuclear charge and first ionisation energy for four elements.

| Element | B | C | N | O |
|---|---|---|---|---|
| Charge of Nucleus | +5 | +6 | +7 | +8 |
| 1st Ionisation Energy (kJ mol⁻¹) | 801 | 1087 | 1402 | 1314 |

a) Write an equation, including state symbols, to represent the first ionisation energy of carbon (C). [2 marks]

b) In these four elements, what is the relationship between nuclear charge and first ionisation energy? [1 mark]

c) Explain why nuclear charge has this effect on first ionisation energy. [2 marks]

Q2 This graph shows the successive ionisation energies of a certain element.

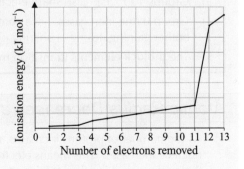

a) To which group of the periodic table does this element belong? [1 mark]

b) Why does it takes more energy to remove each successive electron? [2 marks]

c) What causes the sudden increases in ionisation energy? [1 mark]

d) What is the total number of electron shells in this element? [1 mark]

## Shirt crumpled — ionise it...

*When you're talking about ionisation energies in exams, always use the three main factors — shielding, nuclear charge and distance from nucleus. Recite the definition of the first ionisation energies to yourself until you can't take any more.*

# Periodicity

*One last thing now in this Topic, and then you'll be onto the real juicy stuff. But first have a look at these pages about periodicity. Periodicity describes the trends of elements going across the Periodic Table.*

## The **Modern Periodic Table** Arranges Elements by **Proton Number**

**Dmitri Mendeleev** was one of the first scientists to put the elements in any meaningful order to create the **periodic table** in 1869. It has **changed** a bit and been **added to** since then to give us the **modern** periodic table we use today:

1) The periodic table is arranged into **periods** (rows) and **groups** (columns).

2) All the elements **within a period** have the same number of **electron shells** (if you don't worry about the subshells). The elements of Period 1 (hydrogen and helium) both have 1 electron shell, the elements in Period 2 have 2 electron shells, and so on... This means there are **repeating trends** in the physical and chemical properties of the elements across each period (e.g. decreasing atomic radius). These trends are known as **periodicity**.

3) All the elements **within a group** have the same number of **electrons in their outer shell**. This means they have **similar chemical properties**. The group number tells you the number of electrons in the outer shell, e.g. Group 1 elements have 1 electron in their outer shell, Group 4 elements have 4 electrons, etc... (This isn't the case for Group 0 elements — they all have 8 electrons in their outer shell, except for helium, which has 2.)

## Electronic Configuration Decides the **Chemical Properties** of an Element

The number of **outer shell electrons** decides the chemical properties of an element.

1) The **s-block** elements (Groups 1 and 2) have 1 or 2 outer shell electrons. These are easily **lost** to form positive ions with an **inert gas configuration**. E.g. Na: $1s^2 2s^2 2p^6 3s^1 \rightarrow$ Na$^+$: $1s^2 2s^2 2p^6$ (the electronic configuration of neon).

2) The elements in Groups 5, 6 and 7 (in the **p-block**) can **gain** 1, 2 or 3 electrons to form negative ions with an **inert gas configuration**. E.g. O: $1s^2 2s^2 2p^4 \rightarrow$ O$^{2-}$: $1s^2 2s^2 2p^6$.

3) Groups 4 to 7 can also **share** electrons when they form covalent bonds.

4) Group 0 (the inert gases) have **completely filled** s and p subshells and don't need to bother gaining, losing or sharing electrons — their full subshells make them **inert**.

5) The **d-block** elements (transition metals) tend to **lose** s and d electrons to form positive ions.

## Atomic Radius **Decreases** across a Period

1) As the number of protons increases, the **positive charge** of the nucleus increases. This means electrons are **pulled closer** to the nucleus, making the atomic radius smaller.

2) The extra electrons that the elements gain across a period are added to the **outer energy level** so they don't really provide any extra shielding effect (shielding is mainly provided by the electrons in the inner shells).

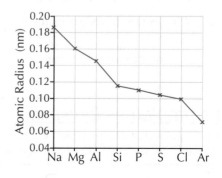

# Periodicity

## Ionisation Energy **Increases** Across a Period

The graph below shows the first ionisation energies of the elements in **Period 2 and Period 3**.

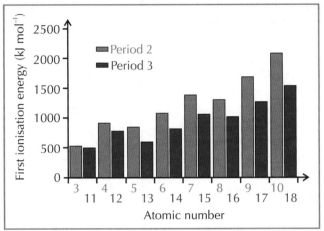

1) As you **move across** a period, the general trend is for the ionisation energies to **increase** — i.e. it gets harder to remove the outer electrons.

2) This can be explained because the number of protons is increasing, which means a stronger **nuclear attraction**.

3) All the extra electrons are at **roughly the same** energy level, even if the outer electrons are in different orbital types.

4) This means there's generally little **extra shielding** effect or **extra distance** to lessen the attraction from the nucleus.

5) But, there are **small drops** between Groups 2 and 3, and 5 and 6. Tell me more, I hear you cry. Well, alright then...

## The Drop between **Groups 2** and **3** Shows **Subshell Structure**

Generally, it requires **more energy** to remove an electron from a **higher energy subshell** than a **lower energy subshell** (see page 10 for a diagram showing the relative energies of subshells 1s to 4f).

> **Example:**  Mg  $1s^2 2s^2 2p^6 3s^2$       1st ionisation energy = 738 kJ mol$^{-1}$
> Al  $1s^2 2s^2 2p^6 3s^2 3p^1$    1st ionisation energy = 578 kJ mol$^{-1}$

1) Aluminium's outer electron is in a **3p orbital** rather than a 3s. The 3p orbital has a **slightly higher** energy than the 3s orbital, so the electron is, on average, to be found **further** from the nucleus.

2) The 3p orbital has additional shielding provided by the **$3s^2$ electrons**.

3) Both these factors together are strong enough to **override** the effect of the increased nuclear charge, resulting in the ionisation energy **dropping** slightly.

4) This pattern in ionisation energies provides **evidence** for the theory of electron subshells.

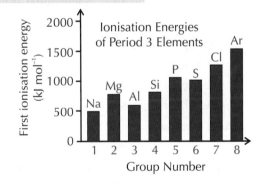

## The Drop between **Groups 5** and **6** is due to **Electron Repulsion**

In general, elements with **singly filled** or **full** subshells are more **stable** than those with **partially filled** subshells, so have **higher** first ionisation energies.

> **Example:**  P   $1s^2 2s^2 2p^6 3s^2 3p^3$    1st ionisation energy = 1012 kJ mol$^{-1}$
> S   $1s^2 2s^2 2p^6 3s^2 3p^4$    1st ionisation energy = 1000 kJ mol$^{-1}$

1) The **shielding is identical** in the phosphorus and sulfur atoms, and the electron is being removed from an identical orbital.

2) In phosphorus's case, the electron is being removed from a **singly-occupied** orbital. But in sulfur, the **electron** is being **removed** from an orbital containing two electrons.

> *This is the 'electrons-in-boxes' notation that you saw on page 10.*

Phosphorus: [Ne]  3s ⬆⬇  3p ⬆ ⬆ ⬆         Sulfur: [Ne]  3s ⬆⬇  3p ⬆⬇ ⬆ ⬆

*The repulsion between two bears in a river means that bears are easier to remove from shared rivers.*

The **repulsion** between two electrons in an orbital means that electrons are **easier to remove** from shared orbitals.

3) Yup, yet more **evidence** for the electronic structure model.

*TOPIC 1 — ATOMIC STRUCTURE AND THE PERIODIC TABLE*

# Periodicity

## Bond Strength Affects Melting and Boiling Points Across a Period

As you go across a period, the **type** of bond formed between the atoms of an element **changes**. This affects the **melting** and **boiling points** of the element. The graph on the right shows the trend in boiling points across **Periods 2 and 3**.

1) For the **metals** (Li, Be, Na, Mg and Al), melting and boiling points **increase** across the period because the **metallic bonds** (see page 27) get stronger. The bonds get stronger because the metal ions have an increasing number of **delocalised electrons** and a decreasing **radius** (i.e. the metal ions have a higher charge density — see page 19). This means there's a stronger attraction between the metal ions and delocalised electrons, so stronger metallic bonding.

2) The elements with **giant covalent lattice** structures (C and Si) have **strong covalent bonds** (see page 26) linking all their atoms together. **A lot** of energy is needed to break all of these bonds. So, for example, carbon (as graphite or diamond) and silicon have the highest boiling points in their periods. (The carbon data in the graph to the right is for graphite — diamond has an even higher boiling point.)

3) Next come the **simple molecular structures** ($N_2$, $O_2$ and $F_2$, $P_4$, $S_8$ and $Cl_2$). Their melting points depend upon the strength of the London forces (see page 30) between their molecules. London forces are weak and easily overcome, so these elements have low melting and boiling points.

4) More electrons in a molecule mean stronger London forces (see page 30). For example, in Period 3 a molecule of sulfur ($S_8$) has the most electrons, so it's got **higher** melting and boiling points than phosphorus and chlorine.

5) The noble gases (Ne and Ar) have the **lowest** melting and boiling points in their periods because they exist as **individual atoms** (they're monatomic) resulting in **very weak** London forces.

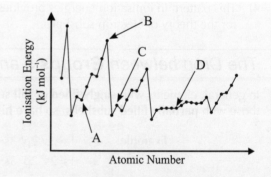

## Practice Questions

Q1 Which elements in Period 3 are found in the s-block of the periodic table?

Q2 Explain the meaning of the term 'periodicity'.

Q3 What happens to the first ionisation energy as you move across a period?

**Exam Questions**

Q1 The graph on the right shows first ionisation energy plotted against atomic number. Which of the labelled points on the graph shows the first ionisation energy of:

a) a Group 2 metal? [1 mark]

b) an element with a full outer electron shell? [1 mark]

c) an element in Period 3? [1 mark]

Q2 This table shows the melting points for the Period 3 elements.

| Element | Na | Mg | Al | Si | P | S | Cl | Ar |
|---|---|---|---|---|---|---|---|---|
| Melting point / K | 371 | 923 | 933 | 1687 | 317 | 392 | 172 | 84 |

In terms of structure and bonding explain why:

a) silicon has a high melting point. [2 marks]

b) the melting point of sulfur is higher than that of phosphorus. [2 marks]

## Periodic trends — my mate Dom's always a couple of decades behind...

*I may not be the trendiest person in the world, but I do love my periodic trends. Yes indeed. That ionisation energy one is my particular favourite. And whether you like it or not, you better learn it so you're not caught out in your exams...*

# Ionic Bonding

*When different elements join or bond together, you get a compound. There are two main types of bonding in compounds — ionic and covalent. You need to make sure you've got them both totally sussed. Let's start with ionic.*

## Ions are Positively or Negatively Charged Atoms (or Groups of Atoms)

1) Ions are formed when electrons are **transferred** from one atom to another. They may be positively charged (**cations**) or negatively charged (**anions**).

2) The simplest ions are single atoms which have either lost or gained 1, 2 or 3 electrons so that they've got a **full outer shell**. Here are some examples of ions:

| | |
|---|---|
| A sodium atom (Na) **loses** 1 electron to form a sodium ion ($Na^+$) | $Na \rightarrow Na^+ + e^-$ |
| A magnesium atom (Mg) **loses** 2 electrons to form a magnesium ion ($Mg^{2+}$) | $Mg \rightarrow Mg^{2+} + 2e^-$ |
| A chlorine atom (Cl) **gains** 1 electron to form a chloride ion ($Cl^-$) | $Cl + e^- \rightarrow Cl^-$ |
| An oxygen atom (O) **gains** 2 electrons to form an oxide ion ($O^{2-}$) | $O + 2e^- \rightarrow O^{2-}$ |

3) You **don't** have to remember what ion **each element** forms — for a lot of them you just look at the periodic table. Elements in the same **group** all have the same number of **outer electrons**, so they have to **lose or gain** the same number to get the full outer shell. And this means that they form ions with the **same charges**. E.g. Mg and Sr are both in **Group 2**. They both lose **2 electrons** to form 2+ ions ($Mg^{2+}$ and $Sr^{2+}$).

4) Generally the charge on a **metal ion** is equal to its **group number**. The charge on a **non-metal ion** is equal to its **group number minus eight**.

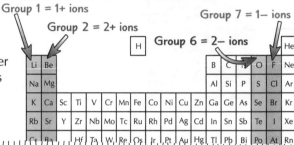

The Group numbers are the bold ones at the top of your periodic table.

## Ionic Bonding is when Ions are Stuck Together by Electrostatic Attraction

**Electrostatic attraction** holds positive and negative ions together — it's **very** strong. When ions are held together like this, it's called **ionic bonding**. Here comes a definition for you to learn...

> An **ionic bond** is the strong **electrostatic attraction** between two **oppositely charged** ions.

When oppositely charged ions form an **ionic bond**, you get an **ionic compound**. The **formula** of an ionic compound tells you what **ions** that compound has in it.

*The positive charges in an ionic compound balance the negative charges exactly — so the total overall charge is zero. This is a dead handy way of checking the formula.*

**Example:** NaCl is made up of $Na^+$ and $Cl^-$ ions in a 1:1 ratio.
$CaCl_2$ is made up of $Ca^{2+}$ and $Cl^-$ ions in a 1:2 ratio.

## Ionic Charges and Ionic Radii Affect Ionic Bonding

**Ionic bonds** are all to do with the **attraction** between **oppositely charged ions**. So, the stronger the **electrostatic attraction**, the stronger the ionic bond. There are **two** things that affect the strength of an ionic bond:

### IONIC CHARGES

In general, the **greater** the **charge** on an ion, the **stronger** the **ionic bond** and therefore, the higher the melting/boiling point.

E.g. the melting point of NaF, (which is made up of **singly charged** $Na^+$ and $F^-$ ions) is **993 °C**, while CaO (which is made up of $Ca^{2+}$ and $O^{2-}$ ions) has a much higher melting point of **2572 °C**.

*Generally, ions with a high charge density (they have a large charge spread over a small area) form stronger ionic bonds than ions with a low charge density (they have a small charge spread out over a large area).*

### IONIC RADII

**Smaller ions** can **pack closer** together than larger ions. Electrostatic attraction gets weaker with distance, so **small, closely packed ions** have **stronger** ionic bonding than larger ions, which sit further apart. Therefore, ionic compounds with small, closely packed ions have higher melting and boiling points than ionic compounds made of large ions.

E.g. the **ionic radius** of $Cs^+$ is **greater** than that of $Na^+$. NaF has a melting point of **992 °C**, whereas CsF has a melting point of **683 °C** since the $Na^+$ and $F^-$ ions can pack closer together in NaF than the $Cs^+$ and $F^-$ ions in CsF.

# Ionic Bonding

## The *Size* of an *Ion* Depends on its *Electron Shells* and *Atomic Number*

There are two trends in ionic radii you need to know about.

1) The **ionic radius increases** as you go **down a group**.

| Ion | Li$^+$ | Na$^+$ | K$^+$ | Rb$^+$ |
|---|---|---|---|---|
| Ionic radius (nm) | 0.060 | 0.095 | 0.133 | 0.148 |

All these **Group 1** ions have the **same charge**. As you go down the group the **ionic radius increases** as the **atomic number increases**. This is because **extra electron shells** are added.

2) **Isoelectronic ions** are ions of different atoms with the **same number of electrons**. The **ionic radius** of a set of **isoelectronic ions decreases** as the **atomic number increases**.

*See page 4 for how to work out the subatomic particles in an ion.*

| Ion | N$^{3-}$ | O$^{2-}$ | F$^-$ | Na$^+$ | Mg$^{2+}$ | Al$^{3+}$ |
|---|---|---|---|---|---|---|
| No. of electrons | 10 | 10 | 10 | 10 | 10 | 10 |
| No. of protons | 7 | 8 | 9 | 11 | 12 | 13 |
| Ionic radius (nm) | 0.171 | 0.140 | 0.136 | 0.095 | 0.065 | 0.050 |

As you go through this series of ions the number of **electrons stays the same**, but the number of **protons increases**.

This means that the electrons are **attracted** to the **nucleus** more strongly, pulling them in a little, so the **ionic radius decreases**.

## *Dot-and-Cross* Diagrams Show Where the Electrons in a Bond Come From

Dot-and-cross diagrams show the **arrangement** of electrons in an atom or ion. Each electron is represented by a dot or a cross. They can also show which **atom** the electrons in a **bond** originally came from.

1) For example, **sodium chloride** (NaCl) is an ionic compound:

Here, the dots represent the Na electrons and the crosses represent the Cl electrons (all electrons are really identical, but this is a good way of following their movement).

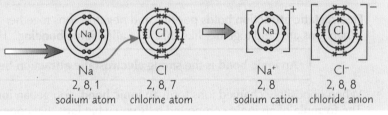

Na 2, 8, 1 sodium atom    Cl 2, 8, 7 chlorine atom    Na$^+$ 2, 8 sodium cation    Cl$^-$ 2, 8, 8 chloride anion

2) When there's a 1:2 ratio of ions, such as in **magnesium chloride**, MgCl$_2$, you draw dot-and-cross diagrams like this:

*Here we've only shown the outer shells of electrons on the dot-and-cross diagram. It makes it easier to see what's going on.*

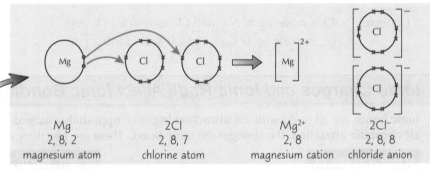

Mg 2, 8, 2 magnesium atom    2Cl 2, 8, 7 chlorine atom    Mg$^{2+}$ 2, 8 magnesium cation    2Cl$^-$ 2, 8, 8 chloride anion

## Ionic Compounds Form *Giant Ionic Lattice* Structures

1) Ionic crystals (e.g. crystals of common salt, such as NaCl) are giant lattices of ions. A lattice is just a regular structure. The structure's called '**giant**' because it's made up of the same basic unit repeated over and over again.

2) It forms because each ion is electrostatically attracted in **all directions** to ions of the **opposite** charge.

3) In **sodium chloride**, the Na$^+$ and Cl$^-$ ions are packed together alternately in a **lattice**.

4) The sodium chloride lattice is **cube** shaped — different ionic compounds have different shaped structures, but they're all still giant lattices.

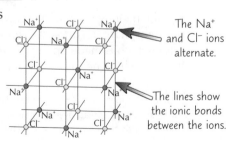

The Na$^+$ and Cl$^-$ ions alternate.

The lines show the ionic bonds between the ions.

# Ionic Bonding

## The **Theory** of Ionic Bonding **Fits the Evidence** from **Physical Properties**

Scientists develop **models** of ionic bonding based on **experimental evidence** — they're an attempt to **explain observations** about how ionic compounds behave. Some evidence is provided by the **physical properties** of ionic compounds:

1) They have **high melting points** — this tells you that the ions are held together by a **strong attraction**. Positive and negative ions are strongly attracted, so the **model** fits the **evidence**.

2) They are often **soluble** in **water** but **not** in **non-polar solvents** — this tells you that the particles are **charged**. The ions are **pulled apart** by **polar molecules** like water, but **not** by **non-polar** molecules. Again, the **model** of ionic structures fits this evidence.

3) Ionic compounds **don't conduct electricity** when they're **solid** — but they **do** when they're **molten or dissolved**. This supports the idea that there are ions, which are **fixed** in position by strong ionic bonds in a solid, but are **free to move** (and carry a charge) as a liquid or in a solution.

4) Ionic compounds can't be **shaped** — for example, if you tried to pull layers of NaCl over each other, you'd get negative chlorine ions directly over other negative chlorine ions (and positive sodium ions directly over each other). The **repulsion** between these ions would be very **strong**, so ionic compounds are **brittle** (they **break** when they're **stretched** or **hammered**). This supports the lattice model.

## The **Migration of Ions** is **Evidence** for the Presence of **Charged Particles**

- When you electrolyse a **green** solution of copper(II) chromate(VI) on a piece of wet filter paper, the filter paper turns **blue** at the **cathode** (the negative electrode) and **yellow** at the **anode** (the positive electrode).

- Copper(II) ions are **blue** in solution and chromate(VI) ions are **yellow**. Copper(II) chromate(VI) solution is **green** because it contains both ions.

- When you pass a current through the solution, the **positive** ions move to the **cathode** and the **negative** ions move to the **anode**.

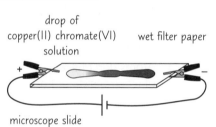

drop of copper(II) chromate(VI) solution        wet filter paper

microscope slide

## Practice Questions

Q1 What is an ionic bond?

Q2 What two factors affect the strength of ionic bonds?

Q3 Why do many ionic compounds dissolve in water?

**Exam Questions**

Q1  a) What type of structure does sodium chloride have? [1 mark]

b) Would you expect sodium chloride to have a high or a low melting point? Explain your answer. [2 marks]

c) How would you expect the melting point of sodium bromide (NaBr) to compare with sodium chloride? Explain your answer. [3 marks]

Q2  Calcium oxide is an ionic compound with ionic formula CaO.

a) Draw a dot-and-cross diagram to show the formation of a bond and subsequent bonding in calcium oxide. Show the outer electrons only. [2 marks]

b) Solid calcium oxide does not conduct electricity, but molten calcium oxide does. Explain this with reference to ionic bonding. [3 marks]

Q3  In terms of electron transfer, what happens when sodium reacts with fluorine to form sodium fluoride? [3 marks]

Q4  Which of the following sets of atoms and ions are isoelectronic?

$\quad$ **A** $\;$ $Ca^{2+}$, $K^+$, Cl $\qquad$ **B** $\;$ $Mg^+$, Ne, $Na^+$ $\qquad$ **C** $\;$ Ar, $S^{2-}$, $Sc^{3+}$ $\qquad$ **D** $\;$ $Ti^{4+}$, $Cl^-$, S $\qquad$ [1 mark]

## The name's Bond... Ionic Bond... Electrons taken, not shared...

*It's all very well learning the properties of ionic compounds, but make sure you can also explain why they do what they do. And practise drawing dot-and-cross diagrams to show ionic bonding— they're easy marks in exams.*

# Covalent Bonding

*And now for covalent bonding — this is when atoms share electrons with one another so they've all got full outer shells.*

## Covalent Bonds Hold Atoms in Molecules Together

Molecules are formed when **2 or more** atoms bond together, and are held together by **covalent bonds**. It doesn't matter if the atoms are the **same** or **different**.

Chlorine gas ($Cl_2$), carbon monoxide (CO), water ($H_2O$) and ethanol ($C_2H_5OH$) are all molecules.

In covalent bonding, two atoms **share** electrons, so they've **both** got full outer shells of electrons. A covalent bond is the **strong electrostatic attraction** between the two **positive nuclei** and the **shared electrons** in the bond.

E.g. two hydrogen atoms bond covalently to form a molecule of hydrogen.

(H) • *H* ⟹ H(•×)H

Covalent bonding usually happens between non-metals. Ionic bonding is usually between a metal and a non-metal.

## Make Sure You Can Draw the Bonding in These Molecules

1) Dot-and-cross diagrams can be used to show how electrons behave in **covalent bonds**.

2) The bonded molecules are drawn with their outer atomic orbitals **overlapping**. The shared electrons that make up the covalent bond are drawn **within** the overlapping area.

3) To simplify the diagrams, not all the electrons in the molecules are shown — just the ones in the **outer shells**.

4) Most of the time the central atom ends up with **eight electrons** in its **outer shell**. This is good for the atom — it's a very **stable** arrangement.

5) Atoms don't have to stick with forming **single bonds** (when there's just **one** pair of electrons shared between two atoms). You can get atoms sharing multiple pairs of electrons. A bond containing **two** electron pairs is a **double bond**, a bond containing **three** electron pairs is a **triple bond** and so on...

The outer electrons in hydrogen are in the first electron shell, which only needs two electrons to be filled.

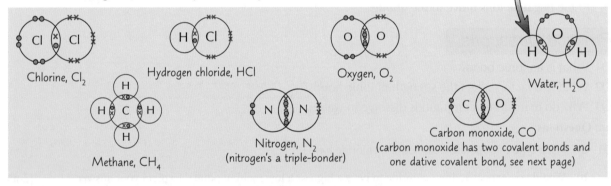

Chlorine, $Cl_2$

Hydrogen chloride, HCl

Oxygen, $O_2$

Water, $H_2O$

Methane, $CH_4$

Nitrogen, $N_2$ (nitrogen's a triple-bonder)

Carbon monoxide, CO (carbon monoxide has two covalent bonds and one dative covalent bond, see next page)

## Bond Enthalpy is Related to the Length of a Bond

1) In covalent molecules, the **positive nuclei** are attracted to the area of electron density between the two nuclei (where the shared electrons are). But there's also a repulsion. The two **positively charged nuclei repel** each other, as do the **electrons**. To maintain the covalent bond there has to be a **balance** between these forces.

2) The distance between the **two nuclei** is the distance where the **attractive** and **repulsive** forces balance each other. This distance is the **bond length**.

3) The **higher the electron density** between the nuclei (i.e. the more electrons in the bond), the **stronger** the attraction between the atoms, the higher the **bond enthalpy** and the **shorter** the bond length. It makes sense really. If there's more attraction, the nuclei are pulled **closer** together.

A C=C bond has a **greater bond enthalpy** and is **shorter** than a C–C bond. Four electrons are shared in C=C and only two in C–C, so the **electron density** between the two carbon atoms is greater and the **bond is shorter**.

C≡C has an even **higher** bond enthalpy and is **shorter** than C=C — six electrons are shared here.

| Bond | C–C | C=C | C≡C |
|---|---|---|---|
| Average Bond Enthalpy (kJ mol⁻¹) | +347 | +612 | +838 |
| Bond length (nm) | 0.154 | 0.134 | 0.120 |

# Covalent Bonding

## *Dative Covalent Bonding is Where Both Electrons Come From One Atom*

1) In the molecules on the last page, the atoms are acting in a bit of an "I'll lend you mine if you lend me yours" way — each atom puts an electron into the bond and, in return, they get use of the electron put in by the other atom.

2) But there's another kind of covalent bond as well — a **dative covalent** (or **coordinate**) bond.
   This is where one atom donates **both electrons** to a bond. You've already seen an example of this in CO.

3) The **ammonium ion** ($NH_4^+$) is formed by dative covalent (or coordinate) bonding.
   It forms when the nitrogen atom in an ammonia molecule **donates a pair of electrons** to a proton ($H^+$).

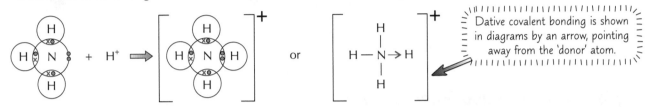

*Dative covalent bonding is shown in diagrams by an arrow, pointing away from the 'donor' atom.*

4) The ammonium ion can go on to form ionic bonds with other ions (see pages 19-21 for more on ionic bonding).

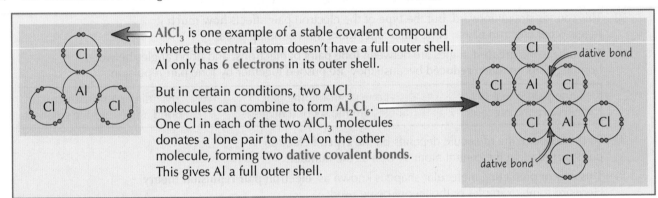

$AlCl_3$ is one example of a stable covalent compound where the central atom doesn't have a full outer shell. Al only has **6 electrons** in its outer shell.

But in certain conditions, two $AlCl_3$ molecules can combine to form $Al_2Cl_6$. One Cl in each of the two $AlCl_3$ molecules donates a lone pair to the Al on the other molecule, forming two **dative covalent bonds**. This gives Al a full outer shell.

## *Practice Questions*

Q1 What happens during covalent bonding?

Q2 Put the following three bonds in order from shortest to longest: C–C, C=C, C≡C.

Q3 What is a dative covalent bond?

Q4 Draw a dot-and-cross diagram to show the arrangement of the outer electrons in a molecule of $Al_2Cl_6$.

**Exam Questions**

Q1 Draw a dot-and-cross diagram (showing outer shell electrons only) to represent the bonding in the molecule silicon hydride ($SiH_4$). [1 mark]

Q2 a) Draw a dot-and-cross diagram of the ammonia molecule ($NH_3$) showing the outer shell electrons only. [1 mark]

 b) Draw a dot-and-cross diagram of the hydrogen chloride molecule (HCl) showing the outer shell electrons only. [1 mark]

 c) Ammonia reacts with hydrogen chloride to form ammonium chloride.
   Draw a dot-and-cross diagram to show the bonding in ammonium chloride. [2 marks]

Q3 a) Would you expect an N–N single bond to be shorter or longer than an N=N bond? Explain your answer. [3 marks]

 b) Draw a dot-and-cross diagram to show the bonding a molecule of nitrogen gas ($N_2$). [1 mark]

 c) How would you expect the bond enthalpy of the bond(s) in a molecule of $N_2$ to compare to those in a)? Explain your answer. [3 marks]

## *Dative covalent bonds — an act of charity on an atomic scale...*

*More pretty diagrams to learn. If you're asked to draw dot-and-cross diagrams in the exam, don't panic. It's a bit of trial and error really. Just sort the outer electrons until every atom has a full outer shell (that's 8 electrons for most atoms, except hydrogen which only has 2 in its outer shell). Watch out for double, triple and dative covalent bonds too...*

# Shapes of Molecules

*Chemistry would be heaps more simple if all molecules were flat. But they're not.*

## Molecular Shape Depends on Electron Pairs Around the Central Atom

Molecules and molecular ions come in loads of **different shapes**.
The shape depends on the **number** of pairs of electrons in the outer shell of the central atom.

In ammonia, the outermost shell
of nitrogen has four pairs of electrons.

Bonding pairs of electrons are shared
with another atom in a covalent bond.

Lone pairs of electrons
are not shared.

*A lone pear.*

## Electron Pairs Repel Each Other

1) Electrons are all **negatively charged**, so electron pairs will **repel** each other as much as they can.

2) This sounds straightforward, but the **type** of the electron pair affects **how much** it repels other electron pairs. Lone pairs repel **more** than bonding pairs.

3) This means the **greatest** angles are between **lone pairs** of electrons, and bond angles between bonding pairs are often **reduced** because they are pushed together by lone pair repulsion.

| Lone pair/lone pair angles are the biggest. | Lone pair/bonding pair angles are the second biggest. | Bonding pair/bonding pair bond angles are the smallest. |
|---|---|---|

4) So the shape of the molecule depends on the **type** of electron pairs surrounding the central atom as well as the **number**.

5) This way of predicting molecular shape is known as '**electron pair repulsion theory**'. Here are some examples of the theory being used:

*Learn the bond angles for these three examples.*

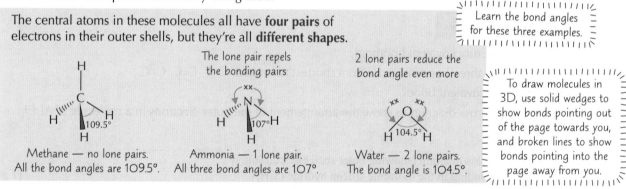

The central atoms in these molecules all have **four pairs** of electrons in their outer shells, but they're all **different shapes**.

The lone pair repels the bonding pairs

2 lone pairs reduce the bond angle even more

Methane — no lone pairs. All the bond angles are 109.5°.

Ammonia — 1 lone pair. All three bond angles are 107°.

Water — 2 lone pairs. The bond angle is 104.5°.

*To draw molecules in 3D, use solid wedges to show bonds pointing out of the page towards you, and broken lines to show bonds pointing into the page away from you.*

## You Can Use Electron Pairs to Predict the Shapes of Molecules

To predict the shape of a molecule, you first have to know how many bonding and non-bonding electron pairs are on the central atom. Here's how:

1) Find the **central atom** (the one all the other atoms are bonded to).

2) Work out the number of **electrons** in the **outer shell** of the central atom. Use the periodic table to do this, or you could draw a dot-and-cross diagram.

3) The **molecular formula** tells you how many atoms the central atom is **bonded** to. From this you can work out how many electrons are **shared with** the central atom.

*If there's a double bond, count it as two bonds.*

4) **Add up** the electrons and **divide by 2** to find the **number of electron pairs** on the central atom. If you have an ion remember to account for its **charge**.

5) **Compare** the number of **electron pairs** with the number of **bonds** to find the number of **lone pairs**.

6) You can then use the **number of electron pairs** and the number of **lone pairs** and **bonding centres** around the central atom to work out the **shape** of the molecule (see next page).

*Bonding centres are the atoms bonded to the central atom.*

# Shapes of Molecules

## Practise **Drawing** these Molecules

Once you know how many electron pairs are on the central atom, you can use **electron pair repulsion theory** to work out the **shape** of the molecule. These are the common shapes that you need to be able to draw:

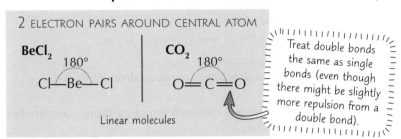

2 ELECTRON PAIRS AROUND CENTRAL ATOM

$BeCl_2$ 180°
Cl—Be—Cl

$CO_2$ 180°
O=C=O

Linear molecules

Treat double bonds the same as single bonds (even though there might be slightly more repulsion from a double bond).

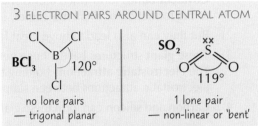

3 ELECTRON PAIRS AROUND CENTRAL ATOM

$BCl_3$ 120°
no lone pairs
— trigonal planar

$SO_2$ 119°
1 lone pair
— non-linear or 'bent'

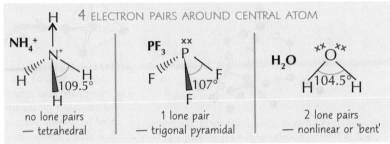

4 ELECTRON PAIRS AROUND CENTRAL ATOM

$NH_4^+$ 109.5°
no lone pairs
— tetrahedral

$PF_3$ 107°
1 lone pair
— trigonal pyramidal

$H_2O$ 104.5°
2 lone pairs
— nonlinear or 'bent'

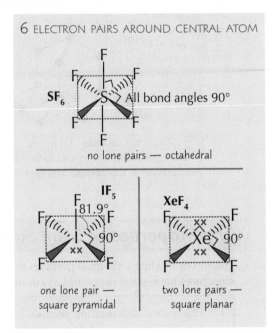

6 ELECTRON PAIRS AROUND CENTRAL ATOM

$SF_6$ All bond angles 90°
no lone pairs — octahedral

$IF_5$ 81.9° 90°
one lone pair —
square pyramidal

$XeF_4$ 90°
two lone pairs —
square planar

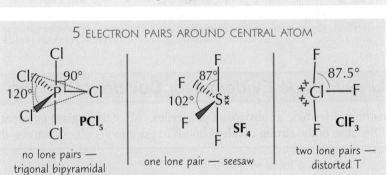

5 ELECTRON PAIRS AROUND CENTRAL ATOM

$PCl_5$ 120° 90°
no lone pairs —
trigonal bipyramidal

$SF_4$ 87° 102°
one lone pair — seesaw

$ClF_3$ 87.5°
two lone pairs —
distorted T

## Practice Questions

Q1 What is a lone pair of electrons?

Q2 Write down the order of the strength of repulsion between different kinds of electron pair.

Q3 Explain why a water molecule is not linear.

Q4 Draw a tetrahedral molecule.

**Exam Questions**

Q1 a) Draw the shapes of the following molecules, showing the approximate values of the bond angles on the diagrams and naming each shape.

   i) $NCl_3$          ii) $BF_3$          [6 marks]

   b) Explain why the shapes of $NCl_3$ and $BCl_3$ are different.          [3 marks]

Q2 The displayed formula of an organic compound is shown. Use electron pair repulsion theory to predict the shape and relevant bond angles of the bonds around atoms A, B and C.          [3 marks]

O=C—C—C—O—H (with H atoms shown; atom A, atom B, atom C labelled)

---

## These molecules ain't square...

*In the exam, those evil examiners might try to throw you by asking you for the shape of an unfamiliar molecule. Don't panic — you can use the steps on page 24 to work out the shape of any covalent molecule. It often helps to draw a dot-and-cross diagram of the molecule you're working out the shape of — it'll help you see where all the electrons are.*

# Giant Covalent and Metallic Structures

*Not all covalent structures are tiny molecules... some form vast structures (well... vast compared to simple molecules).*

## Some **Covalently Bonded** Substances Have **Giant Structures**

1) **Covalent bonds** form when atoms **share** electrons with other atoms. Very often, this leads to the formation of small **molecules**, including $CO_2$, $N_2$ and the others on page 22.

2) But they can also lead to huge great **lattices** too — containing billions and billions of atoms.

3) These **giant** structures have a huge network of **covalently** bonded atoms. The **electrostatic attractions** holding the atoms together in these structures are much **stronger** than the electrostatic attractions between simple covalent molecules.

4) **Carbon** and **silicon** can form these giant networks. This is because they can each form four strong, covalent bonds.

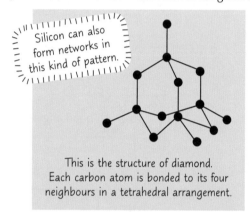

Silicon can also form networks in this kind of pattern.

This is the structure of diamond. Each carbon atom is bonded to its four neighbours in a tetrahedral arrangement.

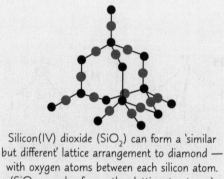

Silicon(IV) dioxide ($SiO_2$) can form a 'similar but different' lattice arrangement to diamond — with oxygen atoms between each silicon atom. ($SiO_2$ can also form other lattice structures.)

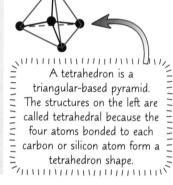

A tetrahedron is a triangular-based pyramid. The structures on the left are called tetrahedral because the four atoms bonded to each carbon or silicon atom form a tetrahedron shape.

## The **Properties** of Giant Structures Provide **Evidence** for **Covalent Bonding**

The forces holding individual particles together help determine a substance's **properties**. All of these **giant covalent structures** have some properties in common. Because of the **strong covalent** bonds in giant molecular structures, they:

1) Have very **high melting points** — you need to break a lot of very strong bonds before the substance melts, which takes a lot of energy.

2) Are often extremely **hard** — again, this is because of the very **strong bonds** all through the lattice arrangement.

3) Are **good thermal conductors** — since vibrations travel easily through the stiff lattices.

4) **Insoluble** — the covalent bonds mean atoms are more attracted to their neighbours in the lattice than to solvent molecules. The fact that they are all **insoluble** in polar solvents (like water) shows that they don't contain ions.

5) **Can't conduct electricity** — since there are (in most giant covalent lattice structures) **no charged ions or free electrons** (all the bonding electrons are held in localised covalent bonds).

## Graphite Can Conduct Electricity

An **exception** to the "can't conduct electricity rule" above is **graphite** (a form of carbon). Carbon atoms form **sheets**, with each carbon atom sharing three of its **outer shell** electrons with three other carbon atoms. This leaves the fourth outer electron in each atom fairly **free** to move between the sheets, making graphite a **conductor**.

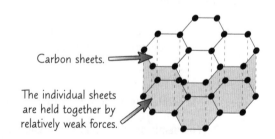

Carbon sheets.

The individual sheets are held together by relatively weak forces.

### Graphene is One Layer of Graphite

Graphene is a **sheet** of carbon atoms joined together in **hexagons**. The sheet is just **one atom** thick, making it a **two-dimensional** compound.

Graphene's **structure** gives it some pretty **useful properties**. Like **graphite**, it can **conduct electricity** as the delocalised electrons are free to move along the sheet. It's also incredibly strong, transparent, and really light.

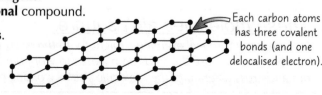

Each carbon atoms has three covalent bonds (and one delocalised electron).

# Giant Covalent and Metallic Structures

## Metals have Giant Structures Too

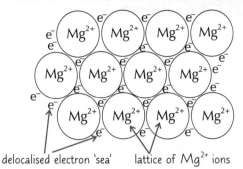

delocalised electron 'sea'   lattice of $Mg^{2+}$ ions

Metal elements exist as **giant metallic lattice structures**.

1) In metallic lattices, the electrons in the outermost shell of the metal atoms are **delocalised** — they're free to move. This leaves a **positive metal ion**, e.g. $Na^+$, $Mg^{2+}$, $Al^{3+}$.

2) The positive metal ions are **electrostatically attracted** to the delocalised negative electrons. They form a lattice of closely packed positive ions in a **sea** of delocalised electrons — this is **metallic bonding**.

3) The overall lattice structure is made up of **layers** of **positive** metal **ions**, **separated** by **layers** of **electrons**.

The **metallic bonding model** explains why metals do what they do —

1) The **melting points** of metals are generally **high** because of the strong metallic bonding, with the **number of delocalised electrons per atom** affecting the melting point. The **more** electrons there are, the **stronger** the bonding will be and the **higher** the melting point. $Mg^{2+}$ has **two** delocalised electrons per atom, so it's got a **higher melting point** than $Na^+$, which only has **one**. The **size** of the metal ion and the **lattice structure** also affect the melting point.

2) As there are **no bonds** holding specific ions together, and the layers of positive metal ions are separated by layers of electrons, metals are **malleable** (can be **shaped**) and are **ductile** (can be drawn into a wire). The layers of metal ions can slide over each other without disrupting the attraction between the positive ions and electrons.

3) The delocalised electrons can pass **kinetic energy** to each other, making metals **good thermal conductors**.

4) Metals are **good electrical conductors** because the **delocalised electrons** are free to move and can carry a **current**. Any **impurities** can dramatically **reduce** electrical conductivity by reducing the number of electrons that are free to move and carry charge — the electrons transfer to the impurities and form anions.

5) Metals are **insoluble**, except in **liquid metals**, because of the **strength** of the metallic bonds.

## Practice Questions

Q1 Are the melting points of giant covalent lattices high or low? Explain why.

Q2 Why won't giant covalent structures dissolve?

Q3 Explain how the model of metallic bonding accounts for: i) the relatively high melting points of metals.
ii) a metal's ability to conduct electricity.

**Exam Questions**

Q1 a) Explain what is meant by metallic bonding. Draw a diagram to illustrate your explanation. [2 marks]

b) Explain why calcium has a higher melting point than potassium. [1 mark]

Q2 Silicon dioxide is a covalent compound that melts at 1610 °C. Explain the high melting point of silicon in terms of its bonding. [2 marks]

Q3 Graphite is a giant covalent structure. However, unlike most giant covalent structures, it is able to conduct electricity. Explain why graphite is able to conduct electricity. [2 marks]

Q4 Electrical grade copper must be 99.99% pure. If sulfur and oxygen impurities react with the copper ions, its electrical conductivity is reduced. Use your knowledge of metallic and ionic bonding to explain this. [3 marks]

Q5 Carborundum (silicon carbide) has the formula SiC and is almost as hard as diamond.

a) What sort of structure would you expect carborundum to have as a solid? [1 mark]

b) Apart from hardness, give two other physical properties you would expect carborundum to have. [2 marks]

## Tetrahedron — sounds like that monster from Greek mythology...

*Close the book and write down a list of the typical properties of a giant covalent lattice — then look back at the page and see what you missed. Then do the same for the typical properties of giant metallic lattices. The fun never stops...*

# Electronegativity and Polarisation

*I find electronegativity an incredibly attractive subject. It's all to do with how strongly an atom attracts electrons.*

## Some Atoms **Attract** Bonding Electrons More than Other Atoms

The ability of an atom to attract the bonding electrons in a covalent bond is called **electronegativity**.

1) Electronegativity is usually measured using the **Pauling scale**. The higher the electronegativity value, the more electronegative the element. **Fluorine** is the most electronegative element — it's given a value of **4.0** on the Pauling scale. Oxygen, chlorine and nitrogen are also very strongly electronegative.

2) The least electronegative elements have electronegativity values of around 0.7.

3) More electronegative elements have **higher nuclear charges** (there are more protons in the nucleus) and **smaller atomic radii**. Therefore, electronegativity **increases** across **periods** and **up** the **groups** (ignoring the noble gases).

4) There'll be a copy of the **periodic table** showing the **Pauling values** of different elements in your exam data book.

## Covalent Bonds may be **Polarised** by **Differences** in **Electronegativity**

1) In a covalent bond, the bonding electrons sit in orbitals between two nuclei. If both atoms have **similar** or **identical** **electronegativities**, the electrons will sit roughly **midway** between the two nuclei and the bond will be **non-polar**.

2) The covalent bonds in homonuclear, diatomic gases (e.g. $H_2$, $Cl_2$) are **non-polar** because the atoms have **equal** electronegativities and so the electrons are equally attracted to both nuclei.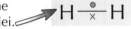

3) Some elements, like carbon and hydrogen, also have pretty **similar** electronegativities, so bonds between them are essentially **non-polar**.

4) If the bond is between two atoms with **different electronegativities**, the bonding electrons will be pulled towards the more electronegative atom. This causes the electrons to be spread unevenly, and so there will be a **charge** across the bond (each atom has a **partial charge** — one atom is slightly positive, and the other slightly negative). The bond is said to be **polar**.

5) In a **polar bond**, the difference in electronegativity between the two atoms causes a **dipole**. A dipole is a **difference in charge** between the two atoms caused by a shift in **electron density** in the bond.

6) So **remember** that the greater the **difference** in electronegativity, the greater the shift in electron density, and the **more polar** the bond.

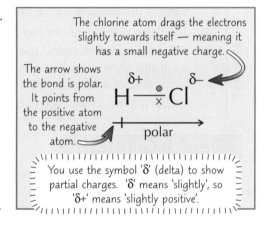

The chlorine atom drags the electrons slightly towards itself — meaning it has a small negative charge.

The arrow shows the bond is polar. It points from the positive atom to the negative atom.

You use the symbol '$\delta$' (delta) to show partial charges. '$\delta$' means 'slightly', so '$\delta+$' means 'slightly positive'.

## Use the **Pauling Scale** to work out the **Percentage Ionic Character**

1) Only bonds between atoms of a **single** element, like diatomic gases, can be **purely covalent**. This is because the **electronegativity difference** between the atoms is **zero** and so the bonding electrons are arranged completely **evenly** within the bond. At the same time, very few compounds are completely ionic.

2) Really, most compounds come somewhere **in between** the two extremes — meaning they've often got ionic **and** covalent properties.

3) You can use electronegativity to **predict** what type of bonding will occur between two atoms. The higher the difference in electronegativity, the more ionic in character the bonding becomes.

4) In your data book, you'll be given a periodic table of all the Pauling values of the elements, and also see a table which tells you **how ionic** a bond is, given the electronegativity difference between the atoms. A copy is shown below:

| Electronegativity difference | 0.1 | 0.3 | 0.5 | 0.7 | 1.0 | 1.3 | 1.5 | 1.7 | 2.0 | 2.5 | 3.0 |
|---|---|---|---|---|---|---|---|---|---|---|---|
| % ionic character | 0.5 | 2 | 6 | 12 | 22 | 34 | 43 | 51 | 63 | 79 | 89 |

**Example:** Predict the % ionic character of a C–Cl bond, given that the Pauling electronegativity values of carbon and chlorine are C = 2.5 and Cl = 3.0.

The difference between the electronegativities of chlorine and carbon is:

$$3.0 - 2.5 = 0.5$$

So the bond will have a percentage ionic character of about **6%**.

Bonds are polar if the difference in electronegativity values is _more_ than about 0.4.

# Electronegativity and Polarisation

## Polar Bonds **Don't** Always Make **Polar Molecules**

Whether a molecule is **polar** or not depends on its **shape** and the **polarity** of its bonds. A **polar molecule** has an **overall dipole**, which is just a dipole caused by the presence of a **permanent charge** across the molecule.

Permanent polar bonding

1) In a simple molecule, such as **hydrogen chloride**, the polar bond gives the whole molecule a permanent dipole — it's a **polar molecule**.

$$\overset{\delta+}{H} \!-\! \overset{\delta-}{\underset{x}{\overset{\circ}{\phantom{.}}}} \overset{\delta-}{Cl}$$

$\xrightarrow{\hspace{1cm}}$ polar

*You may see molecules with an overall dipole referred to as having 'overall polarity'. They're both just ways of saying the molecule is polar.*

2) A more complicated molecule may have **several polar bonds**. If the polar bonds are arranged so they point in opposite directions, they'll **cancel each other out** — the molecule is **non-polar** overall.

No dipole overall.

$$\overset{\delta-}{O} \!=\! \overset{\delta+}{C} \!=\! \overset{\delta-}{O}$$

3) If the polar bonds all point in roughly the **same direction**, then the molecule will be **polar**.

polar

polar

*Be careful with examples like this — the tetrahedral shape means the two dipoles don't cancel out, so the molecule is polar.*

## Practice Questions

Q1 What scale is electronegativity measured on?

Q2 What is the most electronegative element?

Q3 What is a dipole?

Q4 Why isn't $CO_2$ a polar molecule, even though it has polar bonds?

**Exam Questions**

Q1 Many covalent molecules have a permanent dipole, due to differences in electronegativities.

a) Define the term electronegativity. [1 mark]

b) What are the trends in electronegativity as you go across a period and down a group in the periodic table? [1 mark]

c) Which of the following molecules is polar?

    **A** $H_2O$     **B** $Br_2$     **C** $CCl_4$     **D** $SF_6$ [1 mark]

Q2 a) Draw diagrams to show the shape of the covalently bonded molecules below. Mark any partial charges on your diagrams.

    i) Boron trichloride ($BCl_3$) [2 marks]

    ii) Dichloromethane ($CH_2Cl_2$) [2 marks]

b) Explain whether or not the molecules in part a) have an overall dipole. [2 marks]

---

## *I got my tongue stuck on an ice cube last week — it was a polar bond...*

*It's important to remember that just because a molecule has polar bonds, doesn't mean it will have a permanent dipole — you have to look carefully at the shape first to see if the polar bonds will cancel each other out or not. So if you're feeling a bit hazy on how to work out the shape of a molecule, have a read of pages 24-25, and all will be revealed.*

# Intermolecular Forces

*Intermolecular forces hold molecules together. They're pretty important, cos we'd all be gassy clouds without them.*

## Intermolecular Forces are *Very Weak*

Intermolecular forces are forces **between** molecules. They're much **weaker** than covalent, ionic or metallic bonds. There are three types you need to know about:

> You might see intermolecular forces called intermolecular bonds — don't worry, they're exactly the same thing.

1) **London forces (instantaneous dipole-induced dipole bonds).**
2) **Permanent dipole-permanent dipole bonds.**
3) **Hydrogen bonding** (this is the strongest type of intermolecular forces — see pages 32-33).

## *All* Atoms and Molecules Form *London Forces*

**London forces** (also called instantaneous dipole-induced dipole bonds) cause **all** atoms and molecules to be **attracted** to each other.

1) **Electrons** in charge clouds are always **moving** really quickly. At any particular moment, the electrons in an atom are likely to be more to one side than the other. At this moment, the atom would have a **temporary** (or **instantaneous**) **dipole**.

2) This dipole can **induce another** temporary dipole in the opposite direction on a neighbouring atom. The two dipoles are then **attracted** to each other.

3) The second dipole can induce yet another dipole in a **third atom**. It's kind of like the domino effect.

4) Because the electrons are constantly moving, the dipoles are being **created** and **destroyed** all the time. Even though the dipoles keep changing, the **overall effect** is for the atoms to be **attracted** to each other.

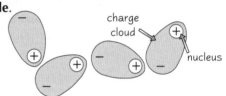

## *London Forces* Can Hold Molecules in a *Lattice*

London forces are responsible for holding **iodine** molecules together in a **lattice**.

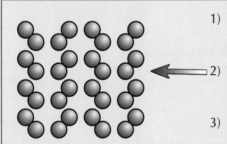

1) Iodine atoms are held together in pairs by **strong** covalent bonds to form molecules of $I_2$.
2) But the molecules are then held together in a **molecular lattice** arrangement by **weak London forces**.
3) This structure is known as a **simple molecular structure**.

> Look back at pages 22-23 for more on covalent bonding.

## Stronger *London Forces* mean *Higher Melting and Boiling Points*

1) Not all London forces are the same strength — larger molecules have **larger electron clouds**, meaning **stronger** London forces.

2) Molecules with greater **surface areas** also have stronger London forces because they have a **bigger exposed electron cloud** (see next page).

3) When you **boil** a liquid, you need to **overcome** the intermolecular forces, so that the particles can **escape** from the liquid surface. It stands to reason that you need **more energy** to overcome **stronger** intermolecular forces, so liquids with stronger London forces will have **higher boiling points**.

4) Melting solids also involves **overcoming intermolecular forces**, so solids with stronger London forces will have **higher melting points** too.

5) Alkanes demonstrate this nicely...

London Forces.

# Intermolecular Forces

## Intermolecular Forces in Organic Molecules Depend on Their Shape

The **shape** of an organic compound's molecules affects the **strength** of the **intermolecular forces**.
Take alkanes, for example...

1) Alkanes have **covalent bonds** inside the molecules. **Between** the molecules there are **London forces**, which hold them all together.

2) The **longer** the carbon chain, the **stronger** the London forces — because there's **more molecular surface contact** and **more electrons** to interact.

3) So as the molecules get longer, it gets harder to separate them because it takes **more energy** to overcome the London forces.

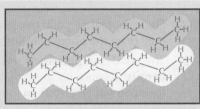

Smaller molecular surface contact, so weaker intermolecular forces.

Greater molecular surface contact, so stronger intermolecular forces.

4) Branched-chain alkanes can't **pack closely** together and their **molecular surface contact** is **small** compared to straight chain alkanes of similar molecular mass. So fewer London forces can form. Look at these **isomers** of $C_4H_{10}$, for example...

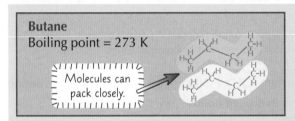

**Butane**
Boiling point = 273 K
Molecules can pack closely.

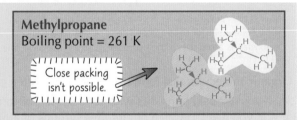

**Methylpropane**
Boiling point = 261 K
Close packing isn't possible.

## Polar Molecules have Permanent Dipole-Permanent Dipole Bonds

The δ+ and δ– charges on polar molecules cause weak electrostatic forces of attraction between molecules. These are known as **permanent dipole-permanent dipole bonds**. E.g., hydrogen chloride gas has polar molecules:

$$\overset{δ+}{H}—\overset{δ-}{Cl}\cdots\cdots\overset{δ+}{H}—\overset{δ-}{Cl}\cdots\cdots\overset{δ+}{H}—\overset{δ-}{Cl}$$

Permanent dipole-permanent dipole bonds happen **as well as** (not instead of) London forces. So, molecules that can form permanent dipole-permanent dipole bonds, in addition to their London forces, will generally have **higher boiling** and **melting points** than those with similar London forces that can't form permanent dipole-permanent dipole bonds.

### Practice Questions

Q1 What's the strongest type of intermolecular force?
Q2 Explain what London forces are.
Q3 Explain what gives rise to permanent dipole-permanent dipole intermolecular forces.

**Exam Questions**

Q1 The molecules in the table on the right all have the molecular formula $C_5H_{12}$.

Explain the differences in the boiling points of these molecules.

| Molecule | Boiling Point (°C) |
|---|---|
| Pentane | 36.1 |
| 2-methylbutane | 27.7 |
| 2,2-dimethylpropane | 9.50 |

[3 marks]

Q2 What intermolecular forces are present in chloroethane ($CH_3CH_2Cl$)? [1 mark]

Q3 $N_2$ and NO are both gases at room temperature. Predict, with reasoning, which gas has a higher boiling point. [2 marks]

## London Forces — the irresistible pull of streets paved with gold...

*You may well see London forces called instantaneous dipole-induced dipole bonds. But don't panic, they're the same thing. It's useful to remember both names though — especially since instantaneous dipole-induced dipole describes what's going on in this sort of intermolecular bonding. It's all to do with the attraction between temporary dipoles.*

# Hydrogen Bonding

*Hydrogen bonds form between certain types of molecule. Water, alcohols, ammonia, hydrogen fluoride... Shall I go on?*

## Hydrogen Bonding is the Strongest Intermolecular Force

1) Hydrogen bonding **only** happens when **hydrogen** is covalently bonded to **fluorine**, **nitrogen** or **oxygen**.

2) Fluorine, nitrogen and oxygen are very **electronegative**, so they draw the bonding electrons away from the hydrogen atom.

   *See page 28 for more about electronegativity.*

3) The bond is so **polarised**, and hydrogen has such a **high charge density** because it's so small, that the hydrogen atoms form weak bonds with **lone pairs of electrons** on the fluorine, nitrogen or oxygen atoms of **other molecules**.

4) **Water**, **ammonia** and **hydrogen fluoride** all have hydrogen bonding:

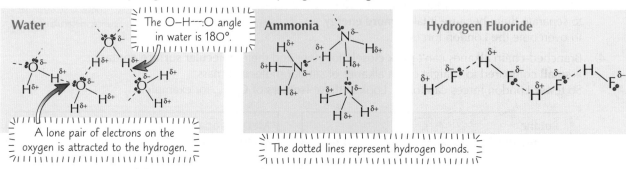

Water — *The O–H---:O angle in water is 180°.* — *A lone pair of electrons on the oxygen is attracted to the hydrogen.*

Ammonia — Hydrogen Fluoride — *The dotted lines represent hydrogen bonds.*

5) **Organic** molecules that form hydrogen bonds often contain **-OH** or **-NH** groups, e.g. **alcohols** and **amines**.

6) So, if you're asked to predict whether a substance forms **hydrogen bonds** or not, you need to watch out for these **groups** of **atoms**.

## Hydrogen Bonds Affect How a Substance Behaves

Hydrogen bonds are the **strongest** type of intermolecular forces and have a huge effect on the properties of substances. Substances that form hydrogen bonds have **high melting and boiling points** because a lot of **energy** is required to overcome the intermolecular forces.

The graph on the right shows how the boiling points of **Group 7 hydrides** vary as you go down Group 7.

- Molecules of **hydrogen fluoride** form hydrogen bonds with each other (see above). Hydrogen bonding is the **strongest** intermolecular force, so the intermolecular bonding in HF is **very strong**. It requires a lot of **energy** to overcome these bonds, so HF has a **high boiling point**.

- From HCl to HI, although the permanent dipole-dipole interactions **decreases**, the **number of electrons** in the molecule increases, so the **strength** of the London forces also **increases**. This effect overrides the decrease in the strength of the permanent dipole-permanent dipole interactions, so the boiling points increase from **HCl** to **HI**.

Boiling Points of Group 7 Hydrides
Boiling point / K — HF 300, 250, HI, HBr, 200, HCl

- **Water** has some pretty weird properties. Despite the fact that it's a pretty small molecule, it has a fairly **high boiling point** (373 K, or 100 °C).

- If you look at the trend in boiling points of **Group 6 hydrides**, you'll see they follow a **similar** trend to the boiling points of the **Group 7 hydrides** above.

- Water's ability to form **hydrogen bonds** with itself gives it a **high boiling point**, while the **increase** in the strength of the **London forces** from $H_2S$ to $H_2Te$ **overrides** the **decrease** in the strength of the **permanent dipole-permanent dipole forces**, causing the boiling point to increase from $H_2S$ to $H_2Te$.

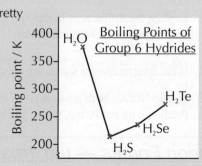

Boiling Points of Group 6 Hydrides
Boiling point / K — $H_2O$ 400, 350, 300, $H_2Te$, 250, $H_2Se$, 200, $H_2S$

Substances that form hydrogen bonds are also **soluble** in water.
This is because they can form hydrogen bonds with the water molecules, allowing them to mix and dissolve.

# Hydrogen Bonding

## Hydrogen Bonds Explains Why *Ice Floats* on *Water*

1) Ice is another example of a **simple molecular** structure.

2) In **ice**, the water molecules are arranged so that there is the maximum number of hydrogen bonds — the **lattice structure** formed in this way 'wastes' lots of space.

3) As the ice **melts**, some of the hydrogen bonds are **broken** and the lattice **breaks down** — allowing molecules to 'fill' the spaces.

4) This effect means ice is much less dense than water — which is why **ice floats**.

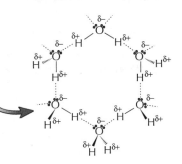

## *Alcohols* are *Less Volatile* than Similar *Alkanes*

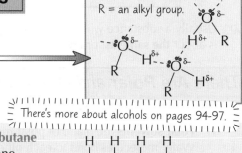

R = an alkyl group.

1) All alcohols contain a **polar hydroxyl group** (-OH) that has a $\delta-$ charge on the oxygen atom and a $\delta+$ charge on the hydrogen atom. This polar group helps alcohols to form **hydrogen bonds**.

2) Hydrogen bonding gives alcohols **low volatilities** (i.e. they have **high boiling points**) compared to **non-polar compounds**, e.g. alkanes, of similar sizes, with similar numbers of electrons.

There's more about alcohols on pages 94-97.

- For example, **butan-1-ol** has a **boiling point of 118 °C**, while **butane** boils at **–1 °C**. The only **intermolecular forces** present in butane are **London forces** which are relatively **weak** — it doesn't take much energy to overcome these forces and for butane to evaporate.

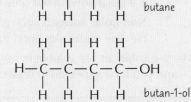

- The strength of the London forces in both butan-1-ol and butane will be **similar**, but butan-1-ol can form **hydrogen bonds** in addition to London forces. Hydrogen bonds are the **strongest** type of intermolecular force and require much **more energy** to break. This gives butan-1-ol a much higher boiling point.

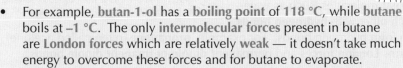

butane

butan-1-ol

## Practice Questions

Q1 What atoms need to be present for hydrogen bonding to occur?

Q2 Name three substances that undergo hydrogen bonding.

Q3 Why is ice less dense than water?

**Exam Questions**

Q1 a) Explain why water's boiling point is higher than expected in comparison to other similar molecules. [2 marks]

b) Draw a labelled diagram showing the intermolecular bonding that takes place in water.
Your diagram should show at least 4 water molecules. [2 marks]

Q2 a) For each of the following pairs of compounds, state which will have the higher boiling point.

i) Ammonia ($NH_3$) and methane ($CH_4$). [1 mark]

ii) Water and hydrogen sulfide ($H_2S$). [1 mark]

iii) Butane and propan-1-ol. [1 mark]

b) Explain your choices in part a). [2 marks]

Q3 An organic compound used as antifreeze is ethane-1,2-diol.
Its structure is shown on the right.

The boiling point of ethane-1,2-diol is 197 °C, whereas
the boiling point of ethanol is 78 °C. Suggest a reason for this difference. [1 mark]

## *I never used to like Chemistry, but after this, I feel we've truly bonded...*

*There you have it, hydrogen bonding. The king of intermolecular bonding in my opinion. If you need to draw a picture of hydrogen bonding in the exam, make sure you draw any lone pairs and all the partial charges (those are the $\delta-$ and $\delta+$ signs). And show any hydrogen bonds with a dotted line (unless you're told otherwise). Don't go missing easy marks.*

# Solubility

*Ever wondered why that teaspoon of sugar dissolves in your afternoon cuppa'?  Or why all the salt doesn't just fall out of the sea onto the seabed?  Well my friend, you're about to find out.  It's all to do with solubility...*

## Solubility is Affected by Bonding

1) For one substance to **dissolve** in another, all these things have to happen:

> • bonds in the **substance** have to **break**,
> • bonds in the **solvent** have to **break**, and
> • **new bonds** have to form **between the substance** and the **solvent**.

2) Usually a substance will only dissolve if the strength of the new bonds **formed** is about **the same as**, or **greater than**, the strength of the bonds that are **broken**.

## There Are Polar and Non-Polar Solvents

There are two main **types of solvent**:

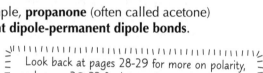

You may see water referred to as an aqueous solvent.  Any solvent that isn't water is known as a non-aqueous solvent.

1) **Polar solvents** are made of polar molecules, such as water.
Water molecules bond to each other with **hydrogen bonds**.
But not all polar solvents can form hydrogen bonds.  For example, **propanone** (often called acetone) is a polar solvent but only forms **London forces** and **permanent dipole-permanent dipole bonds**.

2) **Non-polar solvents** such as hexane.
Hexane molecules bond to each other by **London forces**.

Look back at pages 28-29 for more on polarity, and pages 30-33 for lots on intermolecular forces.

Many substances are soluble in one type of solvent but not the other — and you'll be expected to understand why...

## Ionic Substances Dissolve in Polar Solvents such as Water

1) Water is a **polar solvent** — water molecules have a slightly positively-charged end (the δ+ hydrogens) and a slightly negatively-charged end (the δ– oxygen).

2) When an ionic substance is mixed with water, the ions in the ionic substance are attracted to the **oppositely charged ends** of the water molecules.

3) The ions are pulled away from the ionic lattice by the water molecules, which surround the ions.  This process is called **hydration**.

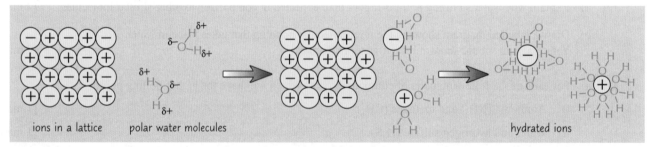

ions in a lattice    polar water molecules    hydrated ions

4) Some ionic substances **don't dissolve** because the bonding between their ions is **too strong**.  For example, aluminium oxide ($Al_2O_3$) is insoluble in water because the bonds between the ions are stronger than the bonds they'd form with the water molecules.  ($Al^{3+}$ has a high charge density, so forms strong ionic bonds — see page 19.)

## Alcohols also Dissolve in Polar Solvents such as Water

1) Alcohols are **covalent** but they dissolve in water...

2) ... because the polar O-H bond in an alcohol is attracted to the polar O-H bonds in water.  **Hydrogen bonds** form between the lone pairs on the δ– oxygen atoms and the δ+ hydrogen atoms.

3) The **carbon chain** part of the alcohol isn't attracted to water, so the more carbon atoms there are, the **less soluble** the alcohol will be.

# Solubility

## Not All **Molecules** with **Polar Bonds** Dissolve in **Water**

1) **Halogenoalkanes** (see page 90) contain **polar bonds** but their dipoles aren't strong enough to form **hydrogen bonds** with water.

See page 32 for what's needed to form hydrogen bonds.

2) The hydrogen bonding **between** water molecules is **stronger** than the bonds that would be formed with halogenoalkanes, so halogenoalkanes don't dissolve.

> **Example:**
> When the halogenoalkane chlorobutane is added to water, they don't mix, but separate into two layers.
>
> chlorobutane layer
> water layer

Henry couldn't understand why the champagne wouldn't dissolve.

3) But, halogenoalkanes can form **permanent dipole-permanent dipole bonds**. They happily dissolve in polar solvents that also form **permanent dipole-permanent dipole bonds** (not hydrogen bonds).

## Non-Polar Substances Dissolve Best in **Non-Polar Solvents**

1) Non-polar substances such as **ethene** have **London forces** between their molecules. They form **similar bonds** with **non-polar solvents** such as hexane — so they tend to dissolve in them.

2) Water molecules are attracted to **each other** more strongly than they are to **non-polar molecules** such as iodine — so non-polar substances don't tend to dissolve easily in water.

> **Like dissolves like** (usually) — substances usually dissolve best in solvents with similar **intermolecular forces**.

## Practice Questions

Q1 Which type of solvent, polar or a non-polar, would you choose to dissolve:  i) sodium chloride?    ii) ethane?

Q2 Why do most ionic substances dissolve in water?

Q3 What is meant by 'hydration'?

Q4 Some ionic substances don't dissolve in water. Why not?

Q5 What type of bonding occurs between an alcohol and water?

Q6 Why are most non-polar substances insoluble in water?

**Exam Questions**

Q1 Hydrogen bonds are present between molecules of water.

  a) i)  Explain why alcohols often dissolve in water while halogenoalkanes do not.        [4 marks]

   ii)  Draw a diagram to show the bonds that form when propan-1-ol dissolves in water.        [2 marks]

  b)  Explain the process by which potassium iodide dissolves in water to form hydrated ions.
   Include a diagram of the hydrated ions.        [5 marks]

Q2 a)  An unknown substance, X is suspected to be a non-polar simple covalent molecule.
   Describe how you could confirm this by testing with two different solvents.
   Name the solvents chosen and give the expected results.        [3 marks]

  b)  Explain these results in terms of the intermolecular bonding within X and the solvents.        [4 marks]

---

## *When the ice-caps melt, where will all the polar solvents live?*

*I reckon it's logical enough, this business of what dissolves what. Remember, water is a polar molecule — so other polar molecules, as well as ions, are attracted to its δ+ and δ– ends. If that attraction's stronger than the existing bonds (which have to break), the substance will dissolve. It's worth remembering that rule of thumb about 'like dissolves like'.*

# Predicting Structures and Properties

*By looking at certain properties that a substance has, such as its melting/boiling points, its solubility and whether it conducts electricity, you can predict what sort of bonding it has. If this doesn't excite you, then I don't know what will.*

## The Physical Properties of a **Solid** Depend on the **Nature** of its Particles

Here are a just a few examples of the ways in which the particles that make up a substance affect it properties:

1) The **melting** and **boiling points** of a substance are determined by the strength of the **attraction** between its particles (the **intermolecular forces**).

2) A substance will only **conduct electricity** if it contains **charged particles** that are **free to move**.

3) How **soluble** a substance is in **water** depends on the **type** of particles that it contains. Water is able to form **hydrogen bonds**, so substances that are also able to form hydrogen bonds, or are **charged** (i.e. ions) will dissolve in it well, whereas **non-polar** or **uncharged** substances won't.

## Learn the **Properties** of the Main Substance Types

Make sure you know this stuff like the back of your hand:

| Bonding | Examples | Melting and boiling points | Typical state at room temperature and pressure | Does solid conduct electricity? | Does liquid conduct electricity? | Is it soluble in water? |
|---|---|---|---|---|---|---|
| Ionic | NaCl MgCl$_2$ | High | Solid | No (ions are held in place) | Yes (ions are free to move) | Yes |
| Simple covalent (molecular) | CO$_2$ I$_2$ H$_2$O | Low (involves breaking intermolecular forces but <u>not</u> covalent bonds) | May be solid (like I$_2$) but usually liquid or gas | No | No | Depends on whether it can form hydrogen bonds |
| Giant covalent | Diamond Graphite SiO$_2$ | High | Solid | No (except graphite) | — (sublimes rather than melting) | No |
| Metallic | Fe Mg Al | High | Solid | Yes (delocalised electrons) | Yes (delocalised electrons) | No |

## You Can Use the **Properties** of a Material to **Predict its Structure**

You need to be able to predict the type of structure from a list of its properties. Here's a quick example.

**Example:** Substance X has a melting point of 1045 K. When solid, it is an insulator, but once melted it conducts electricity. Identify the type of structure present in substance X.

1) Substance X **doesn't** conduct electricity when it's **solid**, but **does** conduct electricity once **melted**. So it looks like it's **ionic** — that would fit with the fact that it has a **high melting point** too.

2) You can also tell that it definitely **isn't simple covalent** because it has a **high melting point**, it definitely **isn't metallic** because it **doesn't** conduct electricity when it's **solid**, and it definitely **isn't giant covalent** because it **does** conduct electricity when **melted**.

So substance X must be **ionic**.

Snowman building — family bonding with a melting point of 0 °C.

# Predicting Structures and Properties

## You can make **Predictions** about a **Substance's Properties** from its **Bonding**

1) You can also **predict** how a substance will behave depending on the **bonding** it has.

2) If you're dealing with **metallic**, **ionic** or **giant covalent substances**, you just need to consider the strong **ionic** or **covalent** bonds between the atoms.

3) If you're dealing with simple molecular compounds, you need to think about the **intermolecular forces** between the molecules, rather than the **covalent bonds** between the atoms.

**Example:** Aminomethane ($CH_3NH_2$) has a simple molecular structure. Predict the properties of aminomethane, including its solubility in water, its electrical conductivity, and its physical state at room temperature.

- Aminomethane contains an -$NH_2$ group, so is likely to form hydrogen bonds with water. This would make aminomethane **soluble in water**.

- Aminomethane has a simple molecular structure. In this type of structure, there are no free particles that can carry a charge, so aminomethane **doesn't conduct electricity**.

- To melt or boil a simple covalent compound you only have to overcome the intermolecular forces that hold the molecules together. You don't need to break the much stronger covalent bonds that hold the atoms together in the molecules. Aminomethane would have weak London forces between its molecules as well as stronger hydrogen bonds. However you would still expect aminomethane to have **low** boiling and melting points, and so be a **gas at room temperature**.

## Practice Questions

Q1 If a substance has a low melting point, what type of structure is it most likely to have?

Q2 Out of the four main types of structure (ionic, simple covalent, giant covalent and metallic), which will conduct electricity when they are liquids?

Q3 Would you expect a substance with a giant covalent structure to be soluble or insoluble in water?

**Exam Questions**

Q1 The table below describes the properties of four compounds, A, B, C and D.

| Substance | Melting point | Electrical conductivity of solid | Electrical conductivity of liquid | Solubility in water |
|-----------|---------------|----------------------------------|-----------------------------------|---------------------|
| A | high | poor | good | soluble |
| B | low | poor | poor | insoluble |
| C | high | good | good | insoluble |
| D | very high | poor | — (compound sublimes rather than melting) | insoluble |

Identify the type of structure present in each substance. [4 marks]

Q2 Iodine, $I_2$, and graphite are both solid at r.t.p.. At 500 K, iodine exists as a gas, while graphite remains solid. Explain this difference in the properties of iodine and graphite in terms of their structures. [4 marks]

Q3 A substance, X, has a melting point of 650 °C and a boiling point of 1107 °C. It conducts electricity in both the solid and liquid states, but is insoluble in water. Which of the follow substances could be substance X?

**A** Carbon dioxide      **B** Magnesium      **C** Caesium chloride      **D** Silicon dioxide      [1 mark]

## *Mystic Molecular Meg — predicting fortunes and properties since 1995...*

*You need to learn the info in the table on page 36. With a quick glance in my crystal ball, I can almost guarantee you'll need a bit of it in your exam... let me look closer and tell you which bit.... hmm.... No, it's clouded over. You'll have to learn the lot. Sorry. Tell you what — close the book and see how much of the table you can scribble out from memory.*

# Oxidation Numbers

*This double page has more occurrences of "oxidation" than the Beatles' "All You Need is Love" features the word "love".*

## Oxidation Numbers Tell You About the Movement of Electrons

When atoms **react** with or **bond** to other atoms, they can **lose** or **gain** electrons. The **oxidation number** (or oxidation state) tells you how many electrons an atom has donated or accepted to form an **ion**, or to form part of a **compound**. There are certain rules you need to remember to help you assign oxidation numbers. Here they are...

1)  All uncombined elements have an oxidation number of **0**. This means they haven't accepted or donated any electrons. Elements that are bonded to identical atoms will also have an oxidation number of **0**.

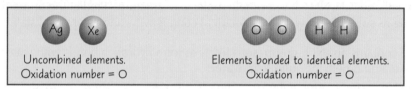

Uncombined elements.
Oxidation number = 0

Elements bonded to identical elements.
Oxidation number = 0

2)  The oxidation number of a simple, monatomic ion (that's an ion consisting of just one atom) is the same as its **charge**.

*Metals generally form ions with a charge that's equal to their Group number. Non-metals form ions with charges equal to their Group number minus 8.*

Oxidation number = +1 ← $Na^+$      $Mg^{2+}$ ← Oxidation number = +2

3)  For **molecular ions** (ions that are made up of a group of atoms with an overall charge), the sum of the oxidation numbers is the same as the overall charge of the ion. Each of the constituent atoms will have an oxidation number of its own, and the **sum** of their oxidation numbers equals the **overall charge**.

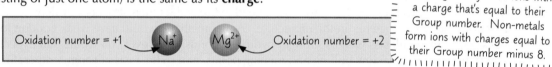

Combined oxygen has an oxidation number of −2 (apart from in $O_2$ and peroxides — see below). There are 4 oxygen atoms in $SO_4^{2-}$ so the total charge from oxygens is $4 \times -2 = -8$.

Overall charge is −2.

So the oxidation number of sulfur is +6, as $-8 + 6 = -2$.

4)  For a neutral compound, the overall charge is **0**, and each atom in the compound will have its own oxidation number. The **sum** of these oxidation numbers is 0.

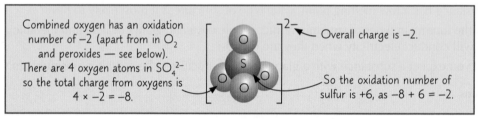

Chlorine forms ions with a charge of −1. So, the oxidation number of each chlorine is −1.

The oxidation number of the magnesium ion is +2.

The overall charge on $MgCl_2$ is $+2 + (2 \times -1) = 0$.

*$MgCl_2$ actually forms an ionic lattice of loads of $MgCl_2$ units.*

5)  **Hydrogen** always has an oxidation number of **+1**, except in **metal hydrides** ($MH_x$, where M = metal) where it's **−1** and in **molecular hydrogen** ($H_2$) where it's **0**.

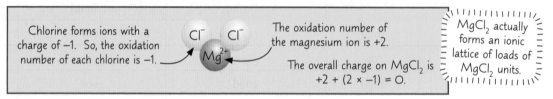

Hydrogen usually has an oxidation number of +1, e.g. in hydrogen chloride: oxidation no. H = +1 oxidation no. Cl = −1

In metal hydrides, e.g. $CaH_2$...

...H has an oxidation number of −1.

*$CaH_2$ has a giant lattice structure.*

The oxidation number of hydrogen in $H_2$ is 0.

6)  **Oxygen** nearly always has an oxidation number of **−2**, except in **peroxides** ($O_2^{2-}$) where it's **−1**, and **molecular oxygen** ($O_2$) where it's **0**.

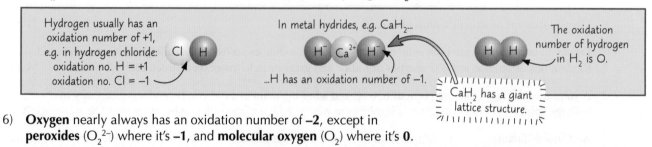

Oxygen usually has an oxidation number of −2, e.g. in water: oxidation no. O = −2 oxidation no. H = +1

In peroxides, each oxygen has an oxidation number of −1.

Overall charge is −2.

The oxidation number of oxygen in $O_2$ is 0.

# Oxidation Numbers

## Roman Numerals tell you the Oxidation Number

1) If an element can have **multiple** oxidation numbers, or **isn't** in its 'normal' oxidation number, its oxidation number can be shown by using **Roman numerals**, e.g. (I) = +1, (II) = +2, (III) = +3 and so on. The Roman numerals are written after the name of the element they correspond to.

> **Example:** In copper(I) oxide, copper has an oxidation number of **+1**. Formula = $Cu_2O$
> In copper(II) sulfate, copper has an oxidation number of **+2**. Formula = $CuSO_4$

2) Ions with names ending in -ate (e.g. sulfate, nitrate, chlorate, carbonate) contain **oxygen** and another element. For example, sulfates contain sulfur and oxygen, nitrates contain nitrogen and oxygen... and so on.

3) Sometimes the 'other' element in the ion can exist with different oxidation numbers, and so form different '-ate ions'. In these cases, the oxidation number is attached as a Roman numeral **after** the name of the -ate compound. The Roman numerals correspond to the **non-oxygen** element in the -ate compound.

> **Example:** In sulfate(VI) ions, the **sulfur** has oxidation number +6 — this is the $SO_4^{2-}$ ion.
> In nitrate(III), **nitrogen** has an oxidation number of +3 — this is the $NO_2^-$ ion.

*If there are no oxidation numbers shown, assume nitrate = $NO_3^-$ and sulfate = $SO_4^{2-}$.*

## You can use Oxidation Numbers to Write Chemical Formulae

1) You might need to use oxidation numbers to work out the **chemical formula** of a certain compound.

2) Unless you're told otherwise, you can assume the overall charge on a **compound** is **0**.

3) To work out the chemical formula, you've just got to work out what ratio of **anions** (negatively charged ions) and **cations** (positively charged ions) gives an overall charge of 0.

> **Example:** What is the formula of barium(II) nitrate?
>
> From the systematic name, you can tell barium has an **oxidation number** of +2.
> The formula of the nitrate ion is $NO_3^-$ and it has an **overall charge** of –1.
> The overall charge of the compound is 0, so you need to find
> a ratio of $Ba^{2+} : NO_3^-$ that will make the overall charge 0.
> $(+2) + (-1 \times 2) = 2 + -2 = 0$     The ratio of $Ba^{2+} : NO_3^-$ is **1 : 2**.
> So the formula is $Ba(NO_3)_2$.

*Hands up if you like Roman numerals...*

## Practice Questions

Q1 What is the oxidation number of H in $H_2$?

Q2 What is the usual oxidation number for oxygen when it's combined with another element?

**Exam Questions**

Q1 Sulfur can exist in a variety of oxidation states.

Work out the oxidation state of sulfur in the following compounds:

a) $S_8$,  b) $SO_3^{2-}$,  c) $H_2SO_4$,  d) $H_2S$.  [4 marks]

Q2 Hydrogen peroxide ($H_2O_2$) is a commonly used component of bleach.

a) In hydrogen peroxide, what is the oxidation number of:  i) hydrogen?  ii) oxygen?  [2 marks]

b) Hydrogen peroxide reacts with sodium sulfite ($Na_2SO_3$) to produce sodium sulfate and water.
What is the oxidation number of sulfur in the sodium sulfite compound?  [1 mark]

---

## *Sockidation number — a measure of how many odd socks are in my drawers...*

*There isn't any tricky maths involved with oxidation numbers, just a bit of adding, some subtracting... maybe a bit of multiplying if you're unlucky. The real trick is to learn all the rules about predicting oxidation numbers. So get cracking.*

# Redox Reactions

*Oxidation numbers are great. They're darn useful for showing where electrons move from and to during redox reactions.*

## If Electrons are Transferred, it's a **Redox Reaction**

1) A **loss** of electrons is called **oxidation**.
2) A **gain** in electrons is called **reduction**.
3) Reduction and oxidation happen **simultaneously** — hence the term "**redox**" reaction.
4) An **oxidising agent accepts** electrons and gets reduced.
5) A **reducing agent donates** electrons and gets oxidised.

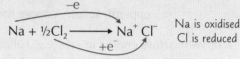

Example: the formation of **sodium chloride** from sodium and chlorine is a **redox reaction**:

$$Na + \tfrac{1}{2}Cl_2 \longrightarrow Na^+Cl^-$$

$-e^-$     $+e^-$

Na is oxidised
Cl is reduced

## Oxidation Numbers go **Up** or **Down** as Electrons are **Lost** or **Gained**

1) The oxidation number for an atom will **increase by 1** for each **electron lost**.
2) The oxidation number will **decrease by 1** for each **electron gained**.
3) To work out whether something has been **oxidised** or **reduced**, you need to assign each element an oxidation number **before** the reaction, and **after** the reaction.
4) If the oxidation number has increased, then the element has **lost** electrons and been **oxidised**.
5) If the oxidation number has decreased, then the element has **gained** electrons and been **reduced**.

**Example:** Identify the oxidising and reducing agents in this reaction: $4Fe + 3O_2 \rightarrow 2Fe_2O_3$

*Check back at the rules for assigning oxidation numbers on page 38 if you're unsure about this.*

Iron has gone from having an oxidation number of 0 to having an oxidation number of +3. It's **lost electrons** and has been **oxidised**. This makes it the **reducing agent** in this reaction.

Oxygen has gone from having an oxidation number of 0 to having an oxidation number of –2. It's **gained electrons** and has been **reduced**. This means it's the **oxidising agent** in this reaction.

6) When **metals** form compounds, they generally **donate** electrons to form **positive ions** and their oxidation numbers **increase** (they usually have **positive oxidation numbers**).

7) When **non-metals** form compounds, they generally **gain** electrons to form **negative ions** and their oxidation numbers **decrease** (they usually have **negative oxidation numbers**).

8) A **disproportionation reaction** is a special redox reaction. During a disproportionation reaction, an **element** in a **single species** is **simultaneously oxidised** and **reduced**. Oxidation numbers can show this happening.

**Example:**
Chlorine and its ions undergo disproportionation reactions:

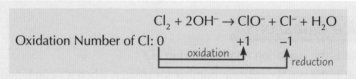

$$Cl_2 + 2OH^- \rightarrow ClO^- + Cl^- + H_2O$$

Oxidation Number of Cl: 0     +1     –1

oxidation     reduction

## You can Write **Half-Equations** and Combine them into **Redox Equations**

1) **Ionic half-equations** show oxidation or reduction.
2) You show the **electrons** that are being lost or gained in a half-equation. For example, this is the half-equation for the **oxidation of sodium**: $Na \rightarrow Na^+ + e^-$

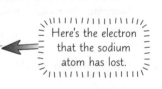

*Here's the electron that the sodium atom has lost.*

3) You can **combine** half-equations for different oxidising or reducing agents together to make **full equations** for redox reactions.

**Example:** Magnesium burns in oxygen to form magnesium oxide.

Oxygen is reduced to $O^{2-}$: $O_2 + 4e^- \rightarrow 2O^{2-}$     Magnesium is oxidised to $Mg^{2+}$: $Mg \rightarrow Mg^{2+} + 2e^-$

You need both equations to contain the same number of electrons. So double everything in the second half-equation: $2Mg \rightarrow 2Mg^{2+} + 4e^-$

Combining the half-equations makes: $2Mg + O_2 \rightarrow 2MgO$     *The electrons aren't included in the full equation. You end up with four on each side — so they cancel.*

# Redox Reactions

## Use e⁻, H⁺ and H₂O to Balance Half-Equations

1) For some redox equations, you'll find that you can't balance the equation by just multiplying up the reactants and products and adding a few electrons.

2) You might have to add some $H^+$ ions and $H_2O$ to your half-equations to make them **balance**.

> **Example:** Acidified manganate(VII) ions ($MnO_4^-$) can be reduced to $Mn^{2+}$ by $Fe^{2+}$ ions. Write the full redox equation for this reaction.

Iron is being oxidised. The half-equation for this is: $Fe^{2+}_{(aq)} \rightarrow Fe^{3+}_{(aq)} + e^-$

The second half-equation is a little bit trickier...

1) Manganate is being reduced. Start by writing this down: $MnO_4^-{}_{(aq)} \rightarrow Mn^{2+}_{(aq)}$

2) To balance the **oxygens**, you need to add **water** to the right-hand side of the equation: $MnO_4^-{}_{(aq)} + \rightarrow Mn^{2+}_{(aq)} + 4H_2O_{(l)}$

3) Now you need to add some $H^+$ **ions** to the left-hand side to balance the **hydrogens**: $MnO_4^-{}_{(aq)} + 8H^+_{(aq)} \rightarrow Mn^{2+}_{(aq)} + 4H_2O_{(l)}$

4) Finally, balance the **charges** by adding some **electrons**: $MnO_4^-{}_{(aq)} + 8H^+_{(aq)} + 5e^- \rightarrow Mn^{2+}_{(aq)} + 4H_2O_{(l)}$

*There's an overall charge of +2 on each side of the equation.*

Now you have to make sure the number of **electrons** produced in the **iron half-equation** equal the number of **electrons** used up in the **manganate half-equation**.

$Fe^{2+}_{(aq)} \rightarrow Fe^{3+}_{(aq)} + e^- \xrightarrow{\times 5} 5Fe^{2+}_{(aq)} \rightarrow 5Fe^{3+}_{(aq)} + 5e^-$

Now combine both half-equations to give a **full redox equation**.

$MnO_4^-{}_{(aq)} + 8H^+_{(aq)} + 5Fe^{2+}_{(aq)} \rightarrow Mn^{2+}_{(aq)} + 5Fe^{3+}_{(aq)} + 4H_2O_{(l)}$

## Practice Questions

Q1 What is a reducing agent?

Q2 What happens to the oxidation number of an element that loses electrons?

Q3 What happens during a disproportionation reaction?

**Exam Questions**

Q1 Lithium oxide forms when lithium is burned in air. Combustion is a redox reaction.
The equation for the combustion of lithium is: $4Li_{(s)} + O_{2(g)} \rightarrow 2Li_2O_{(s)}$

   a) Define oxidation in terms of the movement of electrons. [1 mark]

   b) State which reactant in this reaction is reduced. Write a half-equation for this reduction reaction. [2 marks]

Q2 The half-equation for chlorine acting as an oxidising agent is: $Cl_2 + 2e^- \rightarrow 2Cl^-$

   a) Define the term oxidising agent in terms of electron movement. [1 mark]

   b) Given that indium reacts with chlorine to form indium(III) ions, form a balanced equation for the reaction of indium with chlorine. [2 marks]

Q3 The following reaction is a disproportionation reaction: $2H_2O_2 \rightarrow 2H_2O + O_2$.
By using oxidation numbers, show why this reaction can be classified as a disproportionation reaction. [3 marks]

Q4 Vanadyl(IV) ions ($VO^{2+}$) react with tin(II) ions. During this reaction, the vanadyl(IV) ions are reduced to vanadium(III) ions, and tin is oxidised to tin(IV). Write a full redox equation for this reaction. [3 marks]

## Oxidising agent SALE NOW ON — everything's reduced...

*Half-equations look evil, with all those electrons flying about. But they're not too bad really. Just make sure you get lots of practice using them. (Oh, look, there are some handy questions up there.)*

*And while we're on the redox page, I suppose you ought to learn the most famous memory aid thingy in the world...*

**OIL RIG**
— **O**xidation **I**s **L**oss
— **R**eduction **I**s **G**ain
(of electrons)

# Group 2

*Get ready to learn about the elements magnesium, calcium, strontium and barium. They're lovely.*

## Ionisation Energy **Decreases** Down the Group

1) Each element down Group 2 has an **extra electron shell** compared to the one above.

2) The extra inner shells **shield** the outer electrons from the attraction of the nucleus.

Mr Kelly has one final attempt at explaining electron shielding to his students...

3) Also, the extra shell means that the outer electrons are **further away** from the nucleus, which greatly reduces the electrostatic attraction between the nucleus and the outer electrons.

> Both of these factors make it **easier** to remove outer electrons, meaning the **ionisation energy decreases** as you go down Group 2.

*The positive charge of the nucleus does increase as you go down a group (due to the extra protons), but this effect is overridden by the effect of the extra shells.*

4) This can explain the trend in **reactivity** of the Group 2 elements — most of these elements react by losing their **two outer electrons** (see below). So, the higher their first and second ionisation energies, the less likely they are to lose these electrons and the **less reactive** they will be. So, reactivity **increases** down the group.

## Group 2 Elements React with **Water, Oxygen** and **Chlorine**

*Here, M stands for any Group 2 metal.*

When Group 2 elements react, they form ions with a charge of **2+**. This is because Group 2 atoms contain **2 electrons** in their outer shell. They lose both of these electrons when they react.

$$M \rightarrow M^{2+} + 2e^-$$
E.g. $Ca \rightarrow Ca^{2+} + 2e^-$

### They react with WATER to produce HYDROXIDES.

The Group 2 metals react with water to give a **metal hydroxide and hydrogen**.

$$M_{(s)} + 2H_2O_{(l)} \rightarrow M(OH)_{2\,(aq)} + H_{2\,(g)}$$
e.g. $Ca_{(s)} + 2H_2O_{(l)} \rightarrow Ca(OH)_{2\,(aq)} + H_{2\,(g)}$

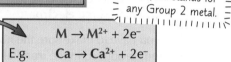

| | |
|---|---|
| Be | doesn't react |
| Mg | VERY slowly |
| Ca | steadily |
| Sr | fairly quickly |
| Ba | rapidly |

### They burn in OXYGEN to form OXIDES.

When Group 2 metals burn in oxygen, you get solid white **oxides**.

$$2M_{(s)} + O_{2\,(g)} \rightarrow 2MO_{(s)}$$
e.g. $2Ca_{(s)} + O_{2\,(g)} \rightarrow 2CaO_{(s)}$

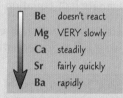

*If you add water to some barium in a test tube, lots of bubbles are produced, showing barium reacts really easily. If you add water to some magnesium in a test tube, you won't see much happening.*

### They react with CHLORINE to form CHLORIDES.

When Group 2 metals react with chlorine, you get solid white **chlorides**.

$$M_{(s)} + Cl_{2\,(g)} \rightarrow MCl_{2\,(s)}$$
e.g. $Ca_{(s)} + Cl_{2\,(g)} \rightarrow CaCl_{2\,(s)}$

## The Oxides and Hydroxides are **Bases**...

1) The **oxides** of the Group 2 metals react readily with **water** to form **metal hydroxides**, which dissolve. The **hydroxide ions, OH⁻**, make these solutions **strongly alkaline**.

2) **Beryllium oxide** is an exception — it **doesn't react** with **water**, and **beryllium hydroxide is insoluble**.

3) **Magnesium oxide** is another exception — it only reacts **slowly** and the hydroxide isn't very soluble.

4) The oxides form **more strongly alkaline** solutions as you go down the group, because the hydroxides get more soluble.

5) Because they're **bases**, both the oxides and hydroxides will **neutralise** dilute acids, forming solutions of the corresponding salts. See the next page for examples of these reactions.

# Group 2

|  | Reaction with Water | Reaction with Dilute Acid |
|---|---|---|
| Oxides | $MO_{(s)} + H_2O_{(l)} \rightarrow M(OH)_{2\,(aq)}$ | $MO_{(s)} + 2HCl_{(aq)} \rightarrow MCl_{2\,(aq)} + H_2O_{(l)}$ |
| Hydroxides | $M(OH)_{2\,(s)} \xrightarrow{+H_2O_{(l)}} M(OH)_{2\,(aq)}$ | $M(OH)_{2\,(aq)} + 2HCl_{(aq)} \rightarrow MCl_{2\,(aq)} + 2H_2O_{(l)}$ |

## Solubility Trends Depend on the **Compound Anion**

1) Generally, compounds of Group 2 elements that contain **singly charged** negative ions (e.g. OH⁻) **increase** in solubility down the group...

2) ...whereas compounds that contain **doubly charged** negative ions (e.g. $SO_4^{2-}$ and $CO_3^{2-}$) **decrease** in solubility down the group.

3) You need to know the solubility trends for the Group 2 **hydroxides** and the **sulfates**.

| Group 2 element | hydroxide (OH⁻) | sulfate ($SO_4^{2-}$) |
|---|---|---|
| magnesium | least soluble | most soluble |
| calcium | | |
| strontium | | |
| barium | most soluble | least soluble |

4) Most sulfates are soluble in water, but **barium sulfate** is **insoluble**.

5) Compounds like magnesium hydroxide that have **very low** solubilities are said to be **sparingly soluble**.

## Practice Questions

Q1 Which is the least reactive metal in Group 2?

Q2 Why does reactivity with water increase down Group 2?

Q3 Describe two reactions of a Group 2 oxide that show it to be a base.

Q4 Which is less soluble, barium hydroxide or magnesium hydroxide?

Q5 Which is more soluble, strontium sulfate or calcium sulfate?

### Exam Questions

Q1 Barium and calcium are both Group 2 elements.

a) Which of the following would be more soluble than calcium hydroxide?

    **A** magnesium hydroxide only          **B** strontium hydroxide and barium hydroxide

    **C** strontium hydroxide only           **D** magnesium hydroxide and barium hydroxide      [1 mark]

b) Which, out of barium and calcium, has the highest, combined first and second ionisation energy? Explain your answer.      [4 marks]

c) Calcium can be burned in chlorine gas. Write an equation, including state symbols, for the reaction.      [1 mark]

Q2 a) Write a balanced equation for the reaction of magnesium hydroxide with dilute hydrochloric acid.      [2 marks]

b) Write a balanced equation for the reaction of calcium oxide with water.      [2 marks]

### *I'm not gonna make it. You've gotta get me out of here, Doc...*

*We're deep in the dense jungle of Inorganic Chemistry now. Those carefree days of atomic structure are well behind us. It's now an endurance test and you've just got to keep going. It's tough, but you've got to stay awake and keep learning.*

# Group 1 and 2 Compounds

*These pages are about Group 1 and 2 compounds, starting with the thermal stability of their carbonates and nitrates. So — quick, get your vest and long johns on before you topple over — we haven't even started yet.*

## Thermal Stability of Carbonates and Nitrates Changes Down the Group

**Thermal decomposition** is when a substance **breaks down** (decomposes) when **heated**.
The more thermally stable a substance is, the more heat it will take to break it down.

### Thermal stability increases down a group

The carbonate and nitrate ions are **large negative ions** (**anions**) and can be made **unstable** by the presence of a **positively charged ion** (a cation). The cation **polarises** the anion, distorting it. The greater the distortion, the less stable the compound.

**Large** cations cause **less distortion** than small cations as they have a lower charge density — the charge on the ion is spread out over a larger area. So the further down the group, the larger the cations, the lower the charge density so the less distortion caused and the **more stable** the carbonate/nitrate compound.

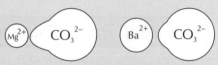

Magnesium ions polarise carbonate ions more than barium ions do, meaning magnesium carbonate is less stable.

### Group 2 compounds are less thermally stable than Group 1 compounds

The greater the **charge** on the cation, the greater the **distortion** and the **less stable** the carbonate/nitrate compound becomes. Group 2 cations have a +2 charge, compared to a +1 charge for Group 1 cations. So Group 2 carbonates and nitrates are less stable than those of Group 1.

| Group 1 | Group 2 |
|---|---|
| Group 1 carbonates* are **thermally stable** — you can't heat them enough with a Bunsen to make them decompose (though they do decompose at higher temperatures).<br>*except $Li_2CO_3$ which decomposes to $Li_2O$ and $CO_2$ (there's always one...). | Group 2 carbonates decompose to form the **oxide** and **carbon dioxide**.<br><br>$$MCO_{3\,(s)} \rightarrow MO_{(s)} + CO_{2\,(g)}$$<br>e.g. $CaCO_{3\,(s)} \rightarrow CaO_{(s)} + CO_{2\,(g)}$<br>calcium      calcium<br>carbonate   oxide |
| Group 1 nitrates** decompose to form the **nitrite** and **oxygen**.<br><br>$$2MNO_{3\,(s)} \rightarrow 2MNO_{2\,(s)} + O_{2\,(g)}$$<br>e.g. $2KNO_{3\,(s)} \rightarrow 2KNO_{2\,(s)} + O_{2\,(g)}$<br>potassium   potassium<br>nitrate       nitrite<br><br>**except $LiNO_3$ which decomposes to form $Li_2O$, $NO_2$ and $O_2$. | Group 2 nitrates decompose to form the **oxide**, **nitrogen dioxide** and **oxygen**.<br><br>$$2M(NO_3)_{2\,(s)} \rightarrow 2MO_{(s)} + 4NO_{2\,(g)} + O_{2\,(g)}$$<br>e.g. $2Ca(NO_3)_{2\,(s)} \rightarrow 2CaO_{(s)} + 4NO_{2\,(g)} + O_{2\,(g)}$<br>calcium     calcium   nitrogen<br>nitrate      oxide      dioxide |

## Here's How to Test the Thermal Stability of Nitrates and Carbonates

### How easily nitrates decompose can be tested by measuring...

- how long it takes until a certain amount of **oxygen** is produced (i.e. enough to relight a glowing splint).
- how long it takes until an amount of **brown gas ($NO_2$)** is produced. This needs to be done in a fume cupboard because $NO_2$ is **toxic**.

Daisy the cow *

### How easily carbonates decompose can be tested by measuring...

- how long it takes for an amount of **carbon dioxide** to be produced. You test for carbon dioxide using lime water — which is a saturated solution of calcium hydroxide. This turns cloudy with carbon dioxide.

You can collect gas using a gas syringe or a test tube upturned in a beaker of water.

\* She wanted to be in the book. I said OK.

# Group 1 and 2 Compounds

## Group 1 and 2 Compounds Burn with Distinctive *Flame Colours*

...not all of them, but quite a few. For compounds containing the ions below, flame tests can help **identify them**.

**Flame colours of Group 1 and 2 metals and their compounds**

| | |
|---|---|
| **Li** red | |
| **Na** orange/yellow | |
| **K** lilac | **Ca** brick-red |
| **Rb** red | **Sr** crimson |
| **Cs** blue | **Ba** green |

Here's how to do a flame test:

1) Mix a small amount of the compound you're testing with a few drops of **hydrochloric acid**.

2) Heat a piece of **platinum** or **nichrome wire** in a hot Bunsen flame to clean it.

3) Dip the wire into the **compound/acid mixture**. Hold it in a very hot flame and note the **colour** produced.

**The explanation:**

The **energy** absorbed from the flame causes electrons to move to **higher energy levels**. The colours are seen as the electrons fall back down to lower energy levels, releasing energy in the form of **light**. The difference in energy between the higher and lower levels determines the **wavelength** of the light released — which determines the **colour** of the light.

*The movement of electrons between energy levels is called electron transition.*

*The principle is the same as for the formation of atomic emission spectra (see page 12).*

## Practice Questions

Q1 What is the trend in the thermal stability of the nitrates of Group 1 elements?

Q2 Write a general equation for the thermal decomposition of a Group 2 carbonate. Use M to represent the Group 2 metal.

Q3 Describe two ways that you could test how easily the nitrates of Group 2 decompose.

Q4 Which Group 1 or 2 metal ions are indicated by the following flame colours?

a) lilac     b) brick-red     c) orange/yellow

**Exam Questions**

Q1 Barium and calcium are both Group 2 elements. They both form carbonates.

a) Write a balanced equation for the thermal decomposition of calcium carbonate, including state symbols. [2 marks]

b) State whether barium carbonate or calcium carbonate is more thermally stable. Explain your answer. [3 marks]

Q2 a) Write a balanced equation, including state symbols, for the thermal decomposition of sodium nitrate. [1 mark]

b) How could you test for the gas produced in the thermal decomposition? [1 mark]

c) Place the following in order of ease of thermal decomposition (easiest first).

**magnesium nitrate**     **potassium nitrate**     **sodium nitrate**

Explain your answer. [3 marks]

Q3 a) When a substance is heated, what changes occur within the atom that give rise to a coloured flame? [2 marks]

b) A compound gives a blue colour in a flame test. What s-block metal ions might this compound contain? [1 mark]

## *Bored of Group 2? Me too. Let's play noughts and crosses...*

*Noughts and crosses is pretty rubbish really, isn't it? It's always a draw. Ho hum. Back to Chemistry then, I guess...*

# Halogens

*Hold on to your hats... here come the halogens...*

## Halogens are the **Highly Reactive Non-Metals** of Group 7

1) The table below gives some of the main properties of the first 4 halogens.

| halogen | formula | colour | physical state (at room temp.) | electronic structure | electronegativity |
|---|---|---|---|---|---|
| fluorine | $F_2$ | pale yellow | gas | $1s^2\ 2s^2\ 2p^5$ | increases up the group |
| chlorine | $Cl_2$ | green | gas | $1s^2\ 2s^2\ 2p^6\ 3s^2\ 3p^5$ | |
| bromine | $Br_2$ | red-brown | liquid | $1s^2\ 2s^2\ 2p^6\ 3s^2\ 3p^6\ 3d^{10}\ 4s^2\ 4p^5$ | |
| iodine | $I_2$ | grey | solid | $1s^2\ 2s^2\ 2p^6\ 3s^2\ 3p^6\ 3d^{10}\ 4s^2\ 4p^6\ 4d^{10}\ 5s^2\ 5p^5$ | |

2) Halogens in their natural state exist as covalent diatomic molecules (e.g. $Br_2$, $Cl_2$). Because they're non-polar, they have **low solubility in water**.

3) But they do dissolve easily in **organic compounds** like hexane. Some of these resulting solutions have distinctive colours that can be used to identify them.

| | colour in water | colour in hexane |
|---|---|---|
| chlorine | virtually colourless | virtually colourless |
| bromine | yellow/orange | orange/red |
| iodine | brown | pink/violet |

## Halogens get **Less Reactive** Down the Group

1) Halogen atoms usually react by **gaining an electron** in their outer p subshell — this means they're **reduced**. As they're reduced, they **oxidise** another substance (it's a redox reaction) — so they're **oxidising agents**.

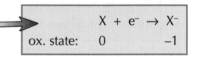

$$X + e^- \rightarrow X^-$$
ox. state:  0  $\quad$ –1

2) As you go down the group, the atoms become **larger**, so their outer electrons are **further** from the nucleus. The outer electrons are also **shielded** more from the attraction of the positive nucleus, because there are more inner electrons. This makes it harder for larger atoms to attract the electron needed to form an ion. So larger atoms are **less reactive** and reactivity **decreases** down the group.

3) This also explains the trend in **electronegativity**. Electronegativity is a measure of how well an atom attracts electrons in a covalent bond (see page 28). Electronegativity **decreases** down Group 7 due to the increase in the number of inner **electron shells** and the increase in **distance** between the nucleus and the bonding electrons.

## **Melting** and **Boiling Points Increase** Down the Group

1) As you go down Group 7, there's an increase in **electron shells** (and therefore electrons). This means the **London forces** (see pages 30-31) between the halogen molecules get stronger.

2) The increase in London forces makes it harder to overcome the intermolecular forces, and so **melting and boiling points** also **increase**.

3) The chemistry of **fluorine** and **astatine** is hard to study. Fluorine is a toxic gas and astatine is highly radioactive and decays quickly. But, you can **predict** how they will behave by looking at the trends in the behaviour of the other halogens. Generally, they **fit** with the trends seen down the other elements in Group 7.

| Halogen | Melting Point / °C | Boiling Point / °C |
|---|---|---|
| F | –220 | –188 |
| Cl | –102 | –34 |
| Br | –7 | 59 |
| I | 114 | 184 |
| At | | |

Increasing Reactivity

## Halogens can **Displace** Halide Ions from Solution

1) A displacement reaction is a type of reaction where one element **replaces** another element in a compound.

For example, if you add **aqueous chlorine** to a **potassium bromide solution**, the chlorine kicks the bromine out and takes its place:

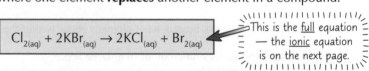

$$Cl_{2(aq)} + 2KBr_{(aq)} \rightarrow 2KCl_{(aq)} + Br_{2(aq)}$$

This is the <u>full</u> equation — the <u>ionic</u> equation is on the next page.

2) The halogens' **relative oxidising strengths** can be seen in their **displacement reactions** with halide ions.

3) In a **displacement reaction**, a **more reactive** halogen will replace a **less reactive** halide in a solution:

- **Chlorine** ($Cl_2$) will displace both **bromide** ($Br^-$) and **iodide** ($I^-$) ions.
- **Bromine** ($Br_2$) will displace **iodide** ($I^-$) but **not** chloride ($Cl^-$) ions.
- **Iodine** ($I_2$) will **not** displace chloride ($Cl^-$) or bromide ($Br^-$) ions.

'Halogen' should be used when describing the atom (X) or molecule ($X_2$), but 'halide' is used to describe the negative ion ($X^-$).

# Halogens

## Halogen-Halide Reactions are Redox Reactions

*Ionic half-equations only show the reacting species. See page 58 for more.*

1) A displacement reaction between halogens and halides is a **redox reaction**.
The thing that is **displaced** is oxidised, and the thing that does the **displacing** is reduced.

*The half-equations for other halogen displacement reactions follow the same pattern.*

Here are the **half-equations** for the reaction of chlorine with potassium bromide:

$Cl_2 + 2e^- \rightarrow 2Cl^-$     Chlorine **displaces** bromine and is **reduced**.

$2Br^- \rightarrow Br_2 + 2e^-$     Bromine **is displaced** by chlorine and gets **oxidised**.

2) This table shows the **ionic equations** for the reactions that happen if you add **aqueous halogen solutions** to solutions containing **halide ions**. (Remember, halogens only displace halides that are below them in the periodic table.)

| | Potassium chloride solution $KCl_{(aq)}$ (colourless) | Potassium bromide solution $KBr_{(aq)}$ (colourless) | Potassium iodide solution $KI_{(aq)}$ (colourless) |
|---|---|---|---|
| Chlorine water $Cl_{2(aq)}$ (colourless) | no reaction | $Cl_{2\,(aq)} + 2Br^-_{\,(aq)} \rightarrow 2Cl^-_{\,(aq)} + Br_{2\,(aq)}$ | $Cl_{2\,(aq)} + 2I^-_{\,(aq)} \rightarrow 2Cl^-_{\,(aq)} + I_{2\,(aq)}$ |
| Bromine water $Br_{2(aq)}$ (orange) | no reaction | no reaction | $Br_{2\,(aq)} + 2I^-_{\,(aq)} \rightarrow 2Br^-_{\,(aq)} + I_{2\,(aq)}$ |
| Iodine solution $I_{2(aq)}$ (brown) | no reaction | no reaction | no reaction |

3) If a reaction takes place, you will see a **colour change**:
- If bromide is displaced and bromine ($Br_2$) is formed, the reaction mixture will turn **orange**.
- If iodide is displaced and iodine ($I_2$) is formed, the reaction mixture will turn **brown**.

*bromine formed    iodine formed*

4) You can make these changes easier to see by shaking the reaction mixture with an **organic solvent** like hexane. The halogen that's present will dissolve in the organic solvent, which settles out as a distinct layer above the aqueous solution.

*bromine formed    iodine formed*

## Practice Questions

Q1 What colour is a solution of bromine in water? And in hexane?

Q2 Going down the group, the halogens become less reactive. Explain why.

Q3 Write an ionic equation for the reaction that occurs when potassium iodide is added to bromine water.

**Exam Questions**

Q1 The halogens can be found in Group 7 of the periodic table.

a) Write an ionic equation for the reaction between chlorine solution and sodium bromide (NaBr).     [1 mark]

b) Describe and explain the trend in the boiling points of the halogens.     [3 marks]

Q2 A student has a sample of an aqueous potassium halide solution. She knows it contains either chloride, bromide or iodide ions. The student adds a few drops of aqueous bromine solution to the test tube and a reaction takes place.

a) Which halide ion is present in the potassium halide solution?     [1 mark]

b) What colour will the aqueous solution in the test tube be after the reaction has finished?     [1 mark]

---

## *Bromine molecules — Chemistry's greatest Bromance...*

*This looks like a lot of tricky stuff, but really it all boils down to just spending a bit of time learning it. Make sure you can remember the Group 7 trends, and that you're able to explain them too. But it's not all bad — you get a periodic table in the exam, so you don't have to remember what order the halogens come in. Sounds like you're being spoilt, to me...*

# Reactions of Halogens

*Here comes another page jam-packed with golden nuggets of halogen fun. Oh yes, I kid you not.*
*This page is the roller coaster of Chemistry... white-knuckle excitement all the way...*

*Halogens are toxic, so make sure you carry out any reactions with them in a fume cupboard.*

## Halogens Can React with **Group 1** and **Group 2 Metals**

Remember, when halogens react they're **reduced** — and they **oxidise** other substances.
For example, they oxidise Group 1 and Group 2 metals in reactions that produce **halide salts**.

### Group 1 Metals...

$$E.g. \quad 2Li_{(s)} + F_{2\,(g)} \rightarrow 2LiF_{(s)}$$

| | | | |
|---|---|---|---|
| ox. state of Li: **0** | $\rightarrow$ **+1** | oxidation | **Lithium is oxidised:** $Li \rightarrow Li^+ + e^-$ |
| ox. state of F: | **0** $\rightarrow$ **−1** | reduction | **Fluorine is reduced:** $F_2 + 2e^- \rightarrow 2F^-$ |

### Group 2 Metals...

$$E.g. \quad Mg_{(s)} + Cl_{2\,(g)} \rightarrow MgCl_{2(s)}$$

| | | | |
|---|---|---|---|
| ox. state of Mg: **0** | $\rightarrow$ **+2** | oxidation | **Magnesium is oxidised:** $Mg \rightarrow Mg^{2+} + 2e^-$ |
| ox. state of Cl: | **0** $\rightarrow$ **−1** | reduction | **Chlorine is reduced:** $Cl_2 + 2e^- \rightarrow 2Cl^-$ |

## Halogens Undergo **Disproportionation** with Cold Alkalis

The halogens will react with cold dilute alkali solutions.
In these reactions, the halogen is simultaneously oxidised and reduced (called **disproportionation**)...

| | | |
|---|---|---|
| | $X_2 + 2NaOH \rightarrow NaOX + NaX + H_2O$ | |
| Ionic equation: | $X_2 + 2OH^- \rightarrow OX^- + X^- + H_2O$ | *X represents any halogen.* |
| Oxidation number of X: | $0 \qquad\qquad +1 \quad -1$ | |
| Example: | $I_2 + 2NaOH \rightarrow NaOI + NaI + H_2O$ | |
| | sodium iodate(I) | |

*Fluorine can't form $F^+$ ions — its oxidation number is always either 0 or −1.*

The halogens (except fluorine) can exist in a wide range of **oxidation states**.
For example:

| Oxidation state | −1 | 0 | +1 | +1 | +3 | +5 | +7 |
|---|---|---|---|---|---|---|---|
| Ion | $Cl^-$ | $Cl$ | $ClO^-$ | $BrO^-$ | $BrO_2^-$ | $IO_3^-$ | $IO_4^-$ |
| Name | chloride | chlorine | chlorate(I) | bromate(I) | bromate(III) | iodate(V) | iodate(VII) |

### *Chlorine* and *Sodium Hydroxide* make Bleach

If you mix chlorine gas with cold, dilute aqueous sodium hydroxide, the above reaction takes
place and you get **sodium chlorate(I) solution**, $NaClO_{(aq)}$, which just happens to be **bleach**.

| | |
|---|---|
| | $2NaOH_{(aq)} + Cl_{2\,(g)} \rightarrow NaClO_{(aq)} + NaCl_{(aq)} + H_2O_{(l)}$ |
| Oxidation number of Cl: | $0 \qquad\qquad +1 \qquad -1$ |

The oxidation number of Cl goes up <u>and</u> down so,
you guessed it, it's <u>disproportionation</u>. Hurray.

The sodium chlorite(I) solution (bleach) has loads of uses — it's used in **water treatment**,
to bleach **paper** and **textiles**... and it's good for **cleaning toilets**, too. Handy...

# Reactions of Halogens

## Halogens Also Undergo **Disproportionation** with Hot Alkalis

In reactions with **hot alkalis**, halogens are also simultaneously oxidised and reduced (disproportionation).

$$3X_2 + 6NaOH \rightarrow NaXO_3 + 5NaX + 3H_2O$$

| | | |
|---|---|---|
| Ionic equation: | $3X_2 + 6OH^- \rightarrow XO_3^- + 5X^- + 3H_2O$ | |
| Oxidation number of X: | 0 +5 -1 | |
| Example: | $3Cl_2 + 6NaOH \rightarrow NaClO_3 + 5NaCl + 3H_2O$ | |
| | sodium chlorate(V) | |

*You can use other alkalis too, e.g. KOH.*

*Reactions using chlorine need to be carried out in a fume cupboard because it's toxic.*

## **Chlorine** is used to Kill Bacteria in Water

**When you mix chlorine with water**, it undergoes disproportionation.
You end up with a mixture of hydrochloric acid and **hypochlorous acid**.

$$Cl_{2\,(g)} + H_2O_{(l)} \rightleftharpoons HCl_{(aq)} + HClO_{(aq)}$$

Oxidation number of Cl: 0      −1      +1

hydrochloric acid    hypochlorous acid

*Bromine and iodine also undergo disproportionation when mixed with water.*

Hypochlorous acid **ionises** to make **chlorate(I) ions** (also called hypochlorite ions).

$$HClO_{(aq)} + H_2O_{(l)} \rightleftharpoons ClO^-_{(aq)} + H_3O^+_{(aq)}$$

Chlorate(I) ions **kill bacteria**.

So, **adding chlorine** (or a compound containing hypochlorite ions) to water can make it safe to **drink** or **swim** in.

Crystal and Shane were thrilled to hear that the water was safe to swim in.

## Practice Questions

Q1 What is formed when a halogen reacts with a Group 1 metal?

Q2 How is common household bleach formed?

Q3 Write the equation for the reaction of chlorine with water. State underneath the oxidation numbers of the chlorine.

**Exam Question**

Q1 If liquid bromine is mixed with cold, dilute potassium hydroxide, potassium bromate(I) is formed.

a) Give the ionic equation for the reaction. [1 mark]

b) What type of reaction is this? [1 mark]

If liquid bromine is reacted with hot, dilute potassium hydroxide, a reaction, different to that outlined in a), occurs.

c) Write the equation for the reaction that occurs when liquid bromine is mixed with hot, dilute potassium hydroxide [2 marks]

---

## Remain seated until the page comes to a halt. Please exit to the right...

*Oooh, what a lovely page, if I do say so myself. I bet the question of how bleach is made and how chlorine reacts with sodium hydroxide has plagued your mind since childhood. Well now you know. And remember... anything that chlorine can do, bromine and iodine can generally do as well. Eeee... it's just fun, fun, fun all the way.*

# Reactions of Halides

*Ah, halides. Personally, I can never get enough of them.*

## The **Reducing Power** of Halides **Increases** Down the Group...

A halide ion can act as a **reducing agent** by losing an electron from its outer shell (see the reaction with halogens on page 47). How easy this is depends on the **attraction** between the halide's **nucleus** and the outer **electrons**. As you go down the group, the attraction gets **weaker** because...

1) ... the ions get bigger, so the electrons are **further** away from the positive nucleus,

2) ... there are extra inner electron shells, so there's a greater **shielding** effect.

## ...which Explains their Reactions with **Sulfuric Acid**

**All** the halides react with concentrated sulfuric acid to give a **hydrogen halide** as a product to start with. But what happens next depends on which halide you've got. Here are the reactions of the Group 1 halides.

### Reaction of KF or KCl with $H_2SO_4$

$$KF_{(s)} + H_2SO_{4(l)} \rightarrow KHSO_{4(s)} + HF_{(g)}$$
$$KCl_{(s)} + H_2SO_{4(l)} \rightarrow KHSO_{4(s)} + HCl_{(g)}$$

1) Hydrogen fluoride (HF) or hydrogen chloride gas (HCl) is formed. You'll see misty fumes as the gas comes into contact with moisture in the air.

2) But fluoride ions ($F^-$) and chloride ions ($Cl^-$) aren't strong enough reducing agents to reduce the sulfuric acid, so the **reaction stops** there.

3) It's **not a redox reaction** — the oxidation numbers of the halide and sulfur stay the same (−1 and +6).

### Reaction of KBr with $H_2SO_4$

$$KBr_{(s)} + H_2SO_{4(l)} \rightarrow KHSO_{4(s)} + HBr_{(g)}$$

$$2HBr_{(aq)} + H_2SO_{4(l)} \rightarrow Br_{2(g)} + SO_{2(g)} + 2H_2O_{(l)}$$

ox. state of S:     +6 → +4     reduction
ox. state of Br:     −1 → 0     oxidation

1) The first reaction gives misty fumes of hydrogen bromide gas (HBr).

2) But bromide ions ($Br^-$) are a stronger reducing agent than chloride ions ($Cl^-$) and react with the $H_2SO_4$ in a **redox reaction**.

3) The reaction produces choking fumes of sulfur dioxide ($SO_2$) and orange fumes of bromine ($Br_2$).

### Reaction of KI with $H_2SO_4$

$$KI_{(s)} + H_2SO_{4(l)} \rightarrow KHSO_{4(s)} + HI_{(g)}$$

$$2HI_{(g)} + H_2SO_{4(l)} \rightarrow I_{2(s)} + SO_{2(g)} + 2H_2O_{(l)}$$

ox. state of S:     +6 → +4     reduction
ox. state of I:     -1 → 0     oxidation

$$6HI_{(g)} + SO_{2(g)} \rightarrow H_2S_{(g)} + 3I_{2(s)} + 2H_2O_{(l)}$$

ox. state of S:     +4 → −2     reduction
ox. state of I:     -1 → 0     oxidation

1) Same initial reaction giving hydrogen iodide (HI) gas.

2) Iodide ions ($I^-$) then reduce $H_2SO_4$ as above.

3) But $I^-$ (being **well 'ard** as far as reducing agents go) keeps going and reduces the $SO_2$ to $H_2S$.

*$H_2S$ gas is toxic and smells of bad eggs. A bit like my mate Andy at times...*

## Hydrogen Halides are **Acidic Gases**

The **hydrogen halides** are **colourless gases**, but you can't forget about them just cos you can't see 'em.

1) The **hydrogen halides** can dissolve in **water** (and moisture in the air) to produce misty fumes of acidic gas. (They'll happily turn damp, blue litmus paper red.)

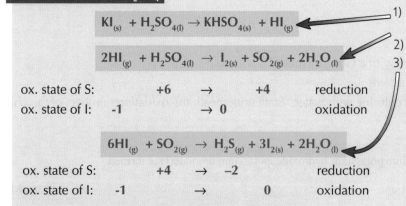

E.g.  $HCl_{(g)} \rightarrow H^+_{(aq)} + Cl^-_{(aq)}$
$HCl_{(g)} + H_2O \rightarrow H_3O^+_{(aq)} + Cl^-_{(aq)}$

2) Hydrogen chloride forms **hydrochloric** acid, hydrogen bromide forms **hydrobromic** acid and hydrogen iodide gives **hydroiodic** acid.

3) The hydrogen halides also react with **ammonia gas** to give **white fumes**. E.g. hydrogen chloride gives ammonium chloride.

E.g. $NH_{3(g)} + HCl_{(g)} \rightarrow NH_4Cl_{(s)}$
(It's an acid-base reaction.)

# Reactions of Halides

## Silver Ions React with Halide Ions to Form a Precipitate

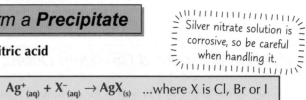

Silver nitrate solution is corrosive, so be careful when handling it.

This can be used as a **test** for halides. First you add **dilute nitric acid** to remove ions which might interfere with the reaction. Then you just add **silver nitrate solution** ($AgNO_{3(aq)}$). A **precipitate** of the silver halide is formed.

$$Ag^+_{(aq)} + X^-_{(aq)} \rightarrow AgX_{(s)} \quad \text{...where X is Cl, Br or I}$$

For example, if you add silver nitrate to **sodium chloride**:

$$Ag^+_{(aq)} + Cl^-_{(aq)} \rightarrow AgCl_{(s)}$$

The **colour** of the precipitate identifies the halide present in the original solution.

| Halide | Precipitate formed |
|---|---|
| Fluoride, $F^-$ | no precipitate (AgF is soluble) |
| Chloride, $Cl^-$ | white precipitate |
| Bromide, $Br^-$ | cream precipitate |
| Iodide, $I^-$ | yellow precipitate |

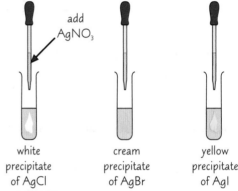

add $AgNO_3$

white precipitate of AgCl

cream precipitate of AgBr

yellow precipitate of AgI

These precipitates can look quite similar, so it can be difficult to identify a halide based on just this test. Thankfully, you can tell them apart by watching what happens when you add some **ammonia solution**.

| Original Precipitate | Observation |
|---|---|
| AgCl | precipitate dissolves in dilute ammonia solution to give a colourless solution |
| AgBr | precipitate remains unchanged if dilute ammonia solution is added, but will dissolve in concentrated ammonia solution to give a colourless solution |
| AgI | precipitate does not dissolve, even in concentrated ammonia solution |

## Practice Questions

Q1 Give two reasons why a bromide ion is a more powerful reducing agent than a chloride ion.

Q2 Name the gaseous products formed when potassium bromide reacts with concentrated sulfuric acid.

Q3 What type of substance is formed when a hydrogen halide is passed through water?

Q4 What would you see if you mixed hydrogen iodide with ammonia?

Q5 What colour precipitate forms during the reaction between silver ions and bromide ions?

**Exam Questions**

Q1 What colour precipitate would be produced from the reaction of sodium iodide with silver ions?

    **A** yellow     **B** white     **C** blue     **D** cream     [1 mark]

Q2 A student carried out chemical tests using concentrated sulfuric acid in order to distinguish between solid samples of sodium chloride and sodium bromide. For each test, state what she would have observed and write an equation for the reaction which occurred.   [6 marks]

Q3 Potassium iodide and potassium bromide both react with sulfuric acid. Compare the reactions of these two potassium halides with sulfuric acid. You should include suitable chemical equations in your answer.   [6 marks]

---

## *Get your umbrella — there's silver halide precipitation heading this way...*

*Having to learn the reactions of the halides with silver nitrate can be a bore, but they're on the specification so you really do need to know 'em. You can't ignore the reactions of the halides with sulfuric acid either, or the reactions of hydrogen halides with ammonia and water. Sorry. Best thing for it is to just crack on I guess. Get yourself a cuppa first.*

# Tests for Ions

*If you've got some unknown ions, there are some nifty little experiments you can do to identify them.  There are tests for both positive ions and for negative ions.  And that's what the next couple of pages are all about.*

## Hydrochloric Acid Can Help Detect Carbonates

The first of the negative ion tests is for **carbonate ions** ($CO_3^{2-}$) and **hydrogencarbonate** ($HCO_3^-$) ions:

With dilute **hydrochloric acid**, **carbonates** will fizz because they give off **carbon dioxide**.

$$CO_3^{2-}{}_{(s)} + 2H^+{}_{(aq)} \rightarrow CO_2{}_{(g)} + H_2O_{(l)}$$

With dilute **hydrochloric acid**, **hydrogencarbonates** will also fizz because they give off **carbon dioxide**.

$$HCO_3^-{}_{(s)} + H^+{}_{(aq)} \rightarrow CO_2{}_{(g)} + H_2O_{(l)}$$

You can test for carbon dioxide using **limewater**.

Carbon dioxide **turns limewater cloudy** — just bubble the gas through a test tube of limewater and watch what happens.  If the water goes cloudy you've identified a **carbonate ion** or a **hydrogencarbonate**.

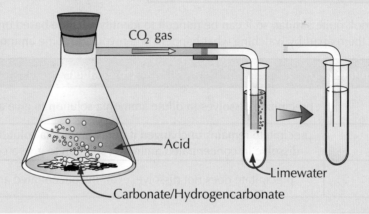

CO$_2$ gas

Acid

Limewater

Carbonate/Hydrogencarbonate

## Test for Sulfates with Hydrochloric Acid and Barium Chloride

To identify a **sulfate** ion ($SO_4^{2-}$), add dilute HCl, followed by **barium chloride solution**, $BaCl_{2(aq)}$.

$$Ba^{2+}{}_{(aq)} + SO_4^{2-}{}_{(aq)} \rightarrow BaSO_4{}_{(s)}$$

*The hydrochloric acid is added to get rid of any traces of carbonate ions before you do the test.  These would also produce a precipitate, so they'd confuse the results.*

If a **white precipitate** of **barium sulfate** forms, it means the original compound contained a sulfate.

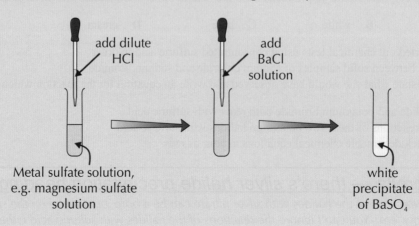

add dilute HCl

add BaCl solution

Metal sulfate solution, e.g. magnesium sulfate solution

white precipitate of BaSO$_4$

# Tests for Ions

## Use *Litmus Paper* and *NaOH* to Test for *Ammonium Compounds*

1) Ammonia gas ($NH_3$) is alkaline, so you can check for it using a damp piece of **red litmus paper**.
   If there's ammonia present, it'll dissolve in the water on the damp litmus paper, turning it **blue**.

2) You can use this to **test** whether a substance contains **ammonium ions** ($NH_4^+$). Add some **sodium hydroxide** to your mystery substance in a test tube and **gently heat** the mixture. If there's ammonia given off this means there are ammonium ions in your mystery substance.

$$NH_4{}^+_{(aq)} + OH^-_{(aq)} \rightarrow NH_{3(g)} + H_2O_{(l)}$$

You should do this experiment in a fume cupboard as it produces an irritant gas.

**Example:** $NH_4Cl_{(aq)} + NaOH_{(aq)} \rightarrow NH_{3(g)} + H_2O_{(l)} + NaCl_{(aq)}$

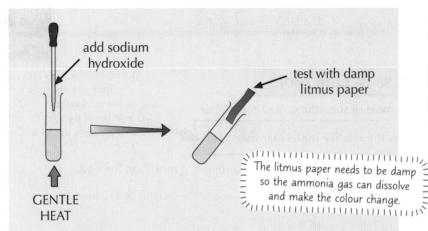

add sodium hydroxide

test with damp litmus paper

The litmus paper needs to be damp so the ammonia gas can dissolve and make the colour change.

GENTLE HEAT

Geoff's iron test had gone well.

## Practice Questions

Q1 What substance do you need to add to a sample to test for hydrogencarbonate ions?

Q2 a) Why is dilute HCl added to a compound as the first step in a test for sulfates?

b) Name the second substance you need to add to a sample to test for sulfates.

Q3 a) In which ion test would you use damp red litmus paper?

b) Why does the litmus paper need to be damp?

**Exam Questions**

Q1 Describe a test that can be used to test for carbonates in a solution. [2 marks]

Q2 a) What colour precipitate would be produced from the reaction of calcium sulfate and barium chloride solution?

   A   yellow            C   white

   B   brick red         D   pale blue            [1 mark]

b) Write an ionic equation to show the formation of the precipitate in the reaction between magnesium sulfate and barium chloride solution, including state symbols. [2 marks]

Q3 A student is given a solution of ammonium bromide.
   Describe how the student could prove that the solution contains ammonium ions. [2 marks]

## *I've got my ion you...*

*Remember, you know some other ways to identify ions too. You learnt about flame tests on p.45, which help to identify Group 1 and 2 metals. You also learnt about identifying halide ions using the colour of the precipitate formed when silver nitrate solution is added (p.51). Armed with this handful of tests, you're ready to do some fine detective work.*

# The Mole

*It'd be handy to be able to count out atoms — but they're way too tiny. You'd never be able to pick them up with tweezers to count them. But never mind — by using the idea of relative mass, you can figure out how many you've got.*

## A *Mole* is Just a (Very Large) *Certain Number of Particles*

Chemists often talk about 'amount of substance'. Basically, all they mean is 'number of particles'.

1) Amount of substance is measured using a unit called the **mole** (or **mol**). The number of moles is given the symbol **n**.

2) The number of **particles** in one mole is $6.02 \times 10^{23}$. This number is **the Avogadro constant**, **L**.
It's given to you in your data booklet in the exam, so don't worry about learning its value, just what it means.

3) It **doesn't matter** what the particles are.
They can be atoms, molecules, penguins — **anything**.

4) Here's a nice simple formula for finding the number of moles from the number of atoms or molecules:

$$\text{Number of moles} = \frac{\text{Number of particles you have}}{\text{Number of particles in a mole}}$$

**Example:** I have $1.50 \times 10^{24}$ carbon atoms. How many moles of carbon is this?

$$\text{Number of moles} = \frac{1.50 \times 10^{24}}{6.02 \times 10^{23}} \approx \textbf{2.49 moles}$$

## *Molar Mass* is the Mass of *One Mole*

Molar mass, **M**, is the mass **per mole** of something. Just remember:

**Molar mass is just the same as the relative molecular mass, $M_r$.**

That's why the mole is such a ridiculous number of particles ($6.02 \times 10^{23}$) — it's the number of particles for which the weight in g is the same as the relative molecular mass.

The only difference is it has units of 'grams per mole', so you stick a 'g mol⁻¹' on the end.

**Example:** Find the molar mass of $CaCO_3$.

Relative formula mass, $M_r$, of $CaCO_3 = 40.1 + 12.0 + (3 \times 16.0) = 100.1$
So the molar mass, M, is **100.1 g mol⁻¹**. — i.e. 1 mole of $CaCO_3$ weighs 100.1 g.

Here's another formula.
This one's really important — you need it **all the time**:

$$\text{Number of moles} = \frac{\text{mass of substance}}{\text{molar mass}}$$

**Example:** How many moles of aluminium oxide are present in 5.1 g of $Al_2O_3$?

Molar mass, M, of $Al_2O_3 = (2 \times 27.0) + (3 \times 16.0) = 102.0$ g mol⁻¹

Number of moles of $Al_2O_3 = \frac{5.1}{102.0} = \textbf{0.050 moles}$

You can re-arrange this equation using this formula triangle:

**Example:** How many moles of chlorine molecules are present in 71.0 g of chlorine gas?

We're talking chlorine **molecules** (not chlorine atoms), so it's $Cl_2$ we're interested in.

Molar mass, M, of $Cl_2 = (2 \times 35.5) = 71.0$ g mol⁻¹

Number of moles of $Cl_2 = \frac{71.0}{71.0} = \textbf{1.00 mole}$

But note that it would be 2 moles of chlorine atoms, since chlorine atoms have a molar mass of 35.5 g mol⁻¹.

## You Need to be Able to Work Out the *Number* of *Atoms* in *Something*

**Example:** How many atoms are in 8.5 g of $H_2S$?

Molar mass, M, of $H_2S = 1.0 + 1.0 + 32.1 = 34.1$ g mol⁻¹

Number of moles of $H_2S = \frac{8.5}{34.1} = 0.249...$ moles

Multiplying moles by the Avogadro constant gives you the number of molecules/particles.

Number of molecules of $H_2S = 0.249... \times 6.02 \times 10^{23} = 1.50... \times 10^{23}$
There are 3 atoms in 1 molecule of $H_2S$ so, total no. atoms $= 1.50... \times 10^{23} \times 3 = \textbf{4.5} \times \textbf{10}^{23}$ (2 s.f.)

# The Mole

## The **Concentration** of a Solution Can be Measured in **mol dm⁻³**...

1) The **concentration** of a solution is how many **moles** are dissolved per **1 dm³** (that's 1 litre) of solution. The units are **mol dm⁻³**.

2) Here's the formula to find the **number of moles**:

> **Number of moles = Concentration (mol dm⁻³) × Volume (dm³)**

*This one can go in a handy formula triangle too:*

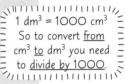

3) Watch out for the units — you might be given the volume in cm³ rather than dm³. If that's the case, you'll have to convert it to dm³ first.

> **Example:** What mass of sodium hydroxide (NaOH) needs to be dissolved in water to give 50.0 cm³ of a solution with a concentration of 2.00 mol dm⁻³?
>
> Volume of solution in dm³ = 50 ÷ 1000 = 0.05 dm³
>
> Number of moles NaOH = 2.00 × 0.0500 = 0.100 mol
>
> Molar mass, $M$, of NaOH = 23.0 + 16.0 + 1.0 = 40.0 g mol⁻¹
>
> Mass = number of moles × $M$ = 0.100 × 40.0 = **4.00 g**

*1 dm³ = 1000 cm³ So to convert from cm³ to dm³ you need to divide by 1000.*

## ...Or in **g dm⁻³**

The concentration of a solution can also be measured by how many **grams** of a substance are dissolved per **1 dm³** of the solution. The units are **g dm⁻³**.

Here's the formula to find the mass of the substance dissolved in a given volume of solution:

> **Mass of substance = Concentration (g dm⁻³) × Volume (dm³)**

> **Example:** What is the concentration, in g dm⁻³, of a solution of sodium chloride (NaCl) that was made by dissolving 0.0210 mol NaCl in 16.0 cm³ of water?
>
> Volume of solution in dm³ = 16.0 ÷ 1000 = 0.0160 dm³
>
> Molar mass, $M$, of NaCl = 23.0 + 35.5 = 58.5 g mol⁻¹
>
> Mass of NaCl = 0.0210 mol × 58.5 = 1.2285 g
>
> Concentration = $\dfrac{\text{Mass of substance}}{\text{Volume}} = \dfrac{1.2285}{0.016}$ = 76.8 g dm⁻³ (3 s.f.)

## Practice Questions

Q1 How many particles are there in one mole?

Q2 What are the units of molar mass?

Q3 What formula links the concentration in mol dm⁻³ to the number of moles and the volume of a solution?

**Exam Questions**

Q1 How many moles of calcium sulfate are there in 34.05 g of CaSO₄? [1 mark]

Q2 Calculate the mass of 0.360 moles of ethanoic acid (CH₃COOH). [1 mark]

Q3 Calculate the concentration, in g dm⁻³, of 0.100 moles of HCl dissolved in 100 cm³ of water. [2 marks]

Q4 What mass of H₂SO₄ is needed to produce 60.0 cm³ of 0.250 mol dm⁻³ solution? [2 marks]

Q5 A 0.500 g sample of sterling silver is dissolved in 15.0 cm³ concentrated nitric acid, and then an excess of potassium iodide is added. All the silver in the solution precipitates out as solid silver iodide (AgI₍ₛ₎). The total mass of the dry silver iodide precipitate formed is 1.01 g. What was the concentration, in mol dm⁻³, of the silver ions in the solution before the addition of potassium iodide? [2 marks]

## *Put your back teeth on the scale and find out your molar mass...*

*You need this stuff for loads of the calculation questions you might get, so learn it inside out. Before you start plugging numbers into formulae, make sure they're in the right units. If they're not, you need to know how to convert them or you'll be tossing marks out the window. Learn all the definitions and formulae, then have a bash at the questions.*

# Empirical and Molecular Formulae

*Here's another page piled high with numbers — it's all just glorified maths really.*

## Empirical and Molecular Formulae are Ratios

You have to know what's what with empirical and molecular formulae, so here goes...

1) The **empirical formula** gives the smallest whole number ratio of atoms of each element in a compound.

2) The **molecular formula** gives the **actual** numbers of atoms of each type of element in a molecule.

3) The molecular formula is made up of a **whole number** of empirical units.

**Example:** A molecule has an empirical formula of $C_4H_3O_2$, and a molecular mass of 166 g mol$^{-1}$. Work out its molecular formula.

*Empirical mass is just like the relative formula mass... (if that helps at all...).*

First find the **empirical mass**: $(4 \times 12.0) + (3 \times 1.0) + (2 \times 16.0)$
$$= 48.0 + 3.0 + 32.0 = 83.0 \text{ g mol}^{-1}$$

*Compare the empirical and molecular masses.*

But the **molecular mass** is 166 g mol$^{-1}$,

so there are $\frac{166}{83.0} = 2$ empirical units in the molecule.

The molecular formula must be the **empirical formula × 2**,

so the molecular formula $= C_8H_6O_4$.

## Empirical Formulae are Calculated from Experiments

You need to be able to work out empirical formulae from **experimental results**.

**Example:** When a hydrocarbon is burnt in excess oxygen, 4.4 g of carbon dioxide and 1.8 g of water are made. What is the empirical formula of the hydrocarbon?

*First work out how many moles of the products you have.*

$$\text{No. of moles of } CO_2 = \frac{\text{mass}}{M} = \frac{4.4}{12.0 + (2 \times 16.0)} = \frac{4.4}{44.0} = 0.10 \text{ moles}$$

1 mole of $CO_2$ contains 1 mole of carbon atoms, so you must have started with **0.10 moles of carbon atoms**.

$$\text{No. of moles of } H_2O = \frac{1.8}{(2 \times 1.0) + 16.0} = \frac{1.8}{18.0} = 0.10 \text{ moles}$$

1 mole of $H_2O$ contains 2 moles of hydrogen atoms (H), so you must have started with **0.20 moles of hydrogen atoms**.

Ratio C:H = 0.10:0.20. Now you divide both numbers by the **smallest** — here it's 0.10. So, the ratio C:H = 1:2. So the empirical formula must be $CH_2$.

*This works because the only place the carbon in the carbon dioxide and the hydrogen in the water could have come from is the hydrocarbon.*

You also need to know how to work out empirical formulae from the **percentages** of the different elements.

**Example:** A compound is found to have percentage composition 56.5% potassium, 8.70% carbon and 34.8% oxygen by mass. Calculate its empirical formula.

*These answers are rounded to 3 significant figures.*

In **100 g** of compound there are:

*Use $n = \frac{\text{mass}}{M}$*

$\frac{56.5}{39.1} = 1.45$ moles of K    $\frac{8.70}{12.0} = 0.725$ moles of C    $\frac{34.8}{16.0} = 2.18$ moles of O

Divide each number of moles by the **smallest number** — in this case it's 0.725.

K: $\frac{1.45}{0.725} = 2.00$    C: $\frac{0.725}{0.725} = 1.00$    O: $\frac{2.18}{0.725} = 3.01$

The ratio of K:C:O ≈ 2:1:3. So you know the empirical formula's got to be $K_2CO_3$.

The calculation above involves using percentage compositions. Sometimes you may have to calculate the **percentage composition** yourself, by working out the **proportions** of different elements in a given compound.

You use the formula: percentage composition of element X $= \dfrac{\text{total mass of element in compound}}{\text{total mass of compound}} \times 100\%$

**Example:** The percentage composition of H in $CH_4$ is $\dfrac{(4 \times 1.0)}{12.0 + (4 \times 1.0)} \times 100 = 25\%$.

*TOPIC 5 — FORMULAE, EQUATIONS & AMOUNTS OF SUBSTANCES*

# Empirical and Molecular Formulae

## Molecular Formulae are Calculated from Experimental Data Too

Once you know the empirical formula, you just need a bit more info and you can work out the **molecular formula** too.

**Example:**

When 4.6 g of an alcohol, with molar mass 46 g mol$^{-1}$, is burnt in excess oxygen, it produces 8.8 g of carbon dioxide and 5.4 g of water.
Calculate the empirical formula for the alcohol and then its molecular formula.

*Alcohols contain C, H and O.*

*The carbon in the $CO_2$ and the hydrogen in the $H_2O$ must have come from the alcohol — work out the number of moles of each of these.*

Number of moles of $CO_2 = \dfrac{mass}{M} = \dfrac{8.8}{44} = 0.20$ moles

1 mole of $CO_2$ contains 1 mole of C. So, 0.20 moles of $CO_2$ contains **0.20 moles of C.**

Number of moles $H_2O = \dfrac{mass}{M} = \dfrac{5.4}{18} = 0.30$ moles

1 mole of $H_2O$ contains 2 moles of H. So, 0.30 moles of $H_2O$ contains **0.60 moles of H.**

Mass of C = no. of moles $\times M = 0.20 \times 12.0 = 2.4$ g
Mass of H = no. of moles $\times M = 0.60 \times 1.0 = 0.60$ g
Mass of O = 4.6 – (2.4 + 0.60) = 1.6 g
Number of moles O = $\dfrac{mass}{M} = \dfrac{1.6}{16.0} =$ **0.10 moles**

*Now work out the mass of carbon and hydrogen in the alcohol. The rest of the mass of the alcohol must be oxygen — so work out that too. Once you know the mass of O, you can work out how many moles there are of it.*

Molar Ratio = C : H : O = 0.20 : 0.60 : 0.10 = 2 : 6 : 1
**Empirical formula = $C_2H_6O$**

*When you know the number of moles of each element, you've got the molar ratio. Divide each number by the smallest.*

Mass of empirical formula = (2 × 12.0) + (6 × 1.0) + 16.0 = 46.0 g

In this example, the mass of the empirical formula equals the molecular mass, so the empirical and molecular formulae are the same.

*Compare the empirical and molecular masses.*

**Molecular formula = $C_2H_6O$**

## Practice Questions

Q1 What's the difference between a molecular formula and an empirical formula?

Q2 What's the formula to work out the percentage composition of an element in a substance?

**Exam Questions**

Q1 In an experiment to determine the formula of an oxide of copper, 2.80 g of the oxide was heated in a stream of hydrogen gas until there was no further mass change. 2.50 g of copper remained.

Calculate the empirical formula of the oxide. [$A_r$(Cu) = 63.5, $A_r$(O) = 16.0] [4 marks]

Q2 Hydrocarbon X has a molecular mass of 78.0 g. It is found to have 92.3% carbon and 7.70% hydrogen by mass. Calculate the empirical and molecular formulae of X. [3 marks]

Q3 When 1.20 g of magnesium ribbon is heated in air, it burns to form a white powder which has a mass of 2.00 g. What is the empirical formula of the powder? [2 marks]

Q4 When 19.8 g of an organic acid, A, is burnt in excess oxygen, 33.0 g of carbon dioxide and 10.8 g of water are produced. Calculate the empirical formula for A and hence its molecular formula, if $M_r$(A) = 132. [4 marks]

## The Empirical Strikes Back...

*With this stuff, you can't just learn some facts parrot-fashion to regurgitate in the exam — you've gotta know how to use them. The only way to do that is to practise. Go through the examples on these two pages again, this time working the answers out for yourself. Then test yourself on the practice exam questions. It'll help you sleep at night — honest.*

# Chemical Equations

*Balancing equations might cause you a few palpitations — as soon as you make one bit right, the rest goes pear-shaped.*

## Balanced Equations Have **Equal Numbers** of Each Atom on **Both Sides**

1) Balanced equations have the **same number** of each atom on **both** sides. They're... well... you know... balanced.

2) You can only add more atoms by adding **whole reactants** or **products**. You do this by putting a number **in front** of a substance or changing one that's already there. You **can't** mess with formulae — ever.

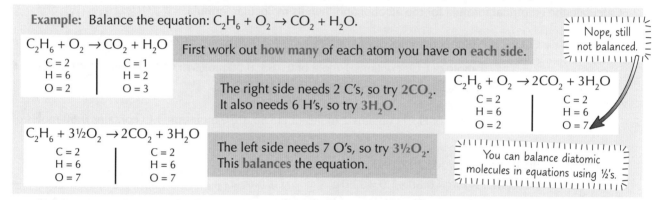

**Example:** Balance the equation: $C_2H_6 + O_2 \rightarrow CO_2 + H_2O$.

$C_2H_6 + O_2 \rightarrow CO_2 + H_2O$

| | |
|---|---|
| C = 2 | C = 1 |
| H = 6 | H = 2 |
| O = 2 | O = 3 |

First work out **how many** of each atom you have on **each side**.

The right side needs 2 C's, so try **2CO$_2$**. It also needs 6 H's, so try **3H$_2$O**.

$C_2H_6 + O_2 \rightarrow 2CO_2 + 3H_2O$

| | |
|---|---|
| C = 2 | C = 2 |
| H = 6 | H = 6 |
| O = 2 | O = 7 |

*Nope, still not balanced.*

$C_2H_6 + 3\frac{1}{2}O_2 \rightarrow 2CO_2 + 3H_2O$

| | |
|---|---|
| C = 2 | C = 2 |
| H = 6 | H = 6 |
| O = 7 | O = 7 |

The left side needs 7 O's, so try **3½O$_2$**. This **balances** the equation.

*You can balance diatomic molecules in equations using ½'s.*

## Ionic Equations Only Show the **Reacting Particles**

1) You can also write an **ionic equation** for any reaction involving **ions** that happens **in solution**.

2) In an ionic equation, only the **reacting particles** (and the **products** they form) are included.

**Example:** Here is the **full balanced equation** for the reaction of **nitric acid** with **sodium hydroxide**:

$$HNO_{3(aq)} + NaOH_{(aq)} \rightarrow NaNO_{3(aq)} + H_2O_{(l)}$$

*These little symbols tell you what state each substance is in (see the next page).*

The **ionic** substances in this equation will **dissolve**, breaking up into ions in solution. You can rewrite the equation to show all the **ions** that are in the reaction mixture:

$$H^+_{(aq)} + NO_3^-{}_{(aq)} + Na^+_{(aq)} + OH^-_{(aq)} \rightarrow Na^+_{(aq)} + NO_3^-{}_{(aq)} + H_2O_{(l)}$$

*Leave anything that isn't an ion in solution (like the H$_2$O) as it is.*

To get from this to the ionic equation, just cross out any ions that appear on **both sides** of the equation — in this case, that's the sodium ions (Na$^+$) and the nitrate ions (NO$_3^-$).

*An ion that's present in the reaction mixture, but doesn't get involved in the reaction is called a spectator ion.*

So the **ionic equation** for this reaction is:

$$H^+_{(aq)} + OH^-_{(aq)} \rightarrow H_2O_{(l)}$$

3) When you've written an ionic equation, check that the **charges** are **balanced**, as well as the atoms — if the charges don't balance, the equation isn't right.

In the example above, the **net charge** on the left hand side is $(+1 + -1) = \mathbf{0}$ and the net charge on the right hand side is **0** — so the charges balance.

## Balanced Equations Can Be Used to Work out **Masses**

Balanced equations show the **reaction stoichiometry**. The reaction stoichiometry tells you the ratios of reactants to products, i.e. how many moles of product are formed from a certain number of moles of reactants.

**Example:** Calculate the mass of iron oxide produced if 28 g of iron is burnt in air. $2Fe + \frac{3}{2}O_2 \rightarrow Fe_2O_3$

The molar mass, $M$, of Fe = 55.8 g mol$^{-1}$, so the number of moles in 28 g of Fe = $\frac{mass}{M} = \frac{28}{55.8} = 0.50$ moles.

From the equation: 2 moles of Fe produces 1 mole of Fe$_2$O$_3$, so 0.50 moles of Fe produce 0.25 moles of Fe$_2$O$_3$.

*Once you know the number of moles and the molar mass ($M$) of Fe$_2$O$_3$, it's easy to work out the mass.*

$M$ of Fe$_2$O$_3$ = $(2 \times 55.8) + (3 \times 16.0) = 159.6$ g mol$^{-1}$

Mass of Fe$_2$O$_3$ = no. of moles × $M$ = $0.25 \times 159.6 = \mathbf{40}$ **g** (2 s.f.)

*TOPIC 5 — FORMULAE, EQUATIONS & AMOUNTS OF SUBSTANCES*

# Chemical Equations

## State Symbols Give a bit More Information about the Substances

**State symbols** are put after each reactant or product in an equation. They tell you what **state of matter** things are in.

| | |
|---|---|
| s = solid | l = liquid |
| g = gas | aq = aqueous (solution in water) |

To show you what I mean, here's an example —

$$CaCO_{3(s)} + 2HCl_{(aq)} \rightarrow CaCl_{2(aq)} + H_2O_{(l)} + CO_{2(g)}$$

solid    aqueous    aqueous    liquid    gas

You can use state symbols and chemical equations to show what's going on during a reaction...

### In Displacement Reactions, One Element Replaces Another

*Have a peek at pages 46-47 for more on the displacement reactions of halogens.*

1) In displacement reactions, a **more reactive** element **reacts** to take the place of a less reactive element in a compound.

2) For example, **chlorine** reacts with **potassium bromide** to form **bromine** and **potassium chloride**.

**Full equation:** $Cl_{2(aq)} + 2KBr_{(aq)} \rightarrow Br_{2(aq)} + 2KCl_{(aq)}$     **Ionic Equation:** $Cl_{2(aq)} + 2Br^-_{(aq)} \rightarrow Br_{2(aq)} + 2Cl^-_{(aq)}$

### In Reactions of Acids, a Salt and Water are Produced

*When acids react with bases, it's a neutralisation reaction.*

When **bases** react with **acids**, a **salt** and **water** are always produced. Sometimes, other compounds such as **carbon dioxide gas** are also formed.

**Example:** Sulfuric acid reacts with sodium hydroxide to form sodium sulfate and water:

$$H_2SO_{4(aq)} + 2NaOH_{(aq)} \rightarrow Na_2SO_{4(aq)} + 2H_2O_{(l)}$$

Ionic equation: $2H^+_{(aq)} + 2OH^-_{(aq)} \rightarrow 2H_2O_{(l)}$

**Example:** Nitric acid and sodium carbonate react to form sodium nitrate, water and carbon dioxide.

$$2HNO_{3(aq)} + Na_2CO_{3(aq)} \rightarrow 2NaNO_{3(aq)} + H_2O_{(l)} + CO_{2(g)}$$

Ionic equation: $2H^+_{(aq)} + CO_3^{2-}_{(aq)} \rightarrow H_2O_{(l)} + CO_{2(g)}$

### In Precipitation Reactions, a Solid is Formed

*This state symbol shows that $BaSO_4$ has formed as a solid precipitate.*

If two **aqueous** compounds react together and one of the products forms as a **solid**, then a **precipitation reaction** has taken place.

E.g. barium chloride and potassium sulfate react to form potassium chloride and a **precipitate** of barium sulfate.

$$BaCl_{2(aq)} + K_2SO_{4(aq)} \rightarrow 2KCl_{(aq)} + BaSO_{4(s)}$$

**Ionic Equation:** $Ba^{2+}_{(aq)} + SO_4^{2-}_{(aq)} \rightarrow BaSO_{4(s)}$

## Practice Questions

Q1 What is the difference between a full balanced equation and an ionic equation?

Q2 What is the state symbol for a solution of hydrochloric acid?

**Exam Questions**

Q1 Balance this equation: $KI_{(aq)} + Pb(NO_3)_{2\,(aq)} \rightarrow PbI_{2\,(s)} + KNO_{3\,(aq)}$ [1 mark]

Q2 Ethene ($C_2H_4$) reacts with hydrochloric acid (HCl) to produce chloroethane ($C_2H_5Cl$). Calculate the mass of ethene required to produce 258 g of chloroethane. [4 marks]

Q3 A solution of magnesium chloride ($MgCl_2$) is mixed with a solution of silver nitrate ($AgNO_3$), resulting in a precipitation reaction to form silver chloride (AgCl) and a solution of magnesium nitrate ($Mg(NO_3)_2$). Write a balanced ionic equation for this reaction, including state symbols. [2 marks]

## Don't get in a state about equations...

*Balancing equations is a really, really important skill in Chemistry, so make sure you can do it. You will ONLY be able to calculate reacting masses if you've got a balanced equation to work from. I've said it once, and I'll say it again — practise, practise, practise... It's the only road to salvation. (By the way, exactly where is salvation anyway?)*

# Calculations with Gases

*You may think this page is full of hot air, but there are some important equations for calculating amounts of gases coming up.*

## All Gases Take Up the **Same Volume** under the Same Conditions

1) The space that one mole of a gas occupies at a certain temperature and pressure is known as the **molar gas volume**. It has units of $dm^3 \, mol^{-1}$.

2) If temperature and pressure stay the same, **one mole** of **any** gas always has the **same volume**. At **room temperature and pressure** (r.t.p.), this happens to be **24 $dm^3 \, mol^{-1}$** (r.t.p. is 293 K (20 °C) and 101.3 kPa). Meanwhile, at **standard temperature and pressure** (s.t.p.), it's **22.4 $dm^3 \, mol^{-1}$** (s.t.p. is 273 K (0 °C) and 101.3 kPa).

3) Here's the formula for working out the number of moles in a volume of gas:

$$\textbf{Number of moles} = \frac{\textbf{Volume in } dm^3}{\textbf{Molar gas volume}}$$

*At r.t.p., just substitute 24 $dm^3 \, mol^{-1}$ into this equation as the molar gas volume. At s.t.p., substitute 22.4 $dm^3 \, mol^{-1}$.*

**Example:** How many moles are there in 6.0 $dm^3$ of oxygen gas at r.t.p.?

$$\text{Number of moles} = \frac{6.0}{24} = \textbf{0.25 moles of oxygen molecules}$$

## You Can **Measure** the Molar Volume of a Gas

You can find the **volume** of gas evolved in a reaction by **collecting** the gas that is produced in a **gas syringe** or by **displacing water** from a **measuring cylinder**.

You can use **experiments** to work out the molar volume of a gas.

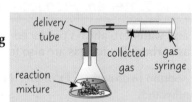

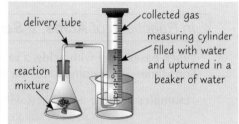

**Example:** Explain how you could measure the molar volume of carbon dioxide, in $dm^3$, at room temperature using this reaction: $Na_2CO_{3\,(aq)} + 2HCl_{(aq)} \rightarrow NaCl_{(aq)} + H_2O_{(l)} + CO_{2\,(g)}$

*1 $dm^3$ = 1000 $cm^3$*

1) Measure out a set volume of hydrochloric acid into a conical flask connected to a **gas syringe**.

2) Add a **known mass** of sodium carbonate to the conical flask, replace the bung and allow the reaction to go to **completion**.

3) Record the **volume** of carbon dioxide gas collected in the gas syringe.

4) **Repeat** the experiment, **varying** the **mass** of sodium carbonate each time.

5) Use your results to draw a **graph** with the **mass** of sodium carbonate on the *x*-axis and the **volume** of gas produced on the *y*-axis.

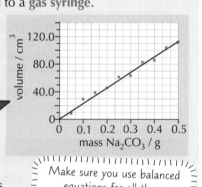

6) Read off the volume of gas produced for a sensible mass of sodium carbonate (e.g. **0.20 g** of **sodium carbonate** produces **45 $cm^3$** of **carbon dioxide**).

7) From the reaction equation, **1 mole** of $Na_2CO_3$ reacts to form **1 mole** of $CO_2$. $M_r \, Na_2CO_3 = 106$, so 0.20 g of $Na_2CO_3$ contain $0.20 \div 106 = 0.00188...$ moles. Therefore, 1 mole of $Na_2CO_3$ will produce $0.045 \div 0.00188... = 23.85 \, dm^3$ of $CO_2$. So the molar volume of a gas under the conditions of this reaction is 24 $dm^3$.

*Make sure you use balanced equations for all these calculations (see page 58 for more on balancing equations).*

## You Can Work Out Gas Volumes Using **Molar Calculations**...

It's handy to be able to work out **how much gas** a reaction will produce, so that you can use **large enough apparatus**.

**Example:** How much gas is produced when 15 g of sodium is reacted with excess water at r.t.p.?

$$2Na_{(s)} + 2H_2O_{(l)} \rightarrow 2NaOH_{(aq)} + H_{2\,(g)}$$

*Excess water means you know all the sodium will react.*

$M$ of Na = 23.0 g mol$^{-1}$, so number of moles in 15 g of Na = $\frac{15}{23.0} = 0.652...$ moles

From the equation, 2 moles of Na produce 1 mole of $H_2$,

so you know 0.652... moles Na produces $\frac{0.652...}{2} = 0.326...$ moles $H_2$.

*The reaction happens at room temperature and pressure, so you know 1 mole takes up 24 $dm^3$.*

So the volume of $H_2 = 0.326... \times 24 = \textbf{7.8 } dm^3$ (2 s.f.)

# Calculations with Gases

## ...Or Using Volume Calculations

If you have a reaction involving **gases**, you can use the **volumes** of **reactant** gases, along with the **reaction equation**, to work out the **volume** of gaseous products that will be produced.

**Example:** Calculate the total volume of gas produced when 8.25 dm³ of dinitrogen pentoxide decomposes:

$$2N_2O_{5(g)} \rightarrow O_{2(g)} + 4NO_{2(g)}$$

From the equation, 2 moles $N_2O_5$ produces 1 mole $O_2$ and 4 moles $NO_2$, which is 5 moles of gas in total.

So 8.25 dm³ $N_2O_5$ decomposes to produce $\frac{5}{2} \times 8.25 = $ **20.6 dm³** gas.

*If you're given the volumes of gas that react and are produced, you can use the ratio of these volumes to work out the reaction equation.*

## Ideal Gas Equation — pV = nRT

The **ideal gas equation** lets you find the **number of moles** in a certain volume at **any temperature and pressure**.

$pV = nRT$ Where: $p$ = pressure (Pa)    $V$ = volume (m³)    $n$ = number of moles

*R is the gas constant.* ⟶ $R = 8.31$ J K⁻¹ mol⁻¹    $T$ = temperature (K)    *K = °C + 273*

**Example:** At a temperature of 60 °C and a pressure of 250 kPa, a gaseous hydrocarbon occupied a volume of 1100 cm³ and had a mass of 1.60 g. Find the molecular formula of the hydrocarbon.

*1 kPa = 1000 Pa*

$$n = \frac{pV}{RT} = \frac{(250 \times 10^3) \times (1.1 \times 10^{-3})}{8.31 \times 333} = 0.0993... \text{ moles}$$

*1100 cm³ = 1.1 × 10⁻³ m³*

If 0.0993... moles is 1.60 g, then 1 mole $= \frac{1.60}{0.0993...} = 16.1...$ g. So the molar mass ($M$) is **16 g mol⁻¹** (2 s.f.)

Hydrocarbons contain only carbon and hydrogen atoms.
The only hydrocarbon with a molecular mass of 16 g mol⁻¹ is **methane, $CH_4$**.

You can use the ideal gas equation to work out the **molar mass** of an unknown, **volatile** liquid:

*Volatile liquids evaporate easily.*

- Put a **known mass** of the liquid in a flask, then attach it to a sealed **gas syringe**. Gently **warm** the apparatus in a water bath, until the liquid completely **evaporates**.
- Record the **volume** of gas in the syringe and the **temperature** of the water bath.
- Use the ideal gas equation to work out how many **moles** of the liquid were in your sample, and the equation **molar mass = mass ÷ moles** to calculate the molar mass.

## Practice Questions

Q1 What volume does 1 mole of gas occupy at r.t.p.?

Q2 Describe two methods you could use to measure the amount of gas produced over the course of a reaction.

Q3 State the ideal gas equation.

**Exam Questions**

Q1  At what temperature will 1.28 g of chlorine gas occupy 98.6 dm³, at a pressure of 175 Pa?    [2 marks]

Q2  What volume will be occupied by 88 g of propane gas ($C_3H_8$) at r.t.p.?    [2 marks]

Q3  What volume of oxygen is required, at room temperature and pressure for the complete combustion of $3.50 \times 10^{-2}$ mol of butane ($C_4H_{10}$)?    [2 marks]

Q4  Magnesium carbonate ($MgCO_3$) thermally decomposes to produce magnesium oxide (MgO) and carbon dioxide. What mass of magnesium carbonate is needed to produce 6.00 dm³ of carbon dioxide at r.t.p.?    [2 marks]

## I can't carry on — I've run out of gas...

*The ideal gas equation is really important, so make sure you know it. To make life a bit easier, the gas constant is in your exam data booklet along with the molar gas volumes at r.t.p. and s.t.p. and conversions between m³, dm³ and cm³.*

# Acid-Base Titrations

*Titrations are used to find out the **concentrations** of acid or alkali solutions.*

## Experiments Involve **Risks** and **Hazards**

1) A **hazard** is anything that has the potential to cause **harm** or **damage**. The **risk** associated with that hazard is the **probability** of someone (or something) being **harmed** if they are exposed to the hazard.

2) Many chemistry experiments have **risks** associated with them. These can include risks associated with the **equipment** you're using (e.g. the risk of burning from an electric heater) as well as risks associated with **chemicals**.

3) When you **plan** an experiment, you need to identify all the hazards and what the risk is from each hazard. This includes working out how **likely** it is that something could go wrong, and how **serious** it would be if it did. You then need to think of ways to **reduce** these risks. This procedure is called **a risk assessment**.

**Example:** A student is going to find the concentration of a solution of sodium hydroxide by titrating it with hydrochloric acid. Identify any hazards in this experiment, and suggest how you could reduce the risk.

Sodium hydroxide and hydrochloric acid are irritants at low concentrations and corrosive at high concentrations. Irritants cause inflammation, and corrosive substances cause **chemical burns** if they come into contact with your skin or eyes. To **reduce** the risks posed by these hazards, the student should try to use **low** concentrations of the substances if possible, and wear **gloves**, a **lab coat** and **goggles** when handling the chemicals.

## A **Standard Solution** Has a **Known** Concentration

Before you start a titration, you have to make up a **standard solution**. A **standard solution** is any solution that you **know** the concentration of. Making a standard solution needs **careful** measuring and a hint of maths:

**Example:** Make 250 cm³ of a solution of benzoic acid ($C_6H_5COOH$) with a concentration of about 0.200 mol dm⁻³.

1) First work out roughly how many **moles** of **solute** you need by using the formula:
$$\text{moles} = \frac{\text{concentration} \times \text{volume (cm}^3)}{1000} = \frac{0.200 \times 250}{1000} = 0.0500 \text{ mol}$$

*The solute is the substance being dissolved into the solution — here it's the solid benzoic acid.*

2) Now work out roughly how many **grams** of solute is needed using the formula
**mass = moles × molar mass** = 0.0500 mol × 122.0 = 6.10 g

3) Carefully **weigh out** this mass of solute using a balance with a precision of at least 2 d.p. — first weigh the **weighing vessel**, note the weight, then **add** the correct mass.

`18.68` grams    `24.78` grams

4) Add the solid acid to a beaker containing about 100 cm³ of **distilled water** and stir until all the solute has **dissolved**.

*Dissolving an acid can release a lot of heat. To stay safe, always add the acid to the water.*

4) **Reweigh** the weighing vessel, and use this value along with the combined mass of the vessel and the acid to calculate the **exact mass** of acid that has been added to the beaker. Use this **exact mass** to calculate what the **concentration** of your standard solution will be:

Mass of acid added to beaker: 24.78 − 18.72 = 6.06 g

Moles of acid added to beaker = 6.06 ÷ 122.0 = 0.0496... moles

`18.72` grams

Exact concentration of standard solution = (0.0496... × 1000) ÷ 250 = **0.199 mol dm⁻³**

5) Tip the solution into a **volumetric flask** — make sure it's the right size for the volume you're making. Use a **funnel** to make sure it all goes in.

6) **Rinse** the beaker and stirring rod with distilled water and add that to the flask too. This makes sure there's no solute clinging to the beaker or rod.

7) Now top the flask up to the **correct volume** (250 cm³) with more distilled water. Make sure the **bottom** of the **meniscus** reaches the **line** — when you get close to the line use a **pipette** to add water drop by drop. If you go **over** the line you'll have to start all over again.

Volumetric flask

8) **Stopper** the bottle and turn it upside down a few times to make sure it's all **mixed**.

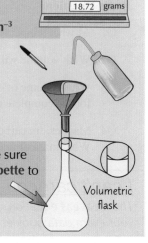

# Acid-Base Titrations

## Titrations Need to Be Done *Accurately*

1) **Titrations** allow you to find out **exactly** how much acid is needed to **neutralise** a quantity of alkali.

2) You measure out some **alkali** of unknown concentration (the analyte), e.g. NaOH using a pipette and put it in a flask, along with some **indicator**, e.g. **phenolphthalein**.

3) **Rinse** the burette with some of your **standard solution** of acid. Then **fill** it with your standard solution.

4) First of all, do a rough titration to get an idea where the **end point** is (the point where the alkali is **exactly neutralised** and the indicator changes colour). To do this, take an initial reading to see how much acid is in the burette to start off with. Then, add the **acid** to the alkali — giving the flask a regular **swirl**. Stop when your indicator shows a permanent colour change (the end point). Record the final reading from your burette.

5) Now do an **accurate** titration. Run the acid in to within 2 cm³ of the end point, then add the acid **dropwise**. If you don't notice exactly when the solution changed colour you've **overshot** and your result won't be accurate.

*You can also do titrations the other way round — adding alkali to acid.*

6) **Work out** the amount of acid used to **neutralise** the alkali. This is just the **final reading minus the initial reading**. This volume is known as the **titre**.

7) It's best to **repeat** the titration a few times, until you get answers that are **concordant** (similar) — your readings should be within 0.1 cm³ of each other. Then calculate a **mean titre** (see page 126), using only your **concordant results**. Also, remember to wash out the conical flask between each titration to remove any acid or alkali left in it.

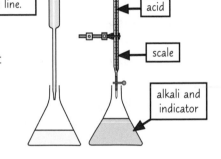

Pipette:
Pipettes measure only one volume of solution. Fill the pipette to just above the line, then take the pipette out of the solution (or the water pressure will hold up the level). Now drop the level down carefully to the line.

Burette:
Burettes measure different volumes and let you add the solution drop by drop.

acid

scale

alkali and indicator

## *Indicators* Show You When the Reaction's *Just Finished*

Indicators change **colour**, as if by magic. In titrations, indicators that change colour quickly over a **very small pH range** are used so you know **exactly** when the reaction has ended.

*Universal indicator is no good here — its colour change is too gradual.*

The main two indicators for **acid/alkali reactions** are —

> **methyl orange** — turns **yellow** to **red** when adding acid to alkali.
> **phenolphthalein** — turns **red** to **colourless** when adding acid to alkali.

It's best to place the flask containing the indicator and the acid or alkali solution on a **white surface**, so the colour change is easy to see.

Car indicators are no good here — they're not always right (because sometimes they're left).

## Practice Questions

Q1 Describe the steps needed to make a standard solution from a solid.

Q2 Describe the procedure for doing a titration.

**Exam Questions**

Q1 Calculate the mass of sulfamic acid ($H_3NSO_3$) needed to make 200 cm³ of 0.500 mol dm⁻³ sulfamic acid solution. [2 marks]

Q2* Describe how indicators are used and explain the importance of selecting an appropriate indicator when carrying out a titration. Include examples of indicators that would and would not be suitable for use in titrations. [6 marks]

---

## *Burettes and pipettes — big glass things, just waiting to be dropped...*

*Titrations work best if the concentration of the standard solution is similar to what you think the concentration of the solution that you're titrating it against is. If the standard solution is too dilute it'll take ages to reach the end point of the titration. If it's too concentrated then tiny amounts will cause large pH changes and your results may be inaccurate.*

---

\* The quality of your extended response will be assessed for this question.

# Titration Calculations

*There's far more to a titration than just simply carrying it out.  There are a whole load of calculations to carry out... Gulp.*

## You can Calculate **Concentrations** from Titrations

**Example:**  25.0 cm³ of 0.500 mol dm⁻³ HCl was used to neutralise 35.0 cm³ of NaOH solution.
Calculate the concentration of the sodium hydroxide solution.

*The method for carrying out this titration was shown on page 63.*

First write a **balanced equation** and decide **what you know** and what you **need to know**:

$$HCl \ + \ NaOH \ \rightarrow \ NaCl + H_2O$$
$$25.0 \text{ cm}^3 \quad 35.0 \text{ cm}^3$$
$$0.500 \text{ mol dm}^{-3} \quad ?$$

*It's just the formula from page 55, but with volume in cm³ rather than dm³.*

Now work out how many **moles of HCl** you have:

$$\text{Number of moles HCl} = \frac{\text{concentration} \times \text{volume (cm}^3)}{1000} = \frac{0.500 \times 25.0}{1000} = 0.0125 \text{ moles}$$

From the equation, you know 1 mole of HCl neutralises 1 mole of NaOH.
So 0.0125 moles of HCl must neutralise **0.0125** moles of NaOH.

*If you're asked for the concentration in g dm⁻³, you need to multiply the concentration by the molar mass.*

Now it's a doddle to work out the **concentration of NaOH**.

$$\text{Concentration of NaOH(aq)} = \frac{\text{moles of NaOH} \times 1000}{\text{volume (cm}^3)} = \frac{0.0125 \times 1000}{35.0} = 0.360 \text{ mol dm}^{-3}$$

## You Can **Also** Use Titrations to Find the **Concentration** of an **Acid**

If you carry out a titration like the one on page 63, but use a standard solution of a **base** and an **acid** of unknown concentration, then your results can be used to find the concentration of the acid.

**Example:**  A student carried out an experiment to find the concentration of a solution of hydrochloric acid (HCl).
He first dissolved 0.987 g of sodium hydroxide (NaOH) in 250 cm³ of distilled water to make a standard solution.  He then titrated this standard solution against 15.0 cm³ of the hydrochloric acid solution of unknown concentration.  Given that the mean titre of NaOH required to neutralise this volume of HCl solution was 21.7 cm³, calculate the concentration of the solution of HCl.

First calculate the concentration of the standard solution of NaOH:

*There's more about the techniques for making a standard solution on page 62.*

Moles of NaOH dissolved = 0.987 ÷ 40.0 = 0.024675 moles
Concentration of standard solution = (0.024675 × 1000) ÷ 250 = **0.0987 mol dm⁻³**

Now write out a **balanced equation** showing what **you do know**, and what you're **trying to find out**.

$$HCl \ + \ NaOH \ \rightarrow \ NaCl \ + \ H_2O$$
$$15.0 \text{ cm}^3 \quad 21.7 \text{ cm}^3$$
$$? \quad 0.0987 \text{ mol dm}^{-3}$$

So, you can use the concentration of the standard solution (that you worked out above) to calculate the concentration of the HCl solution:

$$\text{Number of moles NaOH} = \frac{\text{concentration} \times \text{volume (cm}^3)}{1000} = \frac{0.0987 \times 21.7}{1000} = 0.00214... \text{ moles}$$

Since the reaction equation shows that 1 mole of NaOH neutralises 1 mole of HCl, 0.00214... moles of NaOH will neutralise 0.00214... moles of HCl.  So...

$$\text{Concentration of HCl} = \frac{\text{moles of HCl} \times 1000}{\text{volume (cm}^3)} = \frac{0.00214... \times 1000}{15.0} = 0.143 \text{ mol dm}^{-3}$$

# Titration Calculations

## You use a *Pretty Similar Method* to Calculate *Volumes* for Reactions

This is usually used for **planning experiments**.

You need to use your trusty old **concentration = moles ÷ volume** formula again, but this time you need to **rearrange** it to find the volume.

$$volume\ (cm^3) = \frac{moles \times 1000}{concentration}$$

**Example:** 20.4 cm³ of a 0.500 mol dm⁻³ solution of sodium carbonate reacts with 1.50 mol dm⁻³ nitric acid. Calculate the volume of nitric acid required to neutralise the sodium carbonate.

Like before, first write a **balanced equation** for the reaction and decide **what you know** and what you **want to know**:

$$Na_2CO_3 \quad + \quad 2HNO_3 \rightarrow 2NaNO_3 + H_2O + CO_2$$

20.4 cm³      ?

0.500 mol dm⁻³   1.50 mol dm⁻³

*Writing a balanced equation is really important because not all reactions happen as 1 : 1 molar reactions. This reaction is a 1 : 2 ratio of $Na_2CO_3$ : $HNO_3$.*

Now work out how many **moles** of $Na_2CO_3$ you've got:

$$No.\ of\ moles\ of\ Na_2CO_3 = \frac{concentration \times volume\ (cm^3)}{1000} = \frac{0.500 \times 20.4}{1000} = 0.0102\ moles$$

1 mole of $Na_2CO_3$ neutralises 2 moles of $HNO_3$, so 0.0102 moles of $Na_2CO_3$ neutralises **0.0204 moles of $HNO_3$**.

*If you're given a concentration in g dm⁻³, you should first divide by the molar mass, M, to convert it to mol dm⁻³.*

Now you know the number of moles of $HNO_3$ and the concentration, you can work out the **volume**:

$$Volume\ of\ HNO_3 = \frac{number\ of\ moles \times 1000}{concentration} = \frac{0.0204 \times 1000}{1.50} = \textbf{13.6 cm}^3$$

You might also be asked to calculate the **volume** of a solution required to neutralise a known **mass** of a substance. The calculation is very similar to the one above, except that you start by working out the number of moles of the substance using your old friend '**moles = mass ÷ molar mass**'.

## Practice Questions

Q1 What equation links the number of moles, concentration and volume (in cm³)?

Q2 What equation links the number of moles, the mass of a substance and its molar mass, *M*?

**Exam Questions**

Q1 Calculate the concentration (in mol dm⁻³) of a solution of ethanoic acid, $CH_3COOH$, if 25.4 cm³ of it is neutralised by 14.6 cm³ of 0.500 mol dm⁻³ sodium hydroxide solution.

$$CH_3COOH + NaOH \rightarrow CH_3COONa + H_2O$$

[3 marks]

Q2 You are supplied with 0.750 g of calcium carbonate and a solution of 0.250 mol dm⁻³ sulfuric acid. What volume of acid will be needed to neutralise the calcium carbonate?

$$CaCO_3 + H_2SO_4 \rightarrow CaSO_4 + H_2O + CO_2$$

[4 marks]

Q3 In a titration, 17.1 cm³ of 0.250 mol dm⁻³ hydrochloric acid neutralises 25.0 cm³ calcium hydroxide solution.

a) Write out a balanced equation for this reaction. [1 mark]

b) Work out the concentration of the calcium hydroxide solution. [3 marks]

## DJs can't do titrations — they just keep on dropping the base...

*This just looks like a horrible load of calculations, but it's not that bad. Just remember the equation linking volume, concentration and moles and the one that links moles, mass and molar mass, and you'll be able to work out pretty much everything. They're the only tools you need to become a whizz at titration calculations. And that's the dream.*

# Uncertainty and Errors

*Even if you're a super duper Chemistry whizz, you're not error free. Time to meet errors and... errrmmm... uncertainty?*

## Uncertainty is the Amount of Error Your Measurements Might Have

1) Any measurements you make will have **uncertainty** in them due to the limits to the **sensitivity** of the equipment you used.

2) The **uncertainty** in your measurements **varies** for different equipment. For example, the scale on a 50 cm³ **burette** has marks every **0.1 cm³**. You should be able to tell which mark the level's closest to, so any reading you take won't be more than **0.05 cm³** out (as long as you don't make a daft mistake). The **uncertainty** of a reading from the burette is the **maximum error** you could have — so that's **±0.05 cm³**.

3) The **±** sign tells you the **range** in which the true value could lie. This range can also be called the **margin of error**.

4) For any piece of equipment you use, the uncertainty will be **half** the **smallest increment** the equipment can measure, in either direction.

*The level in this burette is between the 44.9 cm³ and 45.0 cm³ marks. It's closer to 45.0 — so the level is between 44.95 and 45.0. So a reading of 45.0 cm³ can't have an error of more than 0.05 cm³.*

5) Equipment will also have an error based on how **accurately** it has been **made**. The manufacturers should give you these uncertainty values — often they'll be **written** on the equipment somewhere.

6) If you're **combining measurements** that have the same **units**, you'll need to combine their **uncertainties**.

> **Example:** A student is using a set of electronic scales that measures to the nearest 0.05 g. He zeros the scales and measures out 1.35 g of solid. Calculate the total uncertainty of the measurement.
>
> There are two readings here — the initial reading is 0.00 g and the final reading is 1.35 g
> The uncertainty of each reading is 0.05 ÷ 2 = 0.025 g, so the total uncertainty is 0.025 + 0.025 = **0.05 g**.

## The Percentage Uncertainty in a Result Should be Calculated

You can calculate the **percentage uncertainty** of a measurement using this equation:

$$\text{percentage uncertainty} = \frac{\text{uncertainty}}{\text{reading}} \times 100$$

*You might also see percentage uncertainty called 'percentage error'.*

> **Example:** A 250 cm³ volumetric flask has a manufacturer's error of ±0.25 cm³. Calculate the percentage uncertainty of the volumetric flask.
>
> The standard volume of the volumetric flask has an uncertainty of 0.25 cm³, so the percentage uncertainty is $\frac{0.25}{250} \times 100 = \mathbf{0.1\%}$

*The percentage error of a combined uncertainty is $\frac{\text{total uncertainty}}{\text{difference in readings}} \times 100$. So the uncertainty of the mass reading above is $\frac{0.05}{1.35 - 0.00} \times 100 = 4\%$.*

### You Can Minimise the Percentage Uncertainty

1) One obvious way to **reduce errors** in your measurements is to use the most **precise equipment** you can.

2) **Planning** can also improve your results. If you measure out **5 cm³** of liquid in a measuring cylinder that has increments of 0.1 cm³ then the percentage uncertainty is (0.05 ÷ 5) × 100 = **1%**. But if you measure **10 cm³** of liquid in the same measuring cylinder the percentage uncertainty is (0.05 ÷ 10) × 100 = **0.5%** — you've **halved** the percentage uncertainty. So the percentage uncertainty can be reduced by planning an experiment so you use a **larger volume** of liquid.

*In general, the smaller the measurement, the larger the percentage uncertainty.*

## Errors Can Be Systematic or Random

1) **Systematic errors** are the same every time you repeat the experiment. They may be caused by the **set-up** or **equipment** you used. For example, if the 10.00 cm³ pipette you used to measure out a sample for titration actually measured 9.95 cm³, your sample would have been about 0.05 cm³ too small **every time** you repeated the experiment.

2) **Random errors** vary — they're what make the results a bit **different** each time you repeat an experiment. The errors when you make a reading from a burette are random. You have to estimate or round the level when it's between two marks — so sometimes your figure will be **above** the real one, and sometimes it will be **below**.

3) **Repeating an experiment** and finding the mean of your results helps to deal with **random errors**. The results that are a bit high will be **cancelled out** by the ones that are a bit low. But repeating your results won't get rid of any **systematic errors**, so your results won't get more **accurate**.

*Topic 5 — Formulae, Equations & Amounts of Substances*

# Uncertainty and Errors

## The **Total Uncertainty** in a Result Should be Calculated

In **titrations**, here's how you find the **total uncertainty in the final result**:
- Find the **percentage uncertainty** for each bit of equipment.
- Add the individual percentage uncertainties together. This gives the **percentage uncertainty in the final result**.
- Use this to work out the **actual total uncertainty** in the final result.

**Example:** 10.00 cm³ of KOH solution is neutralised by 27.30 cm³ of HCl of known concentration.
The volume of KOH has an uncertainty of 0.060 cm³.
The volume of HCl has an uncertainty of 0.10 cm³.
The concentration of the KOH is calculated to be 1.365 mol dm⁻³.
What is the uncertainty in this concentration?

First work out the **percentage uncertainty** for each **volume measurement**:

The KOH volume of 10.00 cm³ has an uncertainty of 0.060 cm³:

$$\text{percentage uncertainty} = \frac{0.060}{10.00} \times 100 = \textbf{0.60\%}$$

The HCl volume of 27.3 cm³ has an uncertainty of 0.1 cm³:

$$\text{percentage uncertainty} = \frac{0.10}{27.30} \times 100 = \textbf{0.36...\%}$$

Find the **percentage uncertainty in the final result**:

Total percentage uncertainty = 0.60% + 0.36...% = **0.96...%**

You're not done yet — you still have to calculate the **uncertainty** in the final result.

Uncertainty in the final answer is 0.96...% of 1.365 mol dm⁻³ = **0.013 mol dm⁻³**

*So the actual concentration may be 0.013 mol dm⁻³ bigger or smaller than 1.365 mol dm⁻³.*

## Practice Questions

Q1 If the uncertainty of a reading from a burette is 0.05 cm³, why is the uncertainty of a titre quoted as being 0.1 cm³?

Q2 Write down the equation for the percentage uncertainty of a measurement.

Q3 Other than using more precise equipment, describe one way in which you could minimise the percentage uncertainty of a measurement using a mass balance that reads to the nearest 0.05 g.

**Exam Questions**

Q1 The table shows the data recorded from a titration experiment.

a) Each reading recorded in the experiment has an uncertainty of ±0.05 cm³. Calculate the percentage uncertainty in the **titre** in Run 1. [2 marks]

b) Explain how you could reduce the percentage error in these titre values by changing the concentration of the solution in the burette. [2 marks]

| Run | Initial volume (cm³) | Final volume (cm³) | Titre (cm³) |
|---|---|---|---|
| Rough | 1.1 | 5.2 | 4.1 |
| 1 | 1.2 | 4.3 | 3.1 |

Q2 The concentration of a solution of NaOH is measured by titration against 0.100 mol dm⁻³ HCl. 25.00 cm³ of NaOH solution requires 19.25 cm³ of HCl for neutralisation, so the concentration of NaOH is 0.0770 mol dm⁻³.
The volume of NaOH was measured using a pipette with an uncertainty of 0.06 cm³.
The titre reading from the burette has an uncertainty of 0.1 cm³.

By combining percentage uncertainties calculate the uncertainty in the concentration of the NaOH. [4 marks]

## *Random error is human, systematic, divine...*

*Working out errors and uncertainty is important in every experiment you do. So important, in fact, that this topic is covered again in the Practical Skills section on page 130. Remember — if a question asks for the uncertainty of a result, find the uncertainty in the same units as the result. If you work out the total <u>percentage</u> uncertainty, you'll miss out.*

# Atom Economy and Percentage Yield

*How to make a subject like Chemistry even more exciting — introduce the word 'economy'...*

## The **Theoretical Yield** of a Product is the **Maximum** You Could Get

1) The **theoretical yield** is the **mass of product** that **should** be made in a reaction if **no** chemicals are '**lost**' in the process. You can use the **masses of reactants** and a **balanced equation** to calculate the theoretical yield for a reaction.

2) The **actual** mass of product (the **actual yield**) is always **less** than the theoretical yield. Some chemicals are always 'lost', e.g. some solution gets left on filter paper, or is lost during transfers between containers.

3) The **percentage yield** is the **actual** amount of product you collect, written as a percentage of the theoretical yield. You can work out the percentage yield with this formula:

$$\text{percentage yield} = \frac{\text{actual yield}}{\text{theoretical yield}} \times 100\%$$

**Example:** Ethanol can be oxidised to form ethanal: $C_2H_5OH + [O] \rightarrow CH_3CHO + H_2O$
9.2 g of ethanol was reacted with an oxidising agent in excess and 2.1 g of ethanal was produced. Calculate the theoretical yield and the percentage yield.

*[O] is just the symbol for any oxidising agent.*

Number of moles = mass of substance ÷ molar mass

Moles of $C_2H_5OH$ = $9.2 \div [(2 \times 12.0) + (5 \times 1.0) + 16.0 + 1.0] = 9.2 \div 46.0 = 0.20$ moles

1 mole of $C_2H_5OH$ produces 1 mole of $CH_3CHO$, so 0.2 moles of $C_2H_5OH$ will produce 0.20 moles of $CH_3CHO$.

$M$ of $CH_3CHO$ = $(2 \times 12.0) + (4 \times 1.0) + 16.0 = 44.0$ g mol$^{-1}$

Theoretical yield (mass of $CH_3CHO$) = number of moles × $M$ = 0.20 × 44.0 = **8.8 g**

So, if the actual yield was 2.1 g, the percentage yield = $\dfrac{\text{actual yield}}{\text{theoretical yield}} \times 100\% = \dfrac{2.1}{8.8} \times 100\% \approx 24\%$

## Atom Economy is a Measure of the Efficiency of a Reaction

1) The **percentage yield** tells you how wasteful the **process** is — it's based on how much of the product is lost because of things like reactions not completing or losses during collection and purification.

2) But percentage yield doesn't measure how wasteful the **reaction** itself is. A reaction that has a 100% yield could still be very wasteful if a lot of the atoms from the **reactants** wind up in **by-products** rather than the **desired product**.

3) **Atom economy** is a measure of the proportion of reactant **atoms** that become part of the desired product (rather than by-products) in the **balanced** chemical equation. It's calculated using this formula:

$$\% \text{ atom economy} = \frac{\text{molar mass of desired product}}{\text{sum of molar masses of all products}} \times 100\%$$

4) In an **addition reaction**, the reactants **combine** to form a **single product**. The atom economy for addition reactions is **always 100%** since no atoms are wasted.

E.g. ethene ($C_2H_4$) and hydrogen react to form ethane ($C_2H_6$) in an addition reaction: $C_2H_4 + H_2 \rightarrow C_2H_6$
The **only product** is ethane (the desired product). No reactant atoms are wasted so the atom economy is **100%**.

5) In an ideal world, all reactions would have an atom economy of 100%. Unfortunately, this isn't the case, and reactions often have **unwanted by-products** which lead to a **lower** atom economy.

**Example:** Aluminium oxide is formed by heating aluminium hydroxide until it decomposes. Calculate the atom economy of the reaction.
$$2Al(OH)_3 \rightarrow Al_2O_3 + 3H_2O$$

$\% \text{ atom economy} = \dfrac{\text{molar mass of desired product}}{\text{sum of molar masses of all products}} \times 100\%$

$= \dfrac{M(Al_2O_3)}{M(Al_2O_3) + 3 \times M(H_2O)} \times 100\%$

$= \dfrac{(2 \times 27.0) + (3 \times 16.0)}{[(2 \times 27.0) + (3 \times 16.0)] + 3 \times [(2 \times 1.0) + 16.0]} \times 100\% = \dfrac{102}{102 + 54} \times 100\% = \mathbf{65.4\%}$

*TOPIC 5 — FORMULAE, EQUATIONS & AMOUNTS OF SUBSTANCES*

# Atom Economy and Percentage Yield

## Reactions Can Have *High Percentage Yields* and *Low Atom Economies*

A **substitution reaction** is one where some atoms from one reactant are **swapped** with atoms from another reactant. This type of reaction **always** results in **at least two products** — the desired product and at least one by-product.

**Example:** 0.475 g of $CH_3Br$ reacts with an excess of NaOH in this reaction: $CH_3Br + NaOH \rightarrow CH_3OH + NaBr$.
0.153 g of $CH_3OH$ is produced.

a) Calculate the atom economy of this reaction.

$$\% \text{ atom economy} = \frac{\text{molar mass of desired product}}{\text{sum of molar masses of all products}} \times 100\%$$

*Always make sure you're using a balanced equation.*

$$= \frac{M(CH_3OH)}{M(CH_3OH) + M(NaBr)} \times 100\%$$

$$= \frac{12.0 + (3 \times 1.0) + 16.0 + 1.0}{[12.0 + (3 \times 1.0) + 16.0 + 1.0] + [23.0 + 79.9]} \times 100\%$$

$$= \frac{32.0}{32.0 + 102.9} \times 100\% = \textbf{23.7\%}$$

b) Calculate the percentage yield of this reaction.

Number of moles = mass of substance ÷ molar mass

Moles of $CH_3Br$ = 0.475 ÷ (12.0 + (3 × 1.0) + 79.9) = 0.475 ÷ 94.9 = **0.0050... moles**

The reactant : product ratio is 1 : 1, so the maximum number of moles of $CH_3OH$ is **0.00500....**

Theoretical yield = 0.00500... × $M(CH_3OH)$
= 0.00500... × (12.0 + (3 × 1.0) + 16.0 + 1.0) = 0.00500... × 32 = **0.160... g**

$$\text{percentage yield} = \frac{\text{actual yield}}{\text{theoretical yield}} \times 100\% = \frac{0.153}{0.160...} \times 100\% = \textbf{95.5\%}$$

*So this reaction has a very high percentage yield, but the atom economy is low.*

## Practice Questions

Q1 Give the equation for calculating the % atom economy of a reaction.

Q2 How many products are there in an addition reaction?

**Exam Questions**

Q1 Reactions 1 and 2 below show two possible ways of preparing the compound chloroethane ($C_2H_5Cl$):

1 $C_2H_5OH + PCl_5 \rightarrow C_2H_5Cl + POCl_3 + HCl$
2 $C_2H_4 + HCl \rightarrow C_2H_5Cl$

a) Which of these is an addition reaction? [1 mark]

b) Calculate the atom economy for reaction 1. [2 marks]

c) Reaction 2 has an atom economy of 100%. Explain why this is, in terms of the products of the reaction. [1 mark]

Q2 Phosphorus trichloride ($PCl_3$) reacts with chlorine to give phosphorus pentachloride ($PCl_5$):

$PCl_3 + Cl_2 \rightarrow PCl_5$

a) 0.275 g of $PCl_3$ reacts with an excess of chlorine. What is the theoretical yield of $PCl_5$? [2 marks]

b) When this reaction is performed 0.198 g of $PCl_5$ is collected. Calculate the percentage yield. [1 mark]

c) Changing conditions such as temperature and pressure will alter the percentage yield of this reaction. Will changing these conditions affect the atom economy? Explain your answer. [2 marks]

## *I knew a Tommy Conomy once — strange bloke...*

*These pages shouldn't be too much trouble — you've survived worse already. Make sure that you get plenty of practice using the percentage yield and atom economy formulae. And whatever you do, don't get mixed up between percentage yield (which is to do with the process) and atom economy (which is to do with the reaction).*

# TOPIC 6 — ORGANIC CHEMISTRY I

# The Basics

*This topic's all about organic chemistry... carbon compounds, in other words. Read on...*

## There are **Loads of Ways** of **Representing** Organic Compounds

| Type of formula | What it shows you | Formula for Butan-1-ol |
|---|---|---|
| **General formula** | An algebraic formula that can describe **any member** of a family of compounds. | $C_nH_{2n+1}OH$ (for all alcohols) |
| **Empirical formula** | The **simplest whole number ratio** of atoms of each element in a compound (cancel the numbers down if possible). (So ethane, $C_2H_6$, has the empirical formula $CH_3$.) | $C_4H_{10}O$ |
| **Molecular formula** | The **actual** number of atoms of each element in a molecule. | $C_4H_{10}O$ |
| **Structural formula** | Shows the arrangement of atoms **carbon by carbon**, with the attached hydrogens and functional groups. | $CH_3CH_2CH_2CH_2OH$ <br> *This could also be written as $CH_3(CH_2)_3OH$.* |
| **Skeletal formula** | Shows the **bonds** of the carbon skeleton **only**, with any functional groups. The hydrogen and carbon atoms aren't shown. This is handy for drawing large complicated structures, like cyclic hydrocarbons. | OH |
| **Displayed formula** | Shows how all the atoms are **arranged**, and all the bonds between them. | |

## **Nomenclature** is a Fancy Word for the **Naming** of Organic Compounds

Organic compounds used to be given whatever names people fancied, but these names led to **confusion** between different countries.

The **IUPAC** system for naming organic compounds was invented as an **international language** for chemistry. It can be used to give any organic compound a **systematic name** using these **rules** of nomenclature...

1)  Count the carbon atoms in the **longest continuous chain** — this gives you the stem.

| No. of Carbons | 1 | 2 | 3 | 4 | 5 | 6 | 7 | 8 | 9 | 10 |
|---|---|---|---|---|---|---|---|---|---|---|
| Stem | meth- | eth- | prop- | but- | pent- | hex- | hept- | oct- | non- | dec- |

2)  The **main functional group** of the molecule usually tells you what **homologous series** the molecule is in, and so gives you the **prefix** or **suffix** — see the table on the next page.

3)  Number the **longest** carbon chain so that the main functional group has the lowest possible number. If there's more than one longest chain, pick the one with the **most side-chains**.

4)  Any side-chains or less important functional groups are added as prefixes at the start of the name. Put them in **alphabetical** order, after the **number** of the carbon atom each is attached to.

5)  If there's more than one **identical** side-chain or functional group, use **di-** (2), **tri-** (3) or **tetra-** (4) before that part of the name — but ignore this when working out the alphabetical order.

**Example:** $CH_3CH(CH_3)CH(CH_2CH_3)C(CH_3)_2OH$

1)  The longest chain is 5 carbons. So the stem is **pent-**.

2)  The main functional group is **-OH**. So the name will be based on '**pentanol**'.

3)  **Numbering** the longest carbon chain so that -OH has the **lowest** possible number (and you have most side chains) puts -OH on carbon 2, so it's some sort of **pentan-2-ol**.

Longest chain with most side-chains

4)  The side chains are an **ethyl group** on carbon-3, and **methyl groups** on carbon-2 and carbon-4, so the **systematic name** for this molecule is: **3-ethyl-2,4-dimethylpentan-2-ol**.

# The Basics

## Members of **Homologous Series** Have the Same **General Formulae**

1) Organic chemistry is more about **groups** of similar chemicals than individual compounds.

2) These groups are called **homologous series**. A homologous series is a bunch of organic compounds that have the same **functional group** and **general formula**. Consecutive members of a homologous series differ by **–CH$_2$–**.

*A functional group is a group of atoms in a molecule responsible for the characteristic reactions of that compound.*

**Example:**

1) The simplest homologous series is the **alkanes**. They're **straight chain** molecules that contain only **carbon** and **hydrogen** atoms. There's a lot more about the alkanes on pages 76-77.

2) The **general formula** for alkanes is $C_nH_{2n+2}$. So the first alkane in the series is $C_1H_{(2 \times 1)+2} = CH_4$ (you don't need to write the 1 in $C_1$), the second is $C_2H_{(2 \times 2)+2} = C_2H_6$, the seventeenth is $C_{17}H_{(2 \times 17)+2} = C_{17}H_{36}$, and so on...

3) Here are the homologous series you need to know about:

| HOMOLOGOUS SERIES | PREFIX OR SUFFIX | EXAMPLE |
|---|---|---|
| alkanes | –ane | propane — $CH_3CH_2CH_3$ |
| branched alkanes | alkyl– (–yl) | methylpropane — $CH_3CH(CH_3)CH_3$ |
| alkenes | –ene | propene — $CH_3CH=CH_2$ |
| halogenoalkanes | chloro–/bromo–/iodo– | chloroethane — $CH_3CH_2Cl$ |
| alcohols | –ol | ethanol — $CH_3CH_2OH$ |
| aldehydes | –al | ethanal — $CH_3CHO$ |
| ketones | –one | propanone — $CH_3COCH_3$ |
| cycloalkanes | cyclo– ... –ane | cyclohexane $C_6H_{12}$ |
| carboxylic acids | –oic acid | ethanoic acid — $CH_3COOH$ |

*Don't worry if you don't recognise all these series yet — you'll meet them all by the end of the topic.*

## Practice Questions

Q1 Explain the difference between molecular formulae and structural formulae.

Q2 In what order should prefixes be listed in the name of an organic compound?

Q3 What is a homologous series? Give four examples of homologous series.

**Exam Questions**

Q1 1-bromobutane is prepared from butan-1-ol in this reaction: $C_4H_9OH + NaBr + H_2SO_4 \rightarrow C_4H_9Br + NaHSO_4 + H_2O$

a) Draw the displayed formulae for butan-1-ol and 1-bromobutane. [2 marks]

b) What does the '1' in the name butan-1-ol tell you, and why is it necessary to include it in the name? [2 marks]

Q2 a) Name the following molecules.

i)
```
        H
        |
      H—C—H
     H  |  H
     |  |  |
   H—C——C——C—H
     |  |  |
     H  H  Cl
```

ii)
```
        H
        |
      H—C—H
        |
     H  |       H
     |  |      /
   H—C——C——C=C
     |  |  |   \
     H  H  H    H
```

iii)
```
     Br  H
     |   |       H
   H—C———C——C=C /
     |   |     \
     H   H  Br   H
```

HINT: The double bond is the most important functional group, so give it the lowest number. [3 marks]

b) i) Write down the molecular formula for 3-ethylpentane. [1 mark]

ii) Write down the structural formula for this molecule. [1 mark]

## It's as easy as 1,2,3-trichloropentan-2-ol...

*The best thing to do now is find some organic compounds and work out their names. Then have a go at it the other way around — use the name to draw the compound. It might seem boring, but come the exam, you'll be thanking me.*

# Organic Reactions

*This page is chock-full of really good words, like 'radical substitution'. And 'electrophilic addition'. It's well worth a read.*

## You Can **Classify** Reactions by Reaction **Type**...

There are lots of different **reaction types** that organic compounds can take part in.
Here's a run down of the ones that you'll meet in Topic 6:

**Addition** — joining two or more molecules together to **form** a larger molecule.

**Polymerisation** — joining together lots of simple molecules to **form** a **giant molecule**.

**Elimination** — when a **small group** of atoms **breaks away** from a larger molecule.

**Substitution** — when **one species** is **replaced by another**.

**Hydrolysis** — splitting a molecule into two new molecules by **adding H⁺ and OH⁻** derived from **water**.

**Oxidation** — any reaction in which a species **loses electrons**.

**Reduction** — any reaction in which a species **gains electrons**.

*A species is an atom, an ion, a radical or a molecule.*

## A **Mechanism** Breaks Down a Reaction into Individual **Stages**

1)   It's all very well knowing the outcome of a reaction, but it can also be useful to know **how** a reaction happens.

2)   **Mechanisms** are diagrams that break reactions down into individual stages to show how substances react together. Some mechanisms use **curly arrows** to show how **electron pairs** move around when **bonds** are made or broken.

### Curly Arrows Show How **Electron Pairs** Move Around

In order to make or break a bond in a reaction, **electrons** have to move around.
A **curly arrow** shows where a **pair** of electrons goes during a reaction.  They look like this:

The arrow starts at the bond or lone pair where the electrons are at the beginning of the reaction.

The arrow points to where the new bond is formed at the end of the reaction, or to the atom where the electrons go.

**Example:**   Draw a reaction mechanism to show how chloromethane reacts with aqueous potassium hydroxide to form methanol and potassium chloride.

*There are lots of mechanisms coming up in this Topic, so if it all seems a bit strange now, don't worry. Before long you'll be a curly arrow wizard.*

Reaction:

$$H-\overset{\overset{\textstyle H}{|}}{\underset{\underset{\textstyle Cl}{|}}{C}}-H \ + \ NaOH \longrightarrow H-\overset{\overset{\textstyle H}{|}}{\underset{\underset{\textstyle OH}{|}}{C}}-H \ + \ NaCl$$

Mechanism:

Electrons move from the hydroxide lone pair to the carbon to form a new bond.

The overall charge of the reaction stays the same.

The carbon-chlorine bond breaks, and the electrons move onto the chlorine atom.

:OH⁻

$$H-\overset{\overset{\textstyle H}{|}}{\underset{\underset{\textstyle OH}{|}}{C}}-H \ + \ :Cl^{-}$$

*Na⁺ doesn't get involved in the reaction, so you don't need to include it in the mechanism.*

## There are Different **Types** of **Mechanisms** Too

1)   Some reaction types can happen by more than one **mechanism**.  Take addition, for example — you can get **nucleophilic** addition, **electrophilic** addition and **radical** addition.

2)   There are some mechanisms coming up in this Topic that you're expected to **remember**:

- **radical substitution** of halogens in alkanes, to make **halogenoalkanes** — see pages 76-77.
- **electrophilic addition** of halogens and hydrogen halides to alkenes, to make **halogenoalkanes** — see pages 86-87.
- **nucleophilic substitution** of primary halogenoalkanes with aqueous potassium hydroxide to make **alcohols** and with ammonia to make **amines** — see pages 92-93.

# Organic Reactions

## Classifying Reagents Helps to Predict What Reactions Will Happen

Knowing the **type of reagent** that you have helps you **predict** which
chemicals will react together and what products you're likely to end up with.

1) **Nucleophiles** are **electron pair donors**. They're often **negatively charged
   ions** (e.g. halide ions) or species that contain a **lone pair of electrons** (e.g. the
   oxygen atoms in water). They're **electron rich**, so they're **attracted** to places
   that are electron poor. So they like to react with **positive** ions. Molecules with
   **polar bonds** are often attacked by nucleophiles too, as they have δ+ areas.

*Frank put safety first when
he tested his nuclear file...*

> Nucleophiles are attracted to the $C^{\delta+}$ atom in a **polar carbon-halogen bond**.
> The carbon-halogen bond breaks and the nucleophile takes the halogen's
> place — and that's **nucleophilic substitution** (see page 92).

*Remember that 'δ+' and 'δ−' show
partial charges — see page 28.*

2) **Electrophiles** are **electron pair acceptors**. They're often **positively charged ions** (e.g. $H^+$), or δ+ areas (e.g. $H^{\delta+}$ in
   a hydrogen halide H–X bond). They're **electron poor**, so they're **attracted** to places that are electron rich.
   They like to react with **negative** ions, atoms with **lone pairs** and the **electron-rich** area around a **C=C bond**.

> **Alkene** molecules undergo electrophilic addition. In a molecule with a
> polar bond, like HBr, the $H^{\delta+}$ acts as an **electrophile** and is strongly attracted
> to the C=C double bond (which **polarises** the H–Br bond even more, until it
> finally breaks). There's more about this reaction on page 87.

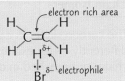

3) **Radicals** have an **unpaired electron**, e.g. the chlorine atoms produced when UV light
   splits a $Cl_2$ molecule. Because they have unpaired electrons, they're very, very **reactive**.
   Unlike electrophiles and nucleophiles, they'll react with anything, positive, negative or neutral.

$$Cl—Cl \rightarrow 2Cl\bullet$$

> **Radicals** will even attack stable non-polar bonds, like C–C and
> C–H (so they're one of the few things that will react with alkanes).
> There's loads about the reactions of radicals with alkanes on pages 76-77.

*Because a radical will react with
anything in sight, you'll probably end
up with a mixture of products. So
radical reactions aren't much use if
you're after a pure product.*

## Practice Questions

Q1 What is a hydrolysis reaction?

Q2 What do curly arrows show?

Q3 What type of reagent accepts a pair of electrons during a reaction?

**Exam Questions**

Q1 Which of the following species would you expect to act as a nucleophile?

   **A** Bromine radicals, Br•.　　　　**B** The non-polar alkane, methane, $CH_4$.

   **C** Hydroxide ions, $OH^-$.　　　　**D** The $C^{\delta+}$ atom in the polar C–OH bond in ethanol, $CH_3CH_2OH$.　　[1 mark]

Q2 Classify each of the following reactions according to its type:

   a) A reaction in which lots of ethene molecules join together to form one long molecule, polyethene.　　[1 mark]

   b) The reaction between chloroethane and water, in which a water molecule
      breaks chloroethane into ethanol and hydrogen chloride.　　[1 mark]

   c) The reaction between chlorine radicals and ethane, in which a hydrogen atom
      in ethane is replaced by chlorine to form chloroethane.　　[1 mark]

## *My brother says I'm rubbish at archery, but I blame the curly arrows...*

*Scientists do love to classify everything, and have it neatly in order. I knew one who liked to alphabetise his socks. But
that's a different issue. Just learn the definitions for the types of reactions and reagents — and what types of reagent
undergo what types of reaction. Then you'll have this page sorted. Without having to alphabetise anything.*

# Isomerism

*Isomerism is great fun. It's all about how many ways there are of making different molecules from the same molecular formula. They can be a bit sneaky, though, so best be on your guard...*

## Isomers Have the Same **Molecular Formula**

1) Two molecules are isomers of one another if they have the same **molecular formula** but the atoms are **arranged differently**.

2) There are two types of isomers you need to know about — **structural isomers** and **stereoisomers**. Structural isomers are coming right up, and you'll meet stereoisomers on pages 83-85.

## **Structural Isomers** Have Different **Structural Arrangements** of Atoms

In structural isomers, the atoms are **connected** in different ways.
So although the **molecular formula** is the same, the **structural formula** is different.
There are **three** different types of structural isomer:

### 1. Chain Isomers

The **carbon skeleton** can be arranged differently — for example, as a **straight chain**, or **branched** in different ways.

These isomers have **similar chemical properties** — but their **physical properties**, like boiling point, will be **different** because of the change in shape of the molecule.

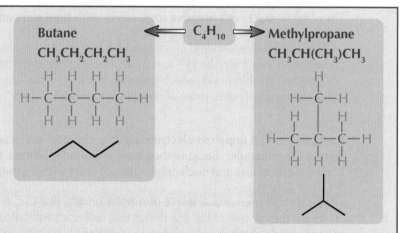

Butane $CH_3CH_2CH_2CH_3$   $\Longleftarrow$ $C_4H_{10}$ $\Longrightarrow$   Methylpropane $CH_3CH(CH_3)CH_3$

### 2. Positional Isomers

The **skeleton** and the **functional group** could be the same, only with the functional group attached to a **different carbon atom**.

These also have **different physical properties**, and the **chemical properties** might be **different** too.

Butan-1-ol $CH_3CH_2CH_2CH_2OH$   $\Longleftarrow$ $C_4H_{10}O$ $\Longrightarrow$   Butan-2-ol $CH_3CH_2CHOHCH_3$

### 3. Functional Group Isomers

The same atoms can be arranged into **different functional groups**.

These have very **different physical** and **chemical** properties.

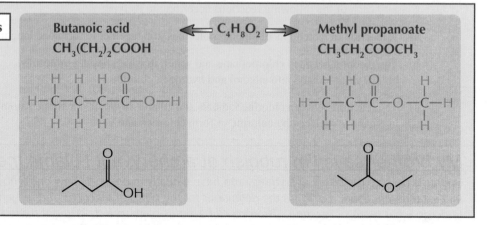

Butanoic acid $CH_3(CH_2)_2COOH$   $\Longleftarrow$ $C_4H_8O_2$ $\Longrightarrow$   Methyl propanoate $CH_3CH_2COOCH_3$

# Isomerism

## Don't be Fooled — What Looks Like an Isomer Might **Not** Be

Atoms can rotate as much as they like around single **C–C bonds**.
Remember this when you work out structural isomers — sometimes what looks like an isomer, isn't.

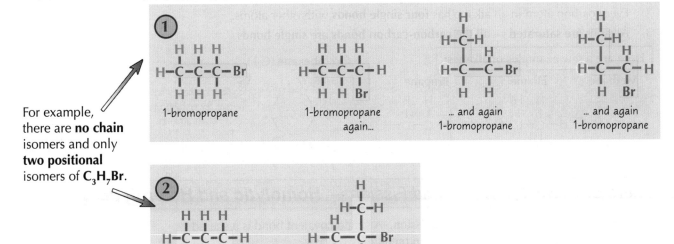

For example, there are **no chain** isomers and only **two positional** isomers of **C₃H₇Br**.

① 1-bromopropane / 1-bromopropane again... / ... and again 1-bromopropane / ... and again 1-bromopropane

② 2-bromopropane / 2-bromopropane again...

## Practice Questions

Q1  What are isomers?

Q2  Name the three types of structural isomerism.

Q3  Draw the skeletal formulae of two isomers that both have the molecular formula C₄H₁₀.

**Exam Questions**

Q1  a)  How many structural isomers are there of the alkane C₆H₁₄?

   **A** 4   **B** 5   **C** 6   **D** 7                                         [1 mark]

   b)  Explain what is meant by the term 'structural isomerism'.                  [1 mark]

Q2  Pentane has the structural formula CH₃CH₂CH₂CH₂CH₃.

   a)  Draw the skeletal formula of a structural isomer of pentane.              [1 mark]

   b)  Draw the displayed formula of an isomer of pentane that is not the molecule you drew in part a).   [1 mark]

Q3  Two structural isomers, A and B, have the molecular formula C₃H₆O.  They both contain a C=O double bond.

   a)  Draw the skeletal formulae of molecules A and B.                          [2 marks]

   b)  Give the structural formulae of isomers A and B.                          [2 marks]

Q4  Which of the following compounds is not an isomer of 1-buten-4-ol, CH₂CHCH₂CH₂OH?

   **A** ⟍OH   **B** ⟍OH   **C** ⟍O   **D** HO⟍                                  [1 mark]

## Human structural isomers...

# Alkanes

*Alkanes are your basic hydrocarbons — like it says on the tin, they've got hydrogen and they've got carbon.*

## Alkanes are **Saturated Hydrocarbons**

1) Alkanes have the **general formula $C_nH_{2n+2}$**. They've only got **carbon** and **hydrogen** atoms, so they're **hydrocarbons**.

2) Every carbon atom in an alkane has **four single bonds** with other atoms.

3) Alkanes are **saturated** — all the **carbon-carbon bonds** are **single bonds**.

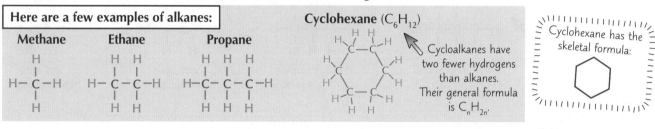

**Here are a few examples of alkanes:**

Methane

$$H-\underset{\underset{H}{|}}{\overset{\overset{H}{|}}{C}}-H$$

Ethane

$$H-\underset{\underset{H}{|}}{\overset{\overset{H}{|}}{C}}-\underset{\underset{H}{|}}{\overset{\overset{H}{|}}{C}}-H$$

Propane

$$H-\underset{\underset{H}{|}}{\overset{\overset{H}{|}}{C}}-\underset{\underset{H}{|}}{\overset{\overset{H}{|}}{C}}-\underset{\underset{H}{|}}{\overset{\overset{H}{|}}{C}}-H$$

**Cyclohexane ($C_6H_{12}$)**

Cycloalkanes have two fewer hydrogens than alkanes. Their general formula is $C_nH_{2n}$.

Cyclohexane has the skeletal formula:

## There are **Two Types** of Bond Fission — **Homolytic** and **Heterolytic**

Breaking a covalent bond is called **bond fission**. A single covalent bond is a shared pair of electrons between two atoms. It can break in two ways:

**Heterolytic Fission:**

In heterolytic fission the bond breaks **unevenly** with one of the bonded atoms receiving **both** electrons from the bonded pair. **Two different** substances can be formed — e.g. a positively charged **cation** ($X^+$), and a negatively charged **anion** ($Y^-$).

$$X \overset{\frown}{—} Y \rightarrow X^+ + Y^-$$

('hetero' means 'different')

**Homolytic Fission:**

In homolytic fission, the bond breaks evenly and each bonding atom receives **one electron** from the bonded pair. Two electrically uncharged 'radicals' are formed. Radicals are particles that have an **unpaired electron**. They are shown in mechanisms by a big dot next to the molecular formula (the dot represents the unpaired electron.)

$$X—Y \rightarrow X\bullet + Y\bullet$$

Because of the unpaired electron, radicals are very **reactive**.

*Carl loved fission at the weekends.*

A curly arrows shows the movement of an electron pair.

## Halogens React with **Alkanes**, Forming **Halogenoalkanes**

1) Halogens react with alkanes in **photochemical** reactions. Photochemical reactions are started by **light** — this reaction requires **ultraviolet light** to get going.

2) A hydrogen atom is **substituted** (replaced) by chlorine or bromine. This is a **radical substitution reaction**.

**Example: Chlorine** and **methane** react with a bit of a bang to form **chloromethane:** $CH_4 + Cl_2 \overset{UV}{\rightarrow} CH_3Cl + HCl$

The **reaction mechanism** has three stages: **initiation**, **propagation** and **termination**.

The reaction between bromine and methane works the same way.
$$CH_4 + Br_2 \overset{UV}{\rightarrow} CH_3Br + HBr$$

### Radicals are Produced by **Initiation** Reactions

In **initiation reactions**, radicals are **produced**.

1) Sunlight provides enough energy to break the Cl–Cl bond — this is **photodissociation**: $Cl_2 \overset{UV}{\rightarrow} 2Cl\bullet$

2) The bond splits **equally** and each atom gets to keep one electron — **homolytic fission**. The atom becomes a highly reactive **radical**, Cl•, because of its **unpaired electron**.

### Radicals are **Used Up** and **Created** in **Propagation** Reactions

During **propagation reactions**, radicals are **used up** and **created** in a **chain reaction**.

1) Cl• attacks a **methane** molecule: $Cl\bullet + CH_4 \rightarrow \bullet CH_3 + HCl$

2) The new **methyl radical**, •CH$_3$, can attack another Cl$_2$ molecule: $\bullet CH_3 + Cl_2 \rightarrow CH_3Cl + Cl\bullet$

3) The new Cl• can attack **another** CH$_4$ molecule, and so on, until all the Cl$_2$ or CH$_4$ molecules are wiped out.

# Alkanes

## Radicals are **Destroyed** in **Termination** Reactions

In **termination reactions**, radicals are mopped up by reacting together to form stable molecules.

1) If two free radicals join together, they make a **stable molecule**.

2) There are **heaps** of possible termination reactions. Here are a couple of them to give you the idea:

$$Cl\bullet + \bullet CH_3 \rightarrow CH_3Cl \qquad \bullet CH_3 + \bullet CH_3 \rightarrow C_2H_6$$ ⟵ Some products formed will be trace impurities in the final sample.

## The Problem is — You End Up With a **Mixture of Products**

1) The big problem with radical substitution if you're trying to make a **particular product** is that you **don't only get** the product you're after, but a **mixture of products**.

2) For example, if you're trying to make chloromethane and there's **too much chlorine** in the reaction mixture, some of the remaining **hydrogen atoms** on the **chloromethane molecule** will be swapped for chlorine atoms. The propagation reactions happen again, this time to make **dichloromethane**.

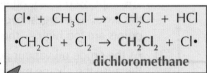

$$Cl\bullet + CH_3Cl \rightarrow \bullet CH_2Cl + HCl$$
$$\bullet CH_2Cl + Cl_2 \rightarrow CH_2Cl_2 + Cl\bullet$$
**dichloromethane**

3) It doesn't stop there. Another substitution reaction can take place to form **trichloromethane**.

$$Cl\bullet + CH_2Cl_2 \rightarrow \bullet CHCl_2 + HCl$$
$$\bullet CHCl_2 + Cl_2 \rightarrow CHCl_3 + Cl\bullet$$
**trichloromethane**

4) **Tetrachloromethane** ($CCl_4$) is formed in the last possible substitution. There are no more hydrogens attached to the carbon atom, so the substitution process has to stop.

5) So the end product is a mixture of $CH_3Cl$, $CH_2Cl_2$, $CHCl_3$ and $CCl_4$. This is a nuisance, because you have to **separate** the **chloromethane** from the other three unwanted by-products.

6) The best way of reducing the chance of these by-products forming is to have an **excess of methane**. This means there's a greater chance of a chlorine radical colliding only with a **methane molecule** and not a **chloromethane molecule**.

7) Another problem with radical substitution is that it can take place at any point along the **carbon chain**. So a mixture of **structural isomers** can be formed. For example, reacting **propane** with chlorine will produce a mixture of **1-chloropropane** and **2-chloropropane**.

## Practice Questions

Q1 What's the general formula for alkanes?

Q2 What's homolytic fission?

Q3 What's a radical?

Q4 Write down the chemical equation for the radical substitution reaction between methane and chlorine.

**Exam Question**

Q1 When irradiated with UV light, methane gas will react with bromine to form a mixture of several organic compounds.

a) Name the type of mechanism involved in this reaction. [1 mark]

b) Write an overall equation to show the formation of bromomethane from methane and bromine. [1 mark]

c) Write down the two equations in the propagation step for the formation of $CH_3Br$. [2 marks]

d) i) Explain why a tiny amount of ethane is found in the product mixture.
You should include the equation for the formation of this ethane in your answer. [2 marks]

ii) Name the mechanistic step that leads to the formation of ethane. [1 mark]

e) Name the major product formed when a large excess of bromine reacts with methane in the presence of UV light. [1 mark]

## *This page is like... totally radical, man...*

*Mechanisms can be a pain in the bum to learn, but unfortunately reactions are what Chemistry's all about. There's no easy trick — you've just got to sit down and learn the stuff. Keep hacking away at it, till you know it all off by heart.*

# Crude Oil

*Crude oil is a big mixture of hydrocarbons. Some parts of the mixture are useful, like the hydrocarbons that make up petrol and diesel, but some aren't. Luckily, it's possible to convert the less useful parts into more usable compounds.*

## Crude Oil is Mainly Alkanes

1) **Petroleum** is just a fancy word for **crude oil** — the sticky black stuff they get out of the ground with oil wells.
2) Petroleum is a mixture of **hydrocarbons**. It's mostly made up of **alkanes**.
   They range from **small alkanes**, like pentane, to **massive alkanes** of more than 50 carbons.
3) Crude oil isn't very useful as it is, but you can **separate** it out into useful bits (**fractions**) by **fractional distillation**.

**Here's how fractional distillation works — don't try this at home.**

1) First, the crude oil is **vaporised** at about 350 °C.
2) The vaporised crude oil goes into a **fractionating column** and rises up through the trays. The largest hydrocarbons don't **vaporise** at all, because their boiling points are too high — they just run to the bottom and form a gooey **residue**.

*You might do fractional distillation in the lab, but if you do you'll use a safer crude oil substitute instead.*

3) As the crude oil vapour goes up the fractionating column, it gets **cooler**. Because the alkane molecules have different chain lengths, they have different **boiling points**, so each fraction **condenses** at a different temperature. The fractions are **drawn off** at different levels in the column.
4) The hydrocarbons with the **lowest boiling points** don't condense. They're drawn off as **gases** at the top of the column.

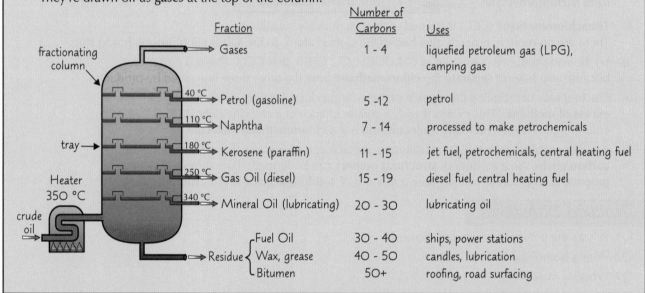

| Fraction | Number of Carbons | Uses |
|---|---|---|
| Gases | 1 - 4 | liquefied petroleum gas (LPG), camping gas |
| Petrol (gasoline) | 5 -12 | petrol |
| Naphtha | 7 - 14 | processed to make petrochemicals |
| Kerosene (paraffin) | 11 - 15 | jet fuel, petrochemicals, central heating fuel |
| Gas Oil (diesel) | 15 - 19 | diesel fuel, central heating fuel |
| Mineral Oil (lubricating) | 20 - 30 | lubricating oil |
| Fuel Oil | 30 - 40 | ships, power stations |
| Wax, grease | 40 - 50 | candles, lubrication |
| Bitumen | 50+ | roofing, road surfacing |

## Heavy Fractions can be 'Cracked' to Make Smaller Molecules

1) People want loads of the **light** fractions of crude oil, like petrol and naphtha. They don't want so much of the **heavier** stuff like bitumen though. Stuff that's in high demand is much more **valuable** than the stuff that isn't.
2) To meet this demand, the less popular heavier fractions are **cracked**. Cracking is **breaking** long-chain alkanes into **smaller** hydrocarbons (which can include alkenes). It involves breaking the **C–C bonds**.

For example, **decane** could crack like this:

$$C_{10}H_{22} \rightarrow C_2H_4 + C_8H_{18}$$

decane     ethene     octane

*Where the chain breaks is random, so you'll get a different mixture of products every time you crack a hydrocarbon.*

Here are **two types** of cracking — **thermal cracking** and **catalytic cracking**.

## Thermal Cracking Produces Lots of Alkenes

1) **Thermal cracking** takes place at **high temperature** (up to 1000 °C) and **high pressure** (up to 70 atm).
2) It produces a lot of **alkenes**.
3) These **alkenes** are used to make heaps of valuable products, like **polymers** (plastics). A good example is **poly(ethene)**, which is made from ethene.

# Crude Oil

## Catalytic Cracking Produces Lots of Aromatic Compounds

1) Catalytic cracking uses something called a **zeolite catalyst** (**hydrated aluminosilicate**), at a **slight pressure** and **high temperature** (about 450 °C).

2) It mostly produces **aromatic** hydrocarbons and **motor fuels**.

3) Using a catalyst **cuts costs**, because the reaction can be done at a **low** pressure and a **lower** temperature. The catalyst also **speeds** up the reaction, saving time (and time is money).

*Aromatic compounds contain benzene rings. Benzene rings contain a ring of 6 carbon atoms with delocalised ring of electrons. But don't worry about this too much now. You'll only meet them again if you're doing the A-Level course.*

## Alkanes can be Reformed into Cycloalkanes and Aromatic Hydrocarbons

1) Most people's cars run on petrol or diesel, both of which contain a mixture of alkanes (as well as other hydrocarbons, impurities and additives).

2) Some of the alkanes in petrol are **straight-chain** alkanes, e.g. hexane — $CH_3CH_2CH_2CH_2CH_2CH_3$.

3) **Knocking** is where alkanes **explode** of their own accord when the fuel/air mixture in the engine is compressed. Straight chain alkanes are the **most likely** hydrocarbons to cause knocking. Adding branched chain and cyclic hydrocarbons to the petrol mixture makes knocking **less likely** to happen, so combustion is more **efficient**.

*Don't worry too much about knocking. You shouldn't be asked about it in the exams, but you do have to know how alkanes are reformed.*

4) You can convert straight-chain alkanes into branched chain alkanes and cyclic hydrocarbons by **reforming**. This uses a catalyst (e.g. platinum stuck on aluminium oxide).

Hexane can be reformed into cyclohexane and hydrogen gas, which can be reformed into benzene ($C_6H_6$) and hydrogen gas:

$CH_3CH_2CH_2CH_2CH_2CH_3 \xrightarrow{Pt}$ (hexane) → cyclohexane + $H_2$ → benzene + $3H_2$

Octane can be reformed into 2,4-dimethylhexane:

$CH_3CH_2CH_2CH_2CH_2CH_2CH_2CH_3 \xrightarrow{Pt} CH_3CHCH_2CH_2CHCH_3$ with two $CH_3$ groups

octane → 2,5-dimethylhexane

## Practice Questions

Q1 How does fractional distillation work?
Q2 What is cracking?
Q3 Why is reforming used?

**Exam Question**

Q1 Crude oil is a source of fuels and petrochemicals.
It's vaporised and separated into fractions using fractional distillation.

a) Some heavier fractions are processed using cracking.

i) Explain why cracking is carried out. [2 marks]

ii) Write a possible equation for the cracking of dodecane, $C_{12}H_{26}$. [1 mark]

b) Some hydrocarbons present in petrol are processed using reforming.

i) Name two types of compound that are produced by reforming. [2 marks]

ii) What effect do these compounds have on the petrol's performance? [1 mark]

## Crude oil — not the kind of oil you could take home to meet your mother...

*This isn't the most exciting topic in the history of the known universe. Although in a galaxy far, far away there may be lots of pages on more boring topics. But, that's neither here nor there, because you've got to learn this stuff anyway. Get fractional distillation and cracking straight in your brain and make sure you know why people bother to do it.*

# Fuels

*If we didn't burn fuels to keep warm and power vehicles, we'd all wear lots of jumpers and use pogo sticks... maybe.*

## Alkanes are Useful as Fuels...

1) If you burn (**oxidise**) alkanes with **oxygen**, you get **carbon dioxide** and water — this is a **combustion reaction**.

> Here's the equation for the combustion of propane — $C_3H_{8(g)} + 5O_{2(g)} \rightarrow 3CO_{2(g)} + 4H_2O_{(g)}$

2) If there isn't much oxygen around, the alkane will still burn, but it will produce a mixture of mainly **carbon monoxide**, **carbon** and **water** (there could also be some carbon dioxide). This is **incomplete combustion**.

> For example, burning ethane with not much $O_2$ — $C_2H_{6(g)} + 2O_{2(g)} \rightarrow C_{(s)} + CO_{(g)} + 3H_2O_{(g)}$

3) Combustion reactions happen between **gases**, so liquid alkanes have to be **vaporised** first. Smaller alkanes turn into **gases** more easily (they're more **volatile**), so they'll **burn** more easily too.

4) Combustion reactions are **exothermic** reactions (they release **heat**).

5) Larger alkanes release heaps more **energy** per mole because they have more bonds to react.

6) Because they release so much energy when they burn, alkanes make excellent **fuels**. For example:

> 1) Methane's used for **central heating** and **cooking** in homes.
> 2) Alkanes with 5-12 carbon atoms are used in **petrol**.
> 3) Kerosene is used as **jet fuel**. Its alkanes have 11-15 carbon atoms.
> 4) **Diesel** is made of a mixture of alkanes with 15-19 carbon atoms.

## ...But They Produce Harmful Emissions

1) We generate most of our **electricity** by burning **fossil fuels** (coal, oil and natural gas) in **power stations**. We also use loads and loads of fossil fuels for **transport** and **heating**. Burning all these fossil fuels causes a lot of **pollution**.

2) Pollutants formed from burning fossil fuels include **carbon monoxide**, **unburnt hydrocarbons** and **carbon particulates** from the **incomplete combustion** of fuels, as well as **oxides** of sulfur ($SO_x$) and **nitrogen** ($NO_x$).

3) These pollutants can cause lots of **problems** for our **health** as well as for the **environment**.

### Carbon Monoxide is Toxic

1) The **oxygen** in your bloodstream is carried around by **haemoglobin**.

2) **Carbon monoxide** is **better** at binding to haemoglobin than oxygen is, so it binds to the haemoglobin in your bloodstream **before** the oxygen can.

3) This means that **less oxygen** can be carried around your body, leading to **oxygen deprivation**. At very high concentrations, carbon monoxide can be fatal.

### Sulfur Dioxide and Oxides of Nitrogen ($NO_x$) Lead to Acid Rain

1) Acid rain can be caused by burning fossil fuels that contain sulfur. The sulfur burns to produce sulfur dioxide gas which then enters the atmosphere, dissolves in the moisture, and is converted into sulfuric acid.

2) Oxides of nitrogen ($NO_x$) are produced when the high pressure and temperature in a car engine cause the nitrogen and oxygen in the air to react together. When oxides of nitrogen ($NO_x$) escape into the atmosphere, they dissolves in moisture and are converted into nitric acid, which can fall as acid rain.

3) Acid rain destroys trees and vegetation, as well as corroding buildings and statues and killing fish in lakes.

## Catalytic Converters Remove Some Pollutants from Car Emissions

1) Catalytic converters sit quietly in a car **exhaust** and stop some **pollutants** from coming out.

2) Without catalytic converters, cars spew out **lots** of bad stuff, like **carbon monoxide**, **oxides of nitrogen** and **unburnt hydrocarbons**.

3) Catalytic converters **get rid** of theses pollutants by using a **platinum catalyst** to change them to **harmless gases**, like **water vapour** and **nitrogen**, or to **less harmful** ones like **carbon dioxide**.

4) For example, **nitrogen monoxide** and **carbon monoxide** can be converted to nitrogen and carbon dioxide: $2NO_{(g)} + CO_{(g)} \rightarrow N_{2(g)} + CO_{2(g)}$

# Fuels

## Fossil Fuels are Non-Renewable

The various kinds of pollution produced by burning fossil fuels aren't the only problems.
They're also becoming more and more scarce as we use more and more of them.

1) The main fossil fuels (**coal, oil,** and **natural gas**) are relatively
   **easily extracted** and produce a **large amount** of energy when burnt.
   But, there's a finite amount of them and they're running out.

2) Oil will be the first to go — and as it gets really scarce, it'll become more **expensive**.
   It's not **sustainable** to keep using fossil fuels willy-nilly.

*"Bruce... bring some more fossils — the barbie's going out."*

## Biofuels Include Biodiesel and Alcohols Made from Renewable Sources

1) Fortunately, there are alternatives to fossil fuels which are renewable.

2) Biofuels are fuels made from **living matter** over a **short period** of time:

   - **bioethanol** is ethanol (an alcohol) made by the **fermentation** of **sugar** from crops such as maize,
   - **biodiesel** is made by **refining** renewable **fats** and **oils** such as vegetable oil,
   - **biogas** is produced by the breakdown of **organic waste matter**.

3) These fuels do produce $CO_2$ when they're burnt, but it's $CO_2$ that the plants
   **absorbed** while growing, so **biofuels** are usually still classed as **carbon neutral**.
   But $CO_2$ is still given out while refining and transporting the fuel, as well as making the fertilisers
   and powering agricultural machinery used to grow and harvest the crops.

4) Biodiesel and biogas can also be made from waste that would otherwise go to **landfill**.

5) But one problem with switching from fossil fuels to biofuels in transport is that
   **petrol car engines** would have to be **modified** to use fuels with high ethanol concentrations.

6) Also, the land used to grow crops for fuel can't be used to grow **food** — this could be a serious problem...
   **Developed** countries (like the UK) will create a huge demand as they try to find fossil fuel alternatives.
   Poorer **developing** countries (in South America, say) could use this as a way of **earning money**, and convert
   farming land to produce 'crops for fuels'. This may mean they won't grow enough food to eat.

## Practice Questions

Q1 Name three products that form when an alkane burns in limited oxygen.

Q2 Why is the production of sulfur dioxide harmful for the environment?

Q3 Describe how bioethanol is produced.

**Exam Questions**

Q1 One of the components in petrol is the alkane pentane ($C_5H_{12}$).

   a) Write a balanced equation for the complete combustion of pentane. [2 marks]

   b) Explain how the incomplete combustion of pentane could cause serious health problems. [2 marks]

Q2 One problem caused by pollution is acid rain.

   a) Name two pollutants which lead to acid rain. [1 mark]

   b) Explain how one of these pollutants can be removed from car emissions. [1 mark]

Q3 Biodiesel is a fuel that can be used as an alternative to fossil fuels.
   Give one advantage and one disadvantage of using biodiesel over fossil fuels. [2 marks]

## Fixing the pollution problem — a fuels errand...

*It's a dirty business, burning fossil fuels. You need to know about the various pollutants they release (such as sulfur oxides, nitrogen oxides, carbon monoxide, unburnt hydrocarbons, carbon particulates) and what damage they do. Then there are the alternatives. Biofuels may well be renewable, but they're not without their own drawbacks.*

# Alkenes

*An alkene is like an alkane's wild younger brother. They look kinda similar, but alkenes are way more reactive.*

## Alkenes are **Unsaturated Hydrocarbons**

1) Alkenes have the **general formula $C_nH_{2n}$**. They're made of carbon and hydrogen atoms, so they're **hydrocarbons**.

2) Alkene molecules **all** have at least one **C=C double covalent bond**. Molecules with C=C double bonds are **unsaturated** because they can make more bonds with extra atoms in **addition** reactions (see pages 86-87).

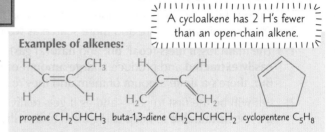

Examples of alkenes:

propene $CH_2CHCH_3$    buta-1,3-diene $CH_2CHCHCH_2$    cyclopentene $C_5H_8$

*A cycloalkene has 2 H's fewer than an open-chain alkene.*

## Bonds in Organic Molecules can be **Sigma** or **Pi Bonds**

Covalent bonds form when **atomic orbitals** from different atoms, each containing a single electron, **overlap**, causing the electrons to become **shared**. A bond forms because the nuclei of the atoms are attracted by **electrostatic attraction** to the bonding electrons. The **way** that atomic orbitals overlap causes different **types** of bond to form.

1) Single covalent bonds in organic molecules are **sigma (σ-) bonds**. A σ-bond is formed when **two orbitals overlap**, in a straight line, in the space between two atoms. This gives the highest possible **electron density** between the two positive nuclei.

2) The **high electron density** between the nuclei means there is a strong **electrostatic attraction** between the nuclei and the shared pair of electrons. This means that σ-bonds have a high **bond enthalpy** — they're the **strongest** type of covalent bonds.

3) A double bond is made up of a **sigma (σ-) bond** and a **pi (π-) bond**. A π-bond is formed when **two lobes** of two orbitals **overlap sideways**. It's got two parts to it — one 'above' and one 'below' the molecular axis. For example, p-orbitals can form π-bonds.

4) In a π-bond, the electron density is **spread out** above and below the nuclei. This causes the **electrostatic attraction** between the nuclei and the shared pair of electrons to be **weaker** in π-bonds than in σ-bonds, so π-bonds have a **relatively low bond enthalpy**.

5) This means that a double bond (π-bond + σ-bond) is less than twice as strong as a single bond (just a σ-bond).

6) Although they're usually written as C=C, double bonds really look **more like this:**

7) In alkenes, the **C–C** and **C–H** bonds are all **σ-bonds**. The **C=C** bonds in **alkenes** contain both a **σ-** and a **π-bond**.

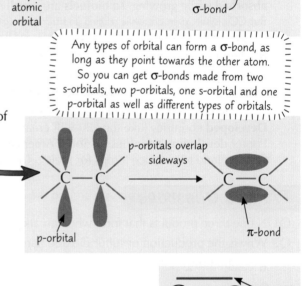

*Any types of orbital can form a σ-bond, as long as they point towards the other atom. So you can get σ-bonds made from two s-orbitals, two p-orbitals, one s-orbital and one p-orbital as well as different types of orbitals.*

## Practice Questions

Q1 What is the general formula of an alkene?

Q2 Describe how a sigma (σ–) bond forms.

**Exam Question**

Q1 The C=C bond in ethene is made up of two different types of bond.

a) Give one similarity between these bonds. [1 mark]

b) Give one difference between these bonds. [1 mark]

---

## *Double, double toil and trouble. Alkene burn and pi bond bubble...*

*Double bonds are always made up of a σ-bond and a π-bond. So even though π-bonds are weaker than σ-bonds, double bonds will be stronger than single bonds because they have the combined strength of a σ- and a π-bond.*

# Stereoisomerism

*The chemistry on these pages isn't so bad.  And don't be too worried when I tell you that a good working knowledge of both German and Latin would be useful.  It's not absolutely essential... You'll be fine without.*

## Double Bonds Can't Rotate

1) Carbon atoms in a C=C double bond and the atoms bonded to these carbons all lie in the **same plane** (they're **planar**). Because of the way they're arranged, they're actually said to be **trigonal planar** — the atoms attached to each double-bonded carbon are at the corners of an imaginary equilateral triangle.

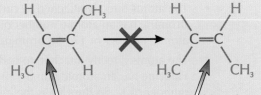

The H–C–H bond angles in the planar unit are all 120°.

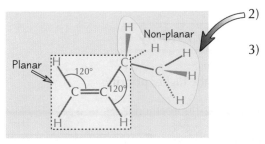

2) Ethene, $C_2H_4$ (like in the diagram above), is completely planar, but in larger alkenes, only the >C=C< unit is planar.

3) Another important thing about C=C double bonds is that atoms **can't rotate** around them like they can around single bonds (because of the way the p-orbitals **overlap** to form a π-**bond** — see previous page).  In fact, double bonds are fairly **rigid** — they don't bend much either.

4) Even though atoms can't rotate about the **double bond**, things can still rotate about any **single bonds** in the molecule.

5) The **restricted rotation** around the C=C double bond is what causes **alkenes** to form **stereoisomers**.

Both these molecules have the structural formula $CH_3CHCHCH_3$.  The restricted rotation around the double bond means you can't turn one into the other so they are isomers.

## E/Z isomerism is a Type of Stereoisomerism

1) **Stereoisomers** have the same structural formula but a **different arrangement** in space. (Just bear with me for a moment... that will become clearer, I promise.)

2) Because of the **lack of rotation** around the double bond, some **alkenes** can have stereoisomers.

3) Stereoisomers occur when the two double-bonded carbon atoms each have two **different atoms** or **groups** attached to them.

4) One of these isomers is called the **'E-isomer'** and the other is called the **'Z-isomer'** (hence the name E/Z isomerism).

> When you're naming stereoisomers, you need to put 'E' or 'Z' at the beginning of the name.

5) The **Z-isomer** has the same groups either **both above** or **both below** the double bond, whilst the **E-isomer** has the same groups positioned **across** the double bond.

**Example:** But-2-ene

The double-bonded carbon atoms in but-2-ene each have an **H** and a **CH₃** group attached.

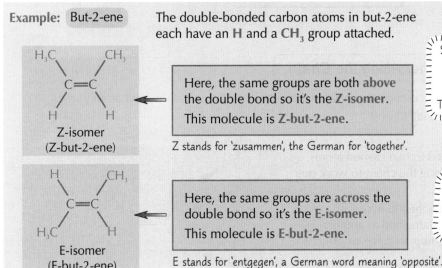

Here, the same groups are both **above** the double bond so it's the **Z-isomer**. This molecule is **Z-but-2-ene**.

Z-isomer (Z-but-2-ene)

Z stands for 'zusammen', the German for 'together'.

> Skeletal formulae (see page 70) are great for showing stereoisomerism.  For example, the skeletal formula of Z-but-2-ene is:
>
> The skeletal formula of E-but-2-ene is:

Here, the same groups are **across** the double bond so it's the **E-isomer**. This molecule is **E-but-2-ene**.

E-isomer (E-but-2-ene)

E stands for 'entgegen', a German word meaning 'opposite'.

> An easy way to work out which isomer is which is to remember that in the Z-isomer, the groups are on 'ze zame zide', but in the E-isomer, they are 'enemies'.

# Stereoisomerism

## The E/Z System Works Even When All the Groups Are Different

1) When the carbons on either end of a double bond both have the **same groups** attached, then it's easy to work out which is the E-isomer and which is the Z-isomer (like in the example on the last page).

2) It only starts to get **problematic** if the carbon atoms both have **totally different groups** attached.

3) Fortunately, a clever person (well, three clever people — Mr Cahn, Mr Ingold and Mr Prelog) came up with a solution to this problem.

4) Using the **Cahn-Ingold-Prelog (CIP) rules** you can work out which is the E-isomer and which is the Z-isomer for any alkene. They're really simple, and they work every time.

## Atoms With a Larger Atomic Number are Given a Higher Priority

1) Look at the atoms **directly bonded** to each of the C=C carbon atoms.
The atom with the higher **atomic number** on each carbon is given the higher **priority**.

**Example:** Here's one of the stereoisomers of 1-bromo-1-chloro-2-fluoroethene:

- The atoms directly attached to **carbon-1** are bromine and chlorine. **Bromine** has an atomic number of **35** and **chlorine** has an atomic number of **17**. So **bromine** is the higher priority group.

- The atoms directly attached to **carbon-2** are fluorine and hydrogen. **Fluorine** has an atomic number of **9** and **hydrogen** has an atomic number of **1**. So **fluorine** is the higher priority group.

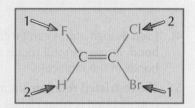

2) Now you can assign the isomers as E- and Z- as before, just by looking at how the groups of the **same priority** are arranged.

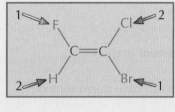

In this stereoisomer of 1-bromo-1-chloro-2-fluoroethene, the **higher priority groups** (bromine and fluorine) are positioned **across** the double bond from one another. So it's the **E-isomer**.

*If you need to look up atomic numbers in the exams, you'll find them on the periodic table in your data booklet.*

This is the Z-isomer.

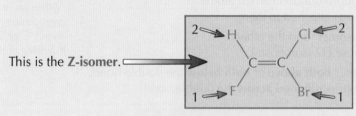

## You May Have to Look Further Along the Chain

If the atoms **directly bonded** to the carbon are the **same** then you have to look at the **next** atom in the groups to work out which has the higher priority.

This carbon is directly bonded to **two carbon** atoms, so you need to go **further along** the chain to work out the ordering.

The methyl carbon is only attached to hydrogen atoms, but the ethyl carbon is attached to another carbon atom. So the **ethyl group** is higher priority.

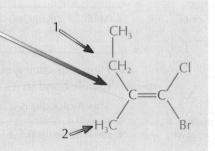

# Stereoisomerism

## *Cis-Trans Isomerism is a Special Type of E/Z isomerism*

1) If the carbon atoms have at least **one group in common** (like in but-2-ene), then you can call the isomers '**cis**' or '**trans**' (as well as E- or Z-) where...

   - '**cis**' means the same groups are on the **same side** of the double bond,
   - '**trans**' means the same groups are on **opposite sides** of the double bond.

   So E-but-2-ene can be called **trans-but-2-ene**, as it has methyl groups on **opposite sides** of the double bond, and Z-but-2-ene can be called **cis-but-2-ene**, as the methyl groups are on the **same side** of the double bond.

   *In cis-trans isomerism, you're looking at how identical groups are positioned, rather than the higher priority groups. This means there isn't a rule for whether the Z-isomer is the cis- or the trans-isomer (and the same for the E-isomer) — you just have to work it out.*

   *We're talking Latin this time... 'cis' means 'on the same side', while 'trans' means 'across'.*

   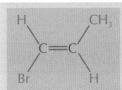

   Here's an example:
   The **H** atoms are on **opposite** sides of the double bond, so this is **trans-1-bromopropene**. No problems there.

2) If the carbon atoms both have totally **different** groups attached to them, the cis-trans naming system can't cope.

   Here, the **cis/trans** naming system doesn't work because the carbon atoms have **different groups** attached so there's no way of deciding **which isomer** is cis and which isomer is trans.

   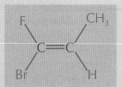

   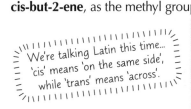

   E-1-bromo-1-fluoropropene        Z-1-bromo-1-fluoropropene

3) The E/Z system keeps on working though — in the E/Z system, Br has a **higher priority** than F, so the names depend on where the Br atom is in relation to the CH₃ group.

## *Practice Questions*

Q1 Why is an ethene molecule said to be planar?

Q2 Define the term 'stereoisomers'.

Q3 Which of the following molecules, **A**, **B** or **C**, is the Z-isomer of but-2-ene?

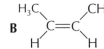

Q4 Is chlorine or bromine higher priority under the Cahn-Ingold-Prelog priority rules?

Q5 Which of the molecules in Question 3 (**A**, **B** or **C**) is the trans-isomer of but-2-ene?

**Exam Questions**

Q1  a)  Draw and name the E/Z isomers of pent-2-ene, using full systematic names.    [2 marks]

   b)  Explain why alkenes can have E/Z isomers but alkanes cannot.    [2 marks]

Q2  How many stereoisomers are there of the molecule CH₃CH=CHCH₂CH=C(CH₃)₂?

   **A** 1        **B** 2        **C** 3        **D** 4    [1 mark]

Q3  a)  Draw and name the E/Z isomers of:

      i)  1-bromo-2-chloroethene,        ii)  1-bromo-2-chloroprop-1-ene.    [4 marks]

   b)  i)  Which of the molecules in part a) exhibits cis-trans isomerism?  Explain your answer.    [2 marks]

      ii)  Draw and name the cis-trans isomers of the molecule identified in part b) i).    [2 marks]

---

## *You've reached the ausfahrt (that's German for exit)...*

*IMPORTANT FACT: If the two groups connected to one of the double-bonded carbons in an alkene are the same, then it won't have E/Z isomers.  So neither propene nor but-1-ene have E/Z isomers.  Try drawing them out if you're not sure.*

# Reactions of Alkenes

*I'll warn you now — some of this stuff gets a bit heavy — but stick with it, as it's pretty important.*

## Electrophilic Addition Reactions Happen to Alkenes

In an **electrophilic addition** reaction, the alkene **double bond** opens up and atoms are **added** to the carbon atoms.

1) Electrophilic addition reactions happen because the double bond has got plenty of **electrons** and is easily attacked by **electrophiles**.

2) **Electrophiles** are **electron-pair acceptors** — they're usually a bit short of electrons, so they're **attracted** to areas where there are lots of electrons about.

3) Electrophiles include **positively charged ions**, like $H^+$ and $NO_2^+$, and **polar molecules** (since the $\delta+$ atom is attracted to places with lots of electrons).

## Adding Hydrogen to C=C Bonds Produces Alkanes

1) Ethene will react with **hydrogen** gas in an addition reaction to produce ethane. It needs a **nickel catalyst** and a temperature of **150 °C** though.

$$H_2C{=}CH_2 + H_2 \xrightarrow[150\,°C]{Ni} CH_3CH_3$$

2) **Margarine's** made by '**hydrogenating**' **unsaturated** vegetable **oils**. By removing some double bonds, you **raise** the **melting point** of the oil so that it becomes **solid** at room temperature.

## Halogens React With Alkenes to Form Dihalogenoalkanes

1) **Halogens** will react with alkenes to form **dihalogenoalkanes** — the halogens add **across** the **double bond**, and each of the carbon atoms ends up bonded to one halogen atom. It's an **electrophilic addition** reaction.

$$H_2C{=}CH_2 + X_2 \longrightarrow CH_2XCH_2X$$

2) Here's the mechanism — bromine is used as an example, but chlorine and iodine react in the same way.

| The double bond repels the electrons in $Br_2$, polarising Br–Br. | Heterolytic (unequal) fission of $Br_2$. The closer Br gives up the bonding electrons to the other Br and bonds to the C atom. | You get a positively charged carbocation intermediate. The $Br^-$ now zooms over... | ...and bonds to the other C atom, forming 1,2-dibromoethane. |

> A carbocation is an organic ion containing a positively charged carbon atom.

3) When you shake an alkene with **brown bromine water**, the solution quickly **decolourises**. This is because bromine is added across the double bond to form a colourless **dibromoalkane**. So **bromine water** is used to test for the presence of **carbon-carbon double bonds**.

bromine water + cyclohexene → SHAKE → solution goes colourless

## Alcohols Can be Made by Steam Hydration

1) Alkenes can be **hydrated** by **steam** at 300 °C and a pressure of 60-70 atm. The reaction needs a solid **phosphoric(V) acid catalyst**.

2) The reaction is used to manufacture **ethanol** from **ethene**:

$$H_2C{=}CH_{2\,(g)} + H_2O_{(g)} \underset{\substack{300\,°C \\ 60\,atm}}{\overset{H_3PO_4}{\rightleftharpoons}} CH_3CH_2OH_{(g)}$$

## Alkenes are Oxidised by Acidified Potassium Manganate(VII)

1) If you shake an alkene with **acidified potassium manganate(VII)**, the **purple** solution is **decolourised**. You've **oxidised** the alkene and made a diol (an alcohol with two -OH groups).

2) For example, here's how **ethene** reacts with acidified potassium manganate(VII):

ethane–1,2–diol

# Reactions of Alkenes

## Alkenes also Undergo *Addition* with *Hydrogen Halides*

Alkenes also undergo **addition** reactions with hydrogen halides — to form **halogenoalkanes**.
For example, this is the reaction between **ethene** and HBr:

$$H_2C=CH_2 + HBr \rightarrow CH_2BrCH_3$$

## Adding *Hydrogen Halides* to *Unsymmetrical Alkenes* Forms *Two Products*

1) If the hydrogen halide adds to an **unsymmetrical** alkene, there are two possible products.

2) The amount of each product depends on how **stable** the **carbocation** formed in the middle of the reaction is.

3) Carbocations with more **alkyl groups** are more stable because the alkyl groups feed **electrons** towards the positive charge. The **more stable carbocation** is much more likely to form.

4) Here's how hydrogen bromide reacts with propene:

$$H_2C=CHCH_3 + HBr \rightarrow CH_3CHBrCH_3$$
2-bromopropane (major product)

$$H_2C=CHCH_3 + HBr \rightarrow CH_2BrCH_2CH_3$$
1-bromopropane (minor product)

This secondary carbocation's more stable because it's got two alkyl groups. This carbocation forms most of the time.

This primary carbocation's less stable as it's only got one alkyl group. It forms less often.

2-bromopropane (major product)

1-bromopropane (small amount only)

5) This can be summed up by **Markownikoff's rule** which says: The **major product** from addition of a hydrogen halide (HX) to an unsymmetrical alkene is the one where **hydrogen** adds to the carbon with the **most hydrogens** already attached.

## Practice Questions

Q1 What is an electrophile?

Q2 Write an equation for the reaction of ethene with hydrogen.

Q3 Give the reagents and conditions needed to convert an alkene into a diol.

**Exam Question**

Q1 But-1-ene is an alkene. Alkenes contain at least one C=C double bond.

a) Describe how bromine water can be used to test for C=C double bonds. [1 mark]

b) Name and show the reaction mechanism involved in the above test. [5 marks]

c) Hydrogen bromide reacts with but-1-ene, producing two isomeric products. Draw the displayed formulae of these two isomers and explain which will be the major product. [4 marks]

## *Electrophiles — they all want a piece of the pi...*

Mechanisms are a classic that examiners just love. You need to know the electrophilic addition examples on these pages, so shut the book and scribble them out. And remember that sometimes the product has more than one isomer.

# Polymers

*Polymers are long, stringy molecules made by joining lots of alkenes together. They're made up of one unit repeated over and over and over and over and over and over and over and over again. Get the idea? OK, let's get started.*

## Alkenes *Join Up* to form *Addition Polymers*

1) The **double bonds** in alkenes can open up and join together to make long chains called **polymers**. It's kind of like they're holding hands in a big line. The individual, small alkenes are called **monomers**.

2) This is called **addition polymerisation**. For example, **poly(ethene)** is made by the **addition polymerisation** of **ethene**.

3) To find the **monomer** used to form an addition polymer, take the **repeat unit**, add a **double bond** between the carbon atoms and **remove** the single bonds from each end.

4) To find the **repeat unit** from a monomer, just do the **reverse** — change the C=C bond into a **single bond**, and add another single bond to each of the C=C carbons.

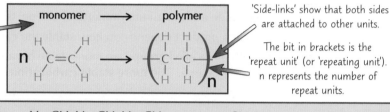

'Side-links' show that both sides are attached to other units.

The bit in brackets is the 'repeat unit' (or 'repeating unit'). n represents the number of repeat units.

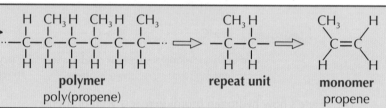

polymer
poly(propene)

repeat unit

monomer
propene

## There are Different *Methods* for *Disposing* of Polymers

In the UK over **2 million** tonnes of plastic waste are produced each year. It's important to find ways to get rid of this waste while minimising **environmental damage**. There are various possible approaches...

### Waste Plastics can be *Buried*

1) **Landfill** is used to dispose of waste plastics when the plastic is:
   - difficult to separate from other waste,
   - not in sufficient quantities to make separation financially worthwhile,
   - too difficult technically to recycle.

2) But because the **amount of waste** we generate is becoming more and more of a problem, there's a need to **reduce** landfill as much as possible.

### Waste Plastics can be *Reused*

1) Many plastics are made from non-renewable **oil-fractions**, so it makes sense to reuse plastics as much as possible.

2) There's more than one way to reuse plastics. After **sorting** into different types:
   - some plastics (poly(propene), for example) can be **recycled** by **melting** and **remoulding** them,
   - some plastics can be **cracked** into **monomers**, and these can be used as an **organic feedstock** to make more plastics or other chemicals.

Infrared spectroscopy (pages 102-103) can be used to help sort plastics into different types before they're recycled.

### Waste Plastics can be *Burned*

1) If recycling isn't possible for whatever reason, waste plastics can be burned — and the heat can be used to generate **electricity**.

2) This process needs to be carefully **controlled** to reduce **toxic** gases. For example, polymers that contain **chlorine** (such as **PVC**) produce **HCl** when they're burned — this has to be removed.

3) Waste gases from the combustion are passed through **scrubbers** which can **neutralise** gases, such as HCl, by allowing them to react with a **base**.

4) Plastics can also be **sorted** before they are burnt to separate out any materials that will produce **toxic gases**.

Rex and Dirk enjoy some waist plastic.

# Polymers

## Chemists Can Work to Make Polymers Sustainably

Lots of **chemicals** that are used in the manufacture of polymers are **pretty dangerous**.
The way that a polymer is made should be designed to **minimise** the impact on human **health** and the **environment**.
There are a set of principles that chemists follow when they design a **sustainable polymer manufacturing process**:

- Use **reactant** molecules that are as **safe** and **environmentally friendly** as possible.
- Use as few **other materials**, like **solvents**, as possible.
  If you have to use other chemicals, choose ones that **won't** harm the environment.
- **Renewable raw materials** should be used wherever possible.
- **Energy use** should be kept to a **minimum**. **Catalysts** are often utilised in polymer synthesis to lower energy use.
- Limit the **waste products** made, especially those which are **hazardous** to **human health** or the **environment**.
- Make sure the **lifespan** of the polymer is **appropriate** for its use. If you make a polymer that just keeps breaking, you'll end up having to make loads more than if you create a more enduring polymer.

## Biodegradable Polymers Decompose in the Right Conditions

1) Scientists can now make **biodegradable** polymers (ones that naturally **decompose**).
   They decompose pretty quickly in certain conditions because organisms can digest them.
2) Biodegradable polymers can be made from **renewable** raw materials such as **starch**
   (from maize and other plants), or from **oil fractions** such as the hydrocarbon **isoprene**.

*Being able to safely dispose of polymers in a way that doesn't harm the environment is part of making polymers sustainable.*

Using **renewable** raw material has several **advantages**.
- Raw materials aren't going to **run out** like oil will.
- When polymers biodegrade, **carbon dioxide** (a greenhouse gas) is produced. If your polymer is **plant-based**,
  then the $CO_2$ released as it decomposes is the same $CO_2$ absorbed by the plant when it grew.
  But with an **oil-based** biodegradable polymer, you're effectively transferring carbon from the oil to the atmosphere.
- Over their 'lifetime' some plant-based polymers **save energy** compared to oil-based plastics.

3) Even though they're biodegradable, these polymers still need the right conditions before they'll decompose.
   This means that you still need to **collect** and **separate** the biodegradable polymers from non-biodegradable
   plastics. At the moment, they're also **more expensive** than non-biodegradable equivalents.

## Practice Questions

Q1 Draw the displayed formulae for the monomer and repeat unit used to make poly(propene).

Q2 Describe three ways in which used polymers such as poly(propene) can be disposed of.

Q3 What is a biodegradable polymer?

**Exam Questions**

Q1 Part of the structure of a polymer is shown on the right.

   a) Draw the repeating unit of the polymer. [1 mark]

   b) Draw the monomer from which the polymer was formed. [1 mark]

Q2 Waste plastics can be disposed of by burning.

   a) Describe one advantage of disposing of waste plastics by burning. [1 mark]

   b) Describe a disadvantage of burning waste plastic that contains chlorine,
   and explain how the impact of this disadvantage could be reduced. [2 marks]

Q3* Outline and discuss some of the considerations an industrial chemist should
make when designing a sustainable polymer manufacturing process. [6 marks]

## Alkenes — join up today, your polymer needs YOU...

*You may have noticed that all this recycling business is a hot topic these days. This suits examiners just fine — they like
you to know how useful and important chemistry is. So learn this stuff, pass your exams, and do some recycling.*

\* The quality of your extended response
will be assessed for this question.

# Halogenoalkanes

*If you haven't had enough of organic chemistry yet, there's more. If you **have** had enough — there's still more.*

## Halogenoalkanes are Alkanes with Halogen Atoms

A **halogenoalkane** is an alkane with at least one **halogen atom** in place of a hydrogen atom.

E.g.

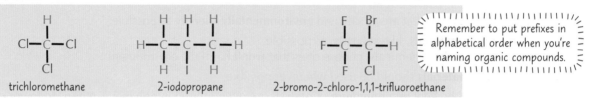

trichloromethane    2-iodopropane    2-bromo-2-chloro-1,1,1-trifluoroethane

*Remember to put prefixes in alphabetical order when you're naming organic compounds.*

## Halogenoalkanes can be Primary, Secondary or Tertiary

Halogenoalkanes with just **one halogen atom** can be **primary**, **secondary** or **tertiary** halogenoalkanes.

On the **carbon** with the **halogen** attached:

1) A **primary** halogenoalkane has **two hydrogen atoms** and just **one alkyl group**.

2) A **secondary** halogenoalkane has **just one hydrogen atom** and **two alkyl groups**.

3) A **tertiary** halogenoalkane has **no hydrogen atoms** and **three alkyl groups**.

X = halogen
R = alkyl group

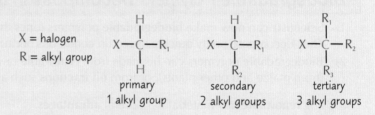

primary
1 alkyl group

secondary
2 alkyl groups

tertiary
3 alkyl groups

## Halogenoalkanes Can be Hydrolysed to Form Alcohols

1) Halogenoalkanes can be hydrolysed to alcohols in a **nucleophilic substitution reaction** (see page 92). One way to do this is to use **water**.

2) The general equation is:
$$R-X + H_2O \rightarrow R-OH + H^+ + X^-$$

*Hydrolysis is when water breaks bonds.*

3) Here's what would happen with bromoethane:
$$CH_3CH_2Br + H_2O \rightarrow C_2H_5OH + H^+ + Br^-$$

*You can also hydrolyse halogenoalkanes using aqueous potassium hydroxide (see page 92).*

## You Can Compare the Reactivities of Halogenoalkanes Using Experiments

1) When you mix a **halogenoalkane** with water, it reacts to form an **alcohol**.
$$R-X + H_2O \rightarrow R-OH + H^+ + X^-$$

2) If you put **silver nitrate solution** in the mixture too, the silver ions react with the **halide ions** as soon as they form, giving a **silver halide precipitate** (see page 51).
$$Ag^+_{(aq)} + X^-_{(aq)} \rightarrow AgX_{(s)}$$

3) To **compare** the reactivities of different halogenoalkanes, set up three test tubes each containing a different halogenoalkane, ethanol (as a solvent) and silver nitrate solution (this contains the water).

4) **Time** how long it takes for a **precipitate** to form in each test tube. The **more quickly** a precipitate forms, the faster the **rate of hydrolysis** is for that halogenoalkane.

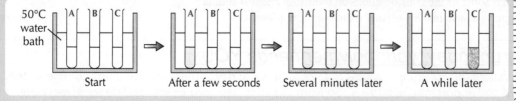

50°C water bath

Start    After a few seconds    Several minutes later    A while later

*You can use the colours of the silver halide precipitates to distinguish between chloro, bromo and iodo alkanes (see page 51). Make sure you learn the colours for the exams.*

# Halogenoalkanes

## Primary, Secondary and Tertiary Halogenoalkanes Have Different Reactivities

You can compare the reactivities of **primary**, **secondary** and **tertiary** halogenoalkanes using the reaction on the last page.

**Example:** A student sets up an experiment to compare the reactivities of a primary, a secondary and a tertiary bromoalkane. His results are shown below. Which is the most reactive halogenoalkane?

| Halogenoalkane | Time taken for precipitate to form / s |
|---|---|
| 1-bromobutane (primary) | 112 |
| 2-bromobutane (secondary) | 62 |
| 2-bromo-2-methylpropane (tertiary) | 8 |

From the results, you can tell that the **tertiary halogenoalkane** is the most reactive, since it reacted **fastest** with the water. The **primary** halogenoalkane is the **least** reactive.

This example uses bromoalkanes, but the order of reactivity is the same whichever halogen you use.

## Iodoalkanes are Hydrolysed the Fastest

1) In order to hydrolyse a halogenoalkane, you have to **break** the **carbon-halogen bond**.

2) How quickly different halogenoalkanes are hydrolysed depends on the carbon-halogen **bond enthalpy** — see page 110 for more on this.

3) **Weaker** carbon-halogen bonds **break** more easily — so they react **faster**.

4) Bond enthalpy depends on the **size** of the halogen — the **larger** the halogen, the **longer** the C–X bond, and the **lower** the bond enthalpy.

5) The **size** of the halogen **increases** down Group 7, so **iodoalkanes** have the **weakest bonds**, and are hydrolysed the **fastest**. **Fluoroalkanes** have the **strongest bonds**, so they're the **slowest** at hydrolysing.

6) You can **compare the reactivity** of chloroalkanes, bromoalkanes and iodoalkanes using an experiment like the one on the previous page.

| bond | bond enthalpy / kJ mol$^{-1}$ |
|---|---|
| C–F | 467 |
| C–Cl | 346 |
| C–Br | 290 |
| C–I | 228 |

Faster hydrolysis as bond enthalpy decreases (the bonds get weaker).

**Example:** A student sets up an experiment to compare the reactivities of a chloroalkane, a bromoalkane and an iodoalkane. Her results are shown below. Which is the most reactive halogenoalkane?

| Halogenoalkane | Time taken for precipitate to form / s |
|---|---|
| 2-iodopropane | 7 |
| 2-bromopropane | 240 |
| 2-chloropropane | 567 |

A pale yellow precipitate quickly forms with **2-iodopropane** — so iodoalkanes must be the **most reactive** of these halogenoalkanes. **Bromoalkanes** react slower than iodoalkanes to form a cream precipitate, and **chloroalkanes** form a white precipitate even more slowly.

The halogenoalkanes should have the same carbon skeleton so it's a fair test.

## Practice Questions

Q1 What is a halogenoalkane?

Q2 What is a secondary halogenoalkane? Draw and name an example of one.

Q3 Put primary, secondary and tertiary halogenoalkanes in order of reactivity with water.

**Exam Question**

Q1 a) A tertiary halogenoalkane has the molecular formula $C_4H_9I$. Draw and name the halogenoalkane. [2 marks]

b) The halogenoalkane in part a) is mixed with water and silver nitrate solution. Give the formula of the precipitate that forms. [1 mark]

c) Predict, with reasoning, whether the tertiary chloroalkane with formula $C_4H_9Cl$ will be hydrolysed faster or slower than the halogenoalkane in part a) if all the other reactant conditions are the same. [3 marks]

## Hydra-lies — stories told by a many-headed monster...

*You can only compare the effect of one variable on the rates of hydrolysis of different halogenoalkanes if you keep the other variables the same. If you're investigating the effect of the halogen, the carbon skeletons of the halogenoalkanes need to be the same, and for the effect of primary, secondary or tertiary, the molecular formulae need to be identical.*

# More on Halogenoalkanes

*Two more pages all about halogenoalkanes. It must be your lucky day...*

## Halogenoalkanes May React by *Nucleophilic Substitution*

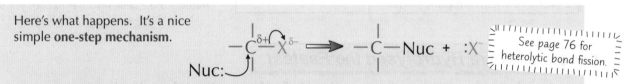

1) Halogens are generally more **electronegative** than carbon. So, the **carbon–halogen bond** is **polar**.

2) The **δ+ carbon** doesn't have enough electrons. This means it can be attacked by a **nucleophile**.
   A nucleophile's an **electron-pair donor**. It donates an electron pair to somewhere without enough electrons.

3) **OH⁻**, **NH₃** and **CN⁻** are examples of **nucleophiles** that react readily with halogenoalkanes.
   **Water** is also a weak nucleophile.

4) A nucleophile can bond with the δ+ carbon of a halogenoalkane, and be **substituted** for the halogen.
   This is called **nucleophilic substitution**:

> Here's what happens. It's a nice
> simple **one-step mechanism**.
>
> See page 76 for heterolytic bond fission.
>
> • **X** is the halogen. **Nuc** is the **nucleophile**, which provides a **pair of electrons** for the **C^δ+**.
> • The C–X bond breaks **heterolytically** — **both** electrons from the bond are taken by the halogen.
> • The halogen falls off as the nucleophile bonds to the carbon.
>
> *This reaction actually goes via a transition state where both the nucleophile and the halogen are weakly attached to the central carbon. You don't need to know about this in this topic though.*

5) There are **three examples** of nucleophilic substitution you need to know. Read on.

## Halogenoalkanes React with *Aqueous KOH* to form *Alcohols*

1) Halogenoalkanes react with **hydroxide ions** by **nucleophilic substitution** to form **alcohols**. You can use **warm aqueous potassium hydroxide** and do the reaction under reflux, otherwise it won't work.

2) Here's the general equation for the reaction:

$$R–X + KOH \rightarrow ROH + KX$$

*R represents an alkyl group. They're alkanes with one H removed, e.g. -CH₃, -C₂H₅. X stands for one of the halogens (F, Cl, Br or I).*

3) And here's how the reaction happens:

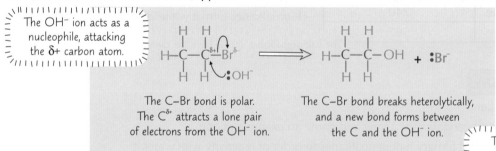

*The OH⁻ ion acts as a nucleophile, attacking the δ+ carbon atom.*

The C–Br bond is polar. The C^δ+ attracts a lone pair of electrons from the OH⁻ ion.

The C–Br bond breaks heterolytically, and a new bond forms between the C and the OH⁻ ion.

*The charges of each step in the mechanism have to balance — here, each step has an overall charge of –1.*

4) As you saw on page 90, you can also use **water** to hydrolyse halogenoalkanes and form **alcohols**. Water is a **worse nucleophile** that hydroxide ions, so the reaction with water is **slower**.

## Cyanide Ions React with Halogenoalkanes to form *Nitriles*

If you **reflux** a halogenoalkane with **potassium cyanide** in **ethanol**, then the cyanide ions will react with the halogenoalkane by **nucleophilic substitution** to form a **nitrile**.

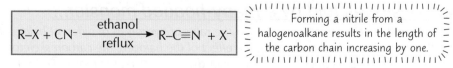

$$R–X + CN^- \xrightarrow[\text{reflux}]{\text{ethanol}} R–C{\equiv}N + X^-$$

*Forming a nitrile from a halogenoalkane results in the length of the carbon chain increasing by one.*

# More on Halogenoalkanes

## Halogenoalkanes React With Ammonia to Form Amines

1) Amines are organic compounds. They're based on **ammonia** ($NH_3$), but one or more of the **hydrogen** atoms are replaced by **alkyl** groups.

2) If you **warm** a halogenoalkane with excess **ethanolic** ammonia, the **ammonia** swaps places with the **halogen** to form a **primary amine** — yes, it's another one of those **nucleophilic substitution reactions**.

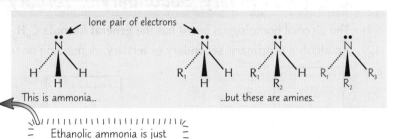

This is ammonia... ...but these are amines.

Ethanolic ammonia is just ammonia dissolved in ethanol.

The first step is the same as in the mechanisms on the previous page, except this time the nucleophile is $NH_3$.

In the second step, an ammonia molecule removes a hydrogen from the $NH_3$ group to leave an amine.

Amines often smell fishy — this can help you identify if an amine's been formed.

## Halogenoalkanes also Undergo Elimination Reactions

You know what happens when a halogenoalkane reacts with an aqueous alkali (yes, you do — it's on the opposite page). But nucleophilic substitution isn't the only game in town. Swap 'aqueous' for '**ethanolic**', and things change.

1) If you react a halogenoalkane with a warm alkali **dissolved in ethanol**, you get an **alkene**. The mixture must be **heated under reflux** or volatile stuff will be lost.

2) Here's bromoethane. Again.

It's possible that more than one isomer will form from elimination, just like with the elimination reaction of alcohols on page 95.

$$H-C-C-Br + KOH \xrightarrow[\text{reflux}]{\text{ethanol}} C=C + H_2O + KBr$$

3) In elimination reactions, the hydroxide ions are acting as a **base** to remove an $H^+$ ion from the halogenoalkane.

## Practice Questions

Q1 What is a nucleophile?

Q2 Sketch the mechanism, including curly arrows, for the reaction of bromoethane with warm aqueous KOH.

Q3 Write a general equation for the reaction under reflux of a halogenoalkane with potassium cyanide in ethanol.

**Exam Question**

Q1 Some reactions of 2-bromopropane, $CH_3CHBrCH_3$, are shown.

a) Give the structural formula of organic product, A. [1 mark]

b) i) Give the reagents and conditions for reaction 2. [2 marks]

ii) Draw a mechanism for reaction 2. [4 marks]

c) Give the structural formula of organic product, B. [1 mark]

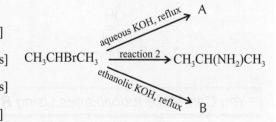

## *If you don't learn this, you will be eliminated. Resistance is nitrile...*

The nucleophilic substitution mechanisms on these pages are all quite similar. They start with the nucleophile attacking the δ+ carbon, causing the C–X bond to break. Then it's a case of getting rid of hydrogens from the substituted group, if necessary, to make the organic product neutral. Practise drawing the mechanisms — they may come up in the exams.

# Alcohols

*These two pages could well be enough to put you off alcohols for life...*

## Alcohols are **Primary, Secondary** or **Tertiary**

1) The alcohol homologous series has the **general formula $C_nH_{2n+1}OH$**.

2) An alcohol is **primary**, **secondary** or **tertiary**, depending on which carbon atom the **-OH** group is bonded to.

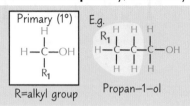

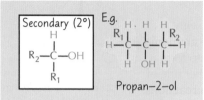

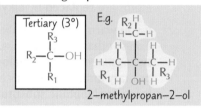

## Alcohols Can React to Form **Halogenoalkanes**

Alcohols can react in **substitution reactions** to form **halogenoalkanes**.
The reagents and method you use depends on the halogenoalkane that you're trying to make.

### Reacting Alcohols with **PCl₅** or **HCl** Produces **Chloroalkanes**

1) If you react an alcohol with phosphorus pentachloride ($PCl_5$), a chloroalkane is produced.
The general equation for this reaction is:

$$ROH + PCl_5 \rightarrow RCl + HCl + POCl_3$$

2) You can also make chloroalkanes if you react an **alcohol** with **hydrochloric acid**. The general equation for this reaction is:

$$ROH + HCl \rightarrow RCl + H_2O$$

*You'll probably do this synthesis as part of a practical in class. You can purify the 2-chloro-2-methylpropane product by separation and then distillation (see page 98).*

3) For example, 2-methylpropan-2-ol reacts with hydrochloric acid at room temperature to form 2-chloro-2-methylpropane:

$$(CH_3)_3COH + HCl \rightarrow (CH_3)_3CCl + H_2O$$

4) The reaction between alcohols and hydrochloric acid is **fastest** if the alcohol is a **tertiary alcohol**, and **slowest** if it is a **primary alcohol** (the rate for secondary alcohols is somewhere in between).

### -OH can be **Swapped** for Bromine to Make a **Bromoalkane**

1) Alcohols will react with compounds containing **bromide ions** (such as KBr) in a **substitution reaction**.

2) The **hydroxyl** (-OH) group is **replaced** by the **bromide**, so the alcohol is transformed into a **bromoalkane**.

3) The reaction also requires an **acid catalyst**, such as **50% concentrated $H_2SO_4$**.

**Example:** To make 2-bromo-2-methylpropane you just need to shake 2-methylpropan-2-ol (a tertiary alcohol) with potassium bromide and 50% concentrated sulfuric acid at room temperature.

First, potassium bromide reacts with sulfuric acid to form hydrogen bromide: $2KBr + H_2SO_4 \rightarrow HBr + K_2SO_4$.

The hydrogen bromide then reacts with the alcohol to form a bromoalkane:

$$\begin{array}{cc} CH_3 & CH_3 \\ | & | \\ H_3C-\underset{|}{\overset{}{C}}-CH_3 + HBr \longrightarrow H_3C-\underset{|}{\overset{}{C}}-CH_3 + H_2O \\ OH & Br \end{array}$$

alcohol
(2-methylpropan-2-ol)

bromoalkane
(2-bromo-2-methylpropane)

*50% concentrated sulfuric acid is made up of 50% $H_2SO_4$ and 50% water.*

### You Can Make Iodoalkanes Using **Red Phosphorus** and **Iodine**

1) You can make an **iodoalkane** from an **alcohol** by reacting it with **phosphorus triiodide ($PI_3$)**.

2) $PI_3$ is usually made **in situ** (within the reaction mixture) by refluxing the alcohol with 'red phosphorus' and iodine.

*There are different types of phosphorus, and red phosphorus is one of them (like how there are different types of carbon, e.g. graphite and diamond).*

3) This is the general equation:

$$3ROH + PI_3 \rightarrow 3RI + H_3PO_3$$

# Alcohols

## Alcohols can be **Dehydrated** to Form **Alkenes**

1) You can make alkenes by **eliminating** water from **alcohols** in an **elimination reaction**.

2) The alcohol is mixed with an **acid catalyst** such as **concentrated phosphoric acid** ($H_3PO_4$). The mixture is then **heated**.

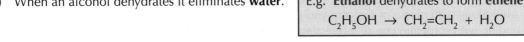
*An elimination reaction where water is eliminated is called a dehydration reaction.*

3) When an alcohol dehydrates it eliminates **water**.

E.g. **Ethanol** dehydrates to form **ethene**.
$$C_2H_5OH \rightarrow CH_2=CH_2 + H_2O$$

4) The water molecule is made up from the hydroxyl group and a hydrogen atom that was bonded to a carbon atom adjacent to the hydroxyl carbon.

5) This means that often there are **two possible** alkene products from one elimination reaction depending on **which side** of the hydroxyl group the **hydrogen** is **eliminated** from.

6) Also, watch out for if any of the alkene products can form **E/Z isomers** (see pages 83-85) — if they can then a mixture of both isomers will form.

**Example:** When butan-2-ol is heated to 170 °C with concentrated phosphoric acid, it dehydrates to form a mixture of products. Give the names and structures of all the organic compounds in this mixture.

- Elimination can occur between the **hydroxyl group** and the hydrogen either on **carbon-1** or **carbon-3**. This results in two possible alkene products — **but-1-ene** and **but-2-ene**.

- In addition, but-2-ene can form **E/Z isomers**.

- So there are **3** possible products — but-1-ene, E-but-2-ene and Z-but-2-ene.

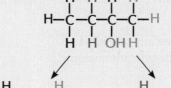

But-1-ene    E-But-2-ene    Z-But-2-ene

## Practice Questions

Q1 What is the general formula for an alcohol?

Q2 Describe two different ways that propan-2-ol could be converted into 2-chloropropane.

Q3 What products are made when ethanol is refluxed with 'red phosphorus' and iodine?

**Exam Questions**

Q1 a) Draw and name a primary alcohol, a secondary alcohol and a tertiary alcohol, each with the formula $C_5H_{12}O$. [3 marks]

b) Describe how ethanol could be converted into bromoethane. [1 mark]

Q2 When 3-methyl-pentan-3-ol is heated with concentrated phosphoric acid, it reacts to form a mixture of organic products.

a) What is the name of this type of reaction? [1 mark]

b) How many organic compounds will be produced?

**A** 4    **B** 3    **C** 2    **D** 1 [1 mark]

---

## *Euuurghh, what a page... I think I need a drink...*

*Not too much to learn here — a few basic definitions, two different ways to make a chloroalkane, a reaction to make a bromoalkane and another to make an iodoalkane, a tricky little dehydration reaction...*
*As I was saying, not much here at all... Think I'm going to faint.* [THWACK]

# Oxidation of Alcohols

*Another two pages of alcohol reactions. Probably not what you wanted for Christmas...*

## The Simplest way to Oxidise Alcohols is to **Burn Them**

It doesn't take much to set ethanol alight and it burns with a **pale blue flame**.
The C–C and C–H bonds break and ethanol is **completely oxidised**
to make carbon dioxide and water. This is a **combustion** reaction.

$$C_2H_5OH_{(l)} + 3O_{2(g)} \rightarrow 2CO_{2(g)} + 3H_2O_{(g)}$$

If you burn any alcohol along with plenty of oxygen, you get carbon dioxide and water as products.
But if you want to end up with something more interesting, you need a more sophisticated way of oxidising...

## How Much an Alcohol can be **Oxidised** Depends on its **Structure**

You can use the **oxidising agent acidified dichromate(VI)** ($Cr_2O_7^{2-}/H^+$, e.g. $K_2Cr_2O_7/H_2SO_4$) to **mildly** oxidise alcohols.

- **Primary** alcohols are oxidised to **aldehydes** and then to **carboxylic acids**.
- **Secondary** alcohols are oxidised to **ketones** only.
- **Tertiary** alcohols won't be oxidised.

*The orange dichromate(VI) ion is reduced to the green chromium(III) ion, $Cr^{3+}$.*

## **Aldehydes** and **Ketones** Contain **C=O** bonds

**Aldehydes** and **ketones** are **carbonyl** compounds — they have the functional group C=O.
Their general formula is $C_nH_{2n}O$.

1) **Aldehydes** have a **hydrogen** and **one alkyl group** attached to the carbonyl carbon atom.
E.g.

propanal
$CH_3CH_2CHO$

2) **Ketones** have **two alkyl groups** attached to the carbonyl carbon atom.
E.g.

propanone
$CH_3COCH_3$

You can test whether a compound is an aldehyde or a ketone using Benedict's solution. This is a **blue** solution of complexed **copper(II) ions** dissolved in **sodium carbonate**.

If it's heated with an **aldehyde** the **blue** copper(II) ions are reduced to a **brick-red precipitate** of **copper(I) oxide**.

*This test can also be done using Fehling's solution, which contains copper(II) ions dissolved in sodium hydroxide. The colour change from blue to red in the presence of an aldehyde is the same. Again, nothing happens with a ketone.*

If it's heated with a ketone, nothing happens as ketones can't be easily oxidised.

## **Primary** Alcohols will Oxidise to **Aldehydes** and **Carboxylic Acids**

Primary alcohols can be oxidised **twice** — first to form **aldehydes** which can then be oxidised to form **carboxylic acids**.

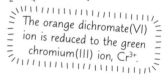

[O] = oxidising agent
e.g. potassium dichromate(VI)

primary alcohol          aldehyde          carboxylic acid

## **Distil** for an **Aldehyde**, and **Reflux** for a **Carboxylic Acid**

You can control how **far** the alcohol is oxidised by controlling the **reaction conditions**. For example...

1) Gently heating ethanol with potassium dichromate(VI) solution and sulfuric acid in a test tube should produce "apple" smelling **ethanal** (an aldehyde). However, it's **really tricky** to control the amount of heat and the aldehyde is usually oxidised to form "vinegar" smelling **ethanoic acid**.

2) To get just the **aldehyde**, you need to get it out of the oxidising solution **as soon** as it's formed. You can do this by gently heating excess alcohol with a **controlled** amount of oxidising agent in **distillation apparatus**, so the aldehyde (which boils at a lower temperature than the alcohol) is distilled off **immediately**.

*There's loads more about distillation and reflux on page 98.*

3) To produce the **carboxylic acid**, the alcohol has to be **vigorously oxidised**.
The alcohol is mixed with excess oxidising agent and heated under **reflux**.

# Oxidation of Alcohols

## Secondary Alcohols will Oxidise to Ketones

1) Refluxing a secondary alcohol, e.g. propan-2-ol, with acidified dichromate(VI) will produce a **ketone**.

2) Ketones can't be oxidised easily, so even prolonged refluxing won't produce anything more.

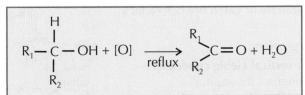

Monty and Bill were getting some much needed rest and refluxation.

## Tertiary Alcohols can't be Oxidised Easily

1) Tertiary alcohols don't react with potassium dichromate(VI) at all — the solution stays orange.

2) The only way to oxidise tertiary alcohols is by **burning** them.

## Practice Questions

Q1 Write an equation for the complete combustion of ethanol in oxygen.

Q2 What's the structural difference between an aldehyde and a ketone?

Q3 Why must you control the reaction conditions when oxidising a primary alcohol to an aldehyde?

Q4 How would you oxidise ethanol to ethanoic acid?

Q5 What will acidified potassium dichromate(VI) oxidise secondary alcohols to?

Q6 How would you oxidise a tertiary alcohol?

### Exam Questions

Q1 A student wanted to produce the aldehyde propanal from propanol, and set up reflux apparatus using acidified potassium dichromate(VI) as the oxidising agent.

    a) The student tested his product and found that he had not produced propanal.

        i) What is the student's product? [1 mark]

        ii) Write equations to show the two-stage reaction.
        You may use [O] to represent the oxidising agent. [2 marks]

        iii) What technique should the student have used and why? [1 mark]

    b) The student also tried to oxidise 2-methylpropan-2-ol, unsuccessfully.

        i) Draw the full structural formula for 2-methylpropan-2-ol. [1 mark]

        ii) Why is it not possible to oxidise 2-methylpropan-2-ol with an oxidising agent? [1 mark]

Q2 What will be produced if 2-methylbutan-2-ol is heated under reflux with acidified dichromate(VI)?

    **A** an aldehyde    **B** a carboxylic acid    **C** a ketone    **D** an unreacted alcohol [1 mark]

Q3 Plan an experiment to prepare 2-methylpropanal ($CH_3CH(CH_3)CHO$) from an appropriate alcohol. Your plan should include details of the chemicals (including an alcohol that could be used as a starting material) and procedure used for the reaction. [2 marks]

---

## I've never been very good at singing — I'm always in the wrong key-tone...

These alcohols couldn't just all react in the same way, could they? Nope — it seems like they're out to make your life difficult. So close the book and write down all the different ways of oxidising primary, secondary and tertiary alcohols, and what the different products are. And don't get caught out by those pesky primary alcohols getting oxidised twice.

# Organic Techniques

*There are some practical techniques that get used a lot in organic chemistry. They may be used during the synthesis of a product, or to purify it from unwanted by-products or unreacted reagents once it's been made.*

## Refluxing *Makes Sure You Don't Lose Any* **Volatile** *Organic Substances*

1) **Organic reactions** are **slow** and the substances are usually **flammable** and **volatile** (they've got **low boiling points**). If you stick them in a beaker and heat them with a Bunsen burner they'll **evaporate** or **catch fire** before they have **time to react**.

2) You can **reflux** a reaction to get round this problem.

3) The mixture's **heated in a flask** fitted with a **vertical Liebig condenser** — this continuously boils, evaporates and condenses the vapours and **recycles** them back into the flask, giving them **time to react**.

4) The **heating** is usually **electrical** — hot plates, heating mantles, or electrically controlled water baths are normally used. This **avoids naked flames** that might ignite the compounds.

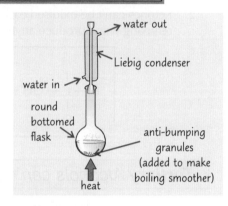

## Distillation *Separates Substances With Different* **Boiling Points**

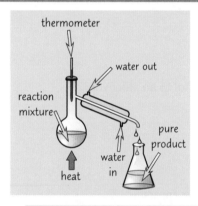

1) Distillation works by **gently heating** a mixture in a distillation apparatus. The substances will evaporate out of the mixture in order of **increasing boiling point**.

2) The thermometer shows the **boiling point** of the substance that is **evaporating** at any given time.

3) If you know the boiling point of your **pure product**, you can use the thermometer to tell you when it's evaporating and therefore when it's condensing.

4) If the **product** of a reaction has a **lower boiling point** than the **starting materials** then the reaction mixture can be **heated** so that the product **evaporates** from the reaction mixture as it forms.

5) If the starting material has a **higher boiling point** than the product, as long as the temperature is controlled, it won't evaporate out from the reaction mixture.

> • Sometimes, a product is formed that will go on to **react further** if it's left in the reaction mixture.
>
> • For example, when you oxidise a **primary alcohol**, it is first oxidised to an **aldehyde** and then oxidised to a **carboxylic acid**. If you want the **aldehyde product**, then you can do your reaction in the **distillation equipment**. The aldehyde product has a **lower boiling point** than the alcohol starting material, so will distil out of the reaction mixture **as soon** as it forms. It is then collected in a separate container.

6) If a product and its impurities have **different boiling points**, then distillation can be used to **separate** them. You use the distillation apparatus shown above, but this time you're heating an **impure product**, instead of the reaction mixture.

7) When the liquid you want **boils** (this is when the thermometer is at the boiling point of the liquid), you place a flask at the open end of the condenser ready to collect your product.

8) When the thermometer shows the temperature is changing, put another flask at the end of the condenser because a **different liquid** is about to be delivered.

## Separation *Removes Any* **Water Soluble Impurities** *From the Product*

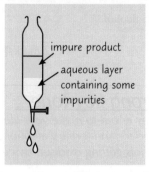

If a product is **insoluble** in water then you can use **separation** to remove any impurities that **do dissolve** in water such as **salts** or water soluble organic compounds (e.g. alcohols).

1) Once the reaction to form the product is completed, pour the mixture into a **separating funnel**, and add **water**.

2) Shake the funnel and then allow it to settle. The **organic layer** and the **aqueous layer** (which contains any water soluble impurities) are **immiscible**, (they don't mix), so separate out into two distinct layers.

3) You can then open the tap and run each layer off into a separate container.
   (In the example on the left, the impurities will be run off first, and the product collected second.)

# Organic Techniques

## You Can Remove **Traces** of **Water** From a Mixture Using an **Anhydrous Salt**

1) If you use separation to purify a product, the organic layer will end up containing **trace amounts** of **water**, so it has to be **dried**.

2) To do this you can add an **anhydrous salt** such as **magnesium sulfate** ($MgSO_4$) or **calcium chloride** ($CaCl_2$). The salt is used as a **drying agent** — it **binds** to any water present to become **hydrated**.

3) When you first add the salt to the organic layer it will be **lumpy**. This means you need to add more. You know that all the water has been removed when you can swirl the mixture and it looks like a snow globe.

4) You can **filter** the mixture to remove the solid **drying agent**.

## Measuring **Boiling Point** is a Good way to **Determine Purity**

1) You can measure the purity of an organic, liquid product by looking at its boiling point.

2) If you've got a reasonable volume of liquid, you can determine its boiling point using a **distillation apparatus**, like the one shown on the previous page.

3) If you **gently heat** the liquid in the distillation apparatus, until it evaporates, you can read the temperature at which it is distilled, using the thermometer in the top of the apparatus. This temperature is the **boiling point**.

*Be careful — different organic liquids can have similar boiling points, so you should use other analytical techniques (see topic 7) to help you determine your product's purity too.*

4) You can then look up the boiling point of the substance in **data books** and compare it to your measurement.

5) If the sample contains **impurities**, then your measured boiling point will be **higher** than the recorded value. You may also find your product boils over a range of temperatures, rather than all evaporating at a single temperature.

## Practice Questions

Q1 Draw a labelled diagram to show the apparatus used in a reflux reaction.

Q2 Why might you want to avoid naked flames when performing an experiment with organic substances?

Q3 Name two ways of purifying organic products.

Q4 Describe a technique you could use to assess the purity of an organic liquid.

**Exam Question**

Q1 a) A student carried out an experiment to make hex-1-ene from hexan-1-ol using the following procedure:

$$HO\text{~~~~} \xrightarrow[\text{heat}]{H_3PO_4} \text{~~~~}$$

1) Mix 1 cm³ hexan-1-ol with concentrated phosphoric acid in a reflux apparatus, and reflux for 30 minutes.

2) Once the mixture has cooled, separate the alkene from any aqueous impurities.

3) Dry the organic layer with anhydrous magnesium sulfate.

  i) What is meant by reflux and why is it a technique sometimes used in organic chemistry? [2 marks]

  ii) What organic compound is removed in the separating step? [1 mark]

  iii) Describe, in detail, how the student would carry out the separation in step 2). [3 marks]

b) In another experiment, the student decides to make 1-hexen-6-ol by carrying out a single dehydration reaction of the diol 1,6-hexanediol.

$$HO\text{~~~~}OH \xrightarrow[\text{heat}]{H_3PO_4} \text{~~~~}OH$$

  i) If the student follows the procedure in part a), why might he produce a mixture of products? [1 mark]

  ii) How could the procedure in part a) be adapted to prevent a mixture of products being formed? [2 marks]

---

## *Thought this page couldn't get any drier? Try adding anhydrous MgSO₄...*

*Learning the fine details of how experiments are carried out may not be the most interesting thing in the world, but you should get to try out some of these methods in practicals, which is a lot more fun.*

# Mass Spectrometry

*This topic's about some of the fancy techniques chemists use to work out what different unknown compounds are. Neat.*

## Mass Spectrometry Can Help to Identify Compounds

1) You saw on page 7 how you can use a mass spectrum showing the relative isotopic abundances of an element to work out its relative atomic mass. You can also get mass spectra for **molecular samples**.

2) A mass spectrum is produced by a **mass spectrometer**. The molecules in the sample are bombarded with electrons, which remove an electron from the molecule to form a **molecular ion**, $M^+_{(g)}$.

3) To find the relative molecular mass of a compound you look at the **molecular ion peak** (the **M peak**). This is the peak with the highest $m/z$ value (ignoring any small M+1 peaks that occur due to the isotope carbon-13). The mass/charge value of the molecular ion peak is the **molecular mass**.

\\\\\|||||||||||||||||||///
Assuming the ion has a +1 charge, which it normally will have.
///||||||||||||||||||\\\\

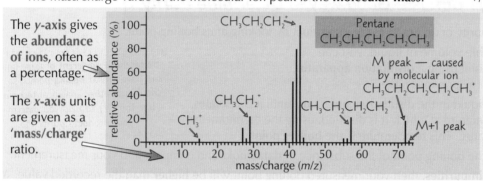

The *y*-axis gives the **abundance of ions**, often as a percentage.

The *x*-axis units are given as a 'mass/charge' ratio.

Here's the mass spectrum of pentane. Its M peak is at 72 — so the compound's $M_r$ is 72.
For most <u>organic compounds</u> the M peak is the one with the second highest mass/charge ratio. The smaller peak to the right of the M peak is called the M+1 peak — it's caused by the presence of the carbon isotope $^{13}C$.

## The Molecular Ion can be Broken into Smaller Fragments

1) The bombarding electrons make some of the molecular ions break up into **fragments**. The fragments that are ions show up on the mass spectrum, making a **fragmentation pattern**. Fragmentation patterns are actually pretty cool because you can use them to identify **molecules** and even their **structure**.

For propane, the molecular ion is $CH_3CH_2CH_3^+$, and the fragments it breaks into include $CH_3^+$ ($M_r = 15$) and $CH_3CH_2^+$ ($M_r = 29$).

Only the **ions** show up on the mass spectrum — the **free radicals** are 'lost'.

$$CH_3CH_2CH_3^+ \nearrow \begin{array}{l} CH_3CH_2\bullet + CH_3^+ \\ \text{free radical} \quad \text{ion} \\ \\ CH_3CH_2^+ + \bullet CH_3 \\ \text{ion} \quad \text{free radical} \end{array}$$

2) To work out the structural formula, you've got to work out what **ion** could have made each peak from its ***m/z* value**. (You assume that the *m/z* value of a peak matches the **mass** of the ion that made it.) Here are some common fragments:

| Fragment | Molecular Mass |
|---|---|
| $CH_3^+$ | 15 |
| $C_2H_5^+$ | 29 |
| $CH_3CH_2CH_2^+$ or $CH_3CHCH_3^+$ | 43 |
| $OH^+$ | 17 |

**Example:** Use this mass spectrum to work out the structure of the molecule:

\\\\||||||||||||||||||///
It's only the *m/z* values you're interested in — ignore the heights of the bars.
///|||||||||||||||||||\\\\

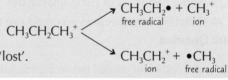

**1. Identify the fragments**

This molecule's got a peak at 15 *m/z*, so it's likely to have a **CH₃ group**.

It's also got a peak at 17 *m/z*, so it's likely to have an **OH group**.

Other ions are matched to the peaks here:

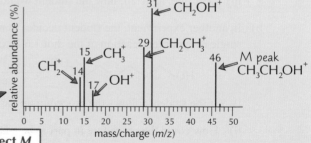

**2. Piece them together to form a molecule with the correct $M_r$**

Ethanol has all the fragments on this spectrum.

Ethanol's **molecular mass** is 46.

This should be the same as the *m/z* value of the M peak — it is.

# Mass Spectrometry

## Mass Spectrometry is Used to **Differentiate** Between **Similar Molecules**

1) Even if two **different compounds** contain **the same atoms**, you can still tell them apart with mass spectrometry because they won't produce exactly the same set of fragments.

2) The formulae of **propanal** and **propanone** are shown below.

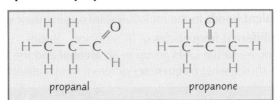

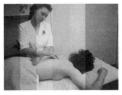

A massage spectrum

They've got the same $M_r$, but different structures, so they produce some **different fragments**. For example, propanal will have a $C_2H_5^+$ fragment but propanone won't.

3) Every compound produces a different mass spectrum — so the spectrum's like a **fingerprint** for the compound. Large computer **databases** of mass spectra can be used to identify a compound from its spectrum.

## Practice Questions

Q1 What is meant by the molecular ion?

Q2 What is the M peak?

Q3 What causes the presence of an M+1 peak on the mass spectra of most organic compounds?

### Exam Questions

Q1 Below is the mass spectrum of an organic compound, Q.

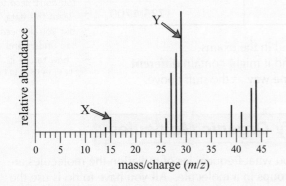

a) What is the $M_r$ of compound Q? [1 mark]

b) What fragments are the peaks marked X and Y most likely to correspond to? [2 marks]

c) Suggest a structure for this compound. [1 mark]

d) Why is it unlikely that this compound is an alcohol? [1 mark]

Q2 Mass spectrometry is run on a sample of but-2-ene ($CH_3CHCHCH_3$) and a mass spectrum is produced. For the following questions, assume that all ions form with a +1 charge.

a) At what $m/z$ value would you expect the M peak of but-2-ene to appear? [1 mark]

b) A peak appears on the spectrum at $m/z = 41$. Suggest which fragment is responsible for this peak. [1 mark]

c) Apart from the M peak and the peak at $m/z = 41$, suggest one other peak that you would expect to be present on the mass spectrum of but-2-ene. What fragment does it correspond to? [2 marks]

Q3 An unknown alcohol has the chemical formula $C_3H_8O$. A sample of the compound was inserted into a mass spectrometer and a mass spectrum was produced. A peak appears on the mass spectrum at $m/z = 31$. Name the unknown alcohol and draw its structure. Explain your answer. [4 marks]

## Use the clues, identify a molecule — mass spectrometry my dear Watson...

*I hate break ups — even if it is to make some lovely ions and a fragmentation pattern. But remember — mass spectrometry only records fragments that have a charge. So, when drawing or writing the fragments that a peak could be responsible for, remember to put that little positive sign next to them — you'll lose marks in the exam if you don't show it.*

# Infrared Spectroscopy

*If you've got some stuff and don't know what it is, don't taste it. You can stick it in an infrared spectrometer. You'll wind up with some scary looking graphs. But just learn the basics, and you'll be fine.*

## Infrared Radiation Makes Some Bonds Vibrate More

1) In infrared (IR) spectroscopy, a beam of **IR radiation** is passed through a sample of a chemical.

2) The IR radiation is absorbed by the **covalent bonds** in the molecules, increasing their **vibrational** energy.

3) **Bonds between different atoms** absorb **different frequencies** of IR radiation. Bonds in different **places** in a molecule absorb different frequencies too — so the O–H group in an **alcohol** and the O–H in a **carboxylic acid** absorb different frequencies. This table shows what **frequencies** different bonds absorb:

| Group | Where it's found | Wavenumber (cm$^{-1}$) |
|---|---|---|
| C–H stretching | Alkanes | 2962-2853 |
| | Alkenes | 3095-3010 |
| | Aldehydes | 2900-2820 and 2775-2700 |
| C–H bending | Alkanes | 1485-1365 |
| N–H stretching | Amines | 3500-3300 |
| O–H stretching | Alcohols | 3750-3200 |
| | Carboxylic Acids | 3300-2500 (broad) |
| C=C stretching | Alkenes | 1669-1645 |
| C=O stretching | Aldehydes | 1740-1720 |
| | Ketones | 1720-1700 |
| | Carboxylic Acids | 1725-1700 |

*Bending is just another sort of vibration.*

4) You'll be given all the infrared spectroscopy data you need in the exams. It may be **presented** a bit differently to the table above and it might contain **different information**. Don't worry though — just **use** it in the **same way** as the stuff above.

*You don't need to learn this data, but you do need to understand how to use it.*

## Infrared Spectroscopy Helps You Identify Organic Molecules

1) An infrared spectrometer produces a **graph** that shows you what frequencies of radiation the molecules are absorbing. So you can use it to identify the **functional groups** in a molecule. All you have to do is use the infrared data table to match up the peaks on the spectrum with the functional groups that made them.

2) The peaks show you **where radiation** is being **absorbed** (the peaks on IR spectra are **upside-down** — they point **downwards**).

3) **Transmittance** is always plotted on the y-axis, and wavenumber on the x-axis. **Wavenumber** is the measure used for the frequency (it's just 1/wavelength in cm).

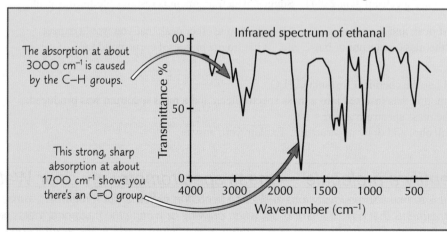

The absorption at about 3000 cm$^{-1}$ is caused by the C–H groups.

This strong, sharp absorption at about 1700 cm$^{-1}$ shows you there's an C=O group.

The toe toucher was Carol's favourite stretch.

# Infrared Spectroscopy

## *Infrared Spectroscopy Can Show if a Reaction's Happened*

Infrared spectroscopy is great for telling if a functional group has **changed** during a reaction. For example, if you **oxidise** an **alcohol** to an **aldehyde** you'll see the O–H absorption **disappear** from the spectrum, and a C=O absorption **appear**. If you then oxidise it further to a **carboxylic acid** an O–H peak at a slightly lower frequency than before will appear, alongside the C=O peak.

*See pages 96-97 for more on the oxidation of alcohols.*

**Example:** A chemical was suspected to be a pure sample of an unknown aldehyde. When the chemical was tested using infrared spectroscopy, the spectrum below was obtained. Is the chemical an aldehyde? Explain your answer.

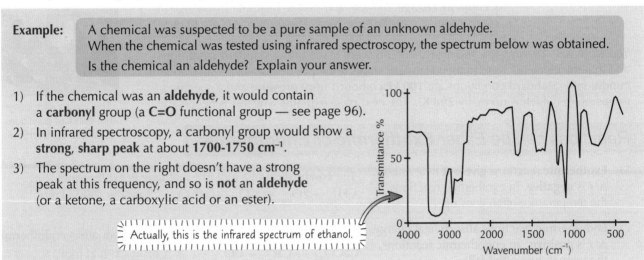

1) If the chemical was an **aldehyde**, it would contain a **carbonyl** group (a **C=O** functional group — see page 96).

2) In infrared spectroscopy, a carbonyl group would show a **strong, sharp peak** at about **1700-1750 cm⁻¹**.

3) The spectrum on the right doesn't have a strong peak at this frequency, and so is **not** an **aldehyde** (or a ketone, a carboxylic acid or an ester).

*Actually, this is the infrared spectrum of ethanol.*

## Practice Questions

Q1 What happens to a covalent bond when it absorbs infrared radiation?

Q2 Why do most infrared spectra of organic molecules have a strong, sharp peak at around 3000 cm⁻¹?

Q3 What functional group would be responsible for a peak on an infrared spectrum at around 1740-1720 cm⁻¹?

### Exam Questions

Q1 The IR spectrum of an organic molecule is shown on the right.

a) Which of the following compounds could be responsible for the spectrum? Use the infrared data on page 102.

  **A** butanoic acid

  **B** butanal

  **C** 1-aminobutane

  **D** butanol             [1 mark]

b) Explain your answer to a).      [2 marks]

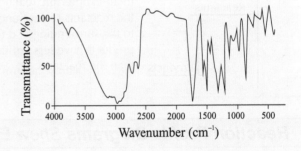

Q2 The molecule that produces the IR spectrum shown on the right has the molecular formula $C_3H_6O_2$.

Use the infrared data on page 102.

a) Which functional groups are responsible for peaks A and B?      [2 marks]

b) Give the structural formula and name of this molecule. Explain your answer.      [2 marks]

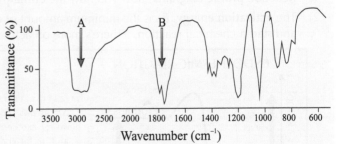

---

## <u>To analyse my sleep patterns, I use into-bed spectroscopy...</u>

*Infrared spectra may just appear to be big, squiggly messes — but they're actually dead handy at telling you what sort of molecule an unknown compound is. Luckily you don't have to remember where any of the infrared peaks are, but you do need to be able to identify them using your data sheet. So get some practice in now and do those exam questions above.*

# Enthalpy Changes

*A whole new topic to enjoy — but don't forget, Big Brother is watching...*

## Chemical Reactions Often Have Enthalpy Changes

When chemical reactions happen, some bonds are **broken** and some bonds are **made**. More often than not, this'll cause a **change in energy**. The souped-up chemistry term for this is **enthalpy change**.

> Enthalpy change, $\Delta H$ (delta H), is the heat energy change in a reaction at **constant pressure**. The units of $\Delta H$ are **kJ mol$^{-1}$**.

You write $\Delta H^{\ominus}$ to show that the measurements were made under **standard conditions** and that the elements were in their **standard states** (their physical states under standard conditions). Standard conditions are **100 kPa** (about 1 atm) **pressure** and a specified temperature (which is normally **298 K**). The next page explains why this is necessary.

*The Smiths were enjoying the standard conditions in British summertime.*

## Reactions can be Either Exothermic or Endothermic

1) **Exothermic** reactions **give out** heat energy. $\Delta H$ is **negative**. In exothermic reactions, the temperature often goes **up**.

The **combustion** of a fuel like methane is **exothermic**:
$$CH_{4(g)} + 2O_{2(g)} \rightarrow CO_{2(g)} + 2H_2O_{(l)} \qquad \Delta_c H^{\ominus} = -890 \text{ kJ mol}^{-1}$$

2) **Endothermic** reactions **absorb** heat energy. $\Delta H$ is **positive**. In endothermic reactions, the temperature often **falls**.

The **thermal decomposition** of calcium carbonate is **endothermic**:
$$CaCO_{3(s)} \rightarrow CaO_{(s)} + CO_{2(g)} \qquad \Delta_r H^{\ominus} = +178 \text{ kJ mol}^{-1}$$

The symbols $\Delta_c H^{\ominus}$ and $\Delta_r H^{\ominus}$ are explained on the next page.

## Enthalpy Level Diagrams Show the Overall Change of a Reaction

1) Enthalpy (or energy) level diagrams show the **relative** energies of the reactants and products in a reaction. The **difference** in the enthalpies is the **enthalpy change** of the reaction.

2) The **less enthalpy** a substance has, the **more stable** it is.

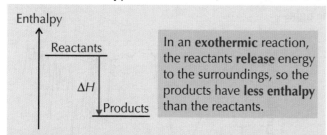

In an **exothermic** reaction, the reactants **release** energy to the surroundings, so the products have **less enthalpy** than the reactants.

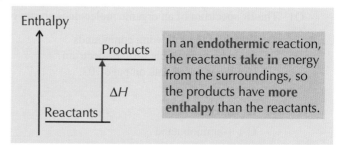

In an **endothermic** reaction, the reactants **take in** energy from the surroundings, so the products have **more enthalpy** than the reactants.

## Reaction Profile Diagrams Show Enthalpy Changes During a Reaction

1) **Reaction profile diagrams** show you how the **enthalpy changes** during reactions.

2) The **activation energy**, $E_a$, is the minimum amount of energy needed to begin breaking reactant bonds and start a chemical reaction. (There's more on activation energy on page 112.)

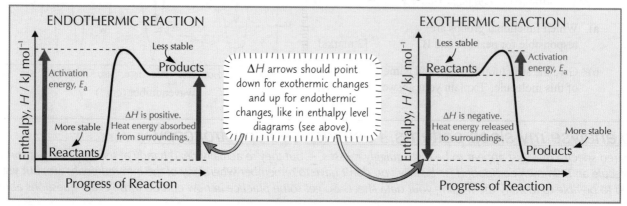

# Enthalpy Changes

## You Need to Specify the **Conditions** for **Enthalpy Changes**

1) You can't directly measure the **actual** enthalpy of a system. In practice, that doesn't matter, because it's only ever **enthalpy change** that matters. You can find enthalpy changes either by **experiment** or in **data books**.

2) Enthalpy changes you find in data books are usually **standard** enthalpy changes — enthalpy changes under **standard conditions** (**100 kPa** and a specified temperature, usually **298 K**).

   *298 K is the same as 25 °C.*

3) This is important because changes in enthalpy are affected by **temperature** and **pressure** — using standard conditions means that everyone can know **exactly** what the enthalpy change is describing.

## There are Different Types of Δ**H** Depending On the **Reaction**

1) **Standard enthalpy change of reaction**, $\Delta_r H^\ominus$, is the enthalpy change when the reaction occurs in the **molar quantities** shown in the **chemical equation**, under standard conditions.

2) **Standard enthalpy change of formation**, $\Delta_f H^\ominus$, is the enthalpy change when **1 mole** of a **compound** is formed from its **elements** in their standard states, under standard conditions, e.g. $2C_{(s)} + 3H_{2(g)} + \frac{1}{2}O_{2(g)} \rightarrow C_2H_5OH_{(l)}$.

3) **Standard enthalpy change of combustion**, $\Delta_c H^\ominus$, is the enthalpy change when **1 mole** of a substance is completely **burned in oxygen**, under standard conditions.

4) **Standard enthalpy change of neutralisation**, $\Delta_{neut} H^\ominus$, is the enthalpy change when an **acid** and an **alkali** react together, under standard conditions, to form **1 mole of water**.

## Practice Questions

Q1 Explain the terms exothermic and endothermic, giving an example reaction in each case.

Q2 Draw and label enthalpy level diagrams for an exothermic and an endothermic reaction.

Q3 Define standard enthalpy change of formation and standard change enthalpy of combustion.

**Exam Questions**

Q1 Hydrogen peroxide, $H_2O_2$, can decompose into water and oxygen.

$$2H_2O_{2(l)} \rightarrow 2H_2O_{(l)} + O_{2(g)} \qquad \Delta H^\ominus = -98 \text{ kJ mol}^{-1}$$

Draw a reaction profile diagram for this reaction. Mark on the activation energy, $E_a$, and $\Delta H$. [3 marks]

Q2 Methanol, $CH_3OH_{(l)}$, when blended with petrol, can be used as a fuel. $\Delta_c H^\ominus[CH_3OH] = -726 \text{ kJ mol}^{-1}$

a) Write an equation, including state symbols, for the standard enthalpy change of combustion of methanol. [1 mark]

b) Write an equation, including state symbols, for the standard enthalpy change of formation of methanol. [1 mark]

c) Petroleum gas is a fuel that contains propane, $C_3H_8$.
   Why does the following equation not represent a standard enthalpy change of combustion? [1 mark]

$$2C_3H_{8(g)} + 10O_{2(g)} \rightarrow 6CO_{2(g)} + 8H_2O_{(g)} \qquad \Delta_r H^\ominus = -4113 \text{ kJ mol}^{-1}$$

Q3 Coal is mainly carbon. It is burned as a fuel. $\Delta_c H^\ominus = -393.5 \text{ kJ mol}^{-1}$

a) Write an equation, including state symbols, for the standard enthalpy change of combustion of carbon. [1 mark]

b) Explain why the standard enthalpy change of formation of carbon dioxide will also be $-393.5$ kJ mol$^{-1}$. [1 mark]

c) How much energy would be released when 1 tonne of carbon is burned? (1 tonne = 1000 kg) [2 marks]

## *Enthalpy changes — ethylpan, thenalpy, panthely, lanthepy, nyapleth...*

*Quite a few definitions here. And you need to know them all. If you're going to bother learning them, you might as well do it properly and learn all the pernickety details. They probably seem about as useful as a dead fly in your custard right now, but all will be revealed over the next few pages. Learn them now, so you've got a bit of a head start.*

# More on Enthalpy Changes

*Now you know what enthalpy changes are, here's how to calculate them...*

## You Can Find **Enthalpy Changes** Using **Experiments**

To find the enthalpy change for a reaction, you only need to know two things:

- the **number of moles** of the stuff that's reacting,
- the change in **temperature** of the reaction.

Once you know these two things, you can work out the change in **heat energy** of the reaction using the equation on the next page. For reactions carried out at **constant pressure**, the heat change is the same as the enthalpy change.

Some enthalpy changes can't be found by measuring a single temperature change. Fear not — there's a way round this on page 109.

## You Can **Directly Measure** the **Temperature Change** of Some **Reaction Mixtures**

For reactions where all the reactants are **solids** or **liquids**, you can just **mix** the reactants together, stick a thermometer in the reaction mixture and measure the **overall temperature change**. The **problem** with this method is that some heat will be **lost** to the surroundings (or gained if the reaction is endothermic), so the **temperature change** you measure will be **less** than the actual temperature change of the reaction. You can account for this problem by using the method below.

You should carry out the reaction in an insulated container, e.g. a polystyrene beaker, so that you don't lose or gain much heat through the sides.

**Example:** Describe an experiment that could be used to find the enthalpy change of the endothermic reaction between citric acid and sodium bicarbonate.

1) Add a set volume of **citric acid** of a known concentration to a polystyrene cup.

2) Put a **lid** on the beaker and measure the **temperature** of the solution every **30 seconds** until it's **stabilised**.

3) Add a set mass of **sodium bicarbonate** to the beaker, and **stir** the mixture.

4) Measure the temperature of the reaction mixture every **30 seconds** until the temperature has reached a **minimum** (or maximum for an exothermic reaction) and has been returning to the **initial temperature** for a couple of minutes.

5) Draw a graph of **temperature** against **time**.

6) To find the temperature change of the reaction, accounting for the fact the heat is gained from the surroundings, **extrapolate** the line from where the reaction is returning to its initial temperature **back** towards the time when the reaction **started**.

7) Read off the **temperature** from the extrapolated line at the time when the reaction started (when the sodium bicarbonate was added). Here, it's 2 minutes and the temperature is 1 °C.

8) Compare this with the **initial reading** to find the **temperature change** of the reaction — the initial temperature was 21 °C, so the temperature change is 1 − 21 = **−20 °C**.

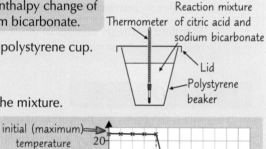

Reaction mixture of citric acid and sodium bicarbonate

Thermometer

Lid

Polystyrene beaker

For an exothermic reaction, the temperature will rise to a maximum and then fall. To find the temperature change, extrapolate the line from the point where the temperature starts falling back to the time where the reaction started.

## To Find Enthalpy Changes of **Combustion** You Need A **Calorimeter**

It's harder to measure the temperature change of a reaction where one of the reactants is a **gas**, such as in **combustion** reactions. You can use a **calorimeter** to find how much heat is given out by a reaction by measuring the **temperature change** of some water.

1) To find the enthalpy of **combustion** of a **flammable liquid**, you burn it — using apparatus like this...

2) As the fuel burns, it heats the water. You can work out the **heat absorbed** by the water if you know the **mass of water**, the **temperature change of the water** ($\Delta T$), and the **specific heat capacity of water** (= 4.18 J g$^{-1}$ K$^{-1}$) — see the next page for the details.

3) Ideally, all the heat given out by the fuel as it burns would be **absorbed** by the water, so you could accurately work out the enthalpy of combustion (next page). But, you **always** lose some heat (you heat the apparatus and the surroundings).

'Calorimetry' means 'measuring heat changes'. The experiments on this page are calorimetry experiments.

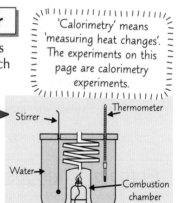

Stirrer

Thermometer

Water

Combustion chamber

Air

Spirit burner containing fuel

# More on Enthalpy Changes

## Calculate *Enthalpy Changes* Using the *Equation q = mcΔT*

It seems there's a snazzy equation for everything these days, and enthalpy change is no exception:

$q = mc\Delta T$ where, $q$ = heat lost or gained (in joules). This is the same as the enthalpy change if the pressure is constant.

The specific heat capacity of water is the amount of heat energy it takes to raise the temperature of 1 g of water by 1 K.

$m$ = mass of water in the calorimeter, or solution in the insulated container (in grams).

$c$ = specific heat capacity of water ($4.18$ J g$^{-1}$ K$^{-1}$).

$\Delta T$ = the change in temperature of the water or solution (in K). This is the same as the change in °C.

**Example:** In a laboratory experiment, 1.16 g of an organic liquid fuel was completely burned in oxygen. The heat formed during this combustion raised the temperature of 100 g of water from 17.5 °C to 80.0 °C. Calculate the standard enthalpy of combustion, $\Delta_c H^{\ominus}$, of the fuel. Its $M_r$ is 58.0.

Remember — m is the mass of water, NOT the mass of fuel.

**1** First, you need to calculate the **amount of heat** given out by the fuel, using $q = mc\Delta T$.

$q = mc\Delta T$

$q = 100 \times 4.18 \times (80.0 - 17.5) = 26\ 125$ J

$26\ 125 \div 1000 = 26.125$ kJ

If you're asked to calculate an enthalpy change, the answer should always be in kJ mol$^{-1}$. So change the amount of heat from J to kJ by dividing by 1000.

**2** The standard enthalpy of combustion involves 1 mole of fuel. So next you need to find out **how many moles** of fuel produced this heat. It's back to the old $n = $ mass $\div M_r$ equation.

$n = 1.16 \div 58.0 = 0.0200$ mol of fuel

It's negative because combustion is an exothermic reaction.

**3** So, the heat produced by 1 mole of fuel = $26.125 \div 0.0200$

$\approx -1310$ kJ mol$^{-1}$ (3 s.f.). This is the standard enthalpy change of combustion.

The actual $\Delta_c H^{\ominus}$ of this compound is $-1615$ kJ mol$^{-1}$ — lots of heat has been **lost** and not measured. For example, it's likely a bit escaped through the **calorimeter**, the fuel might not have **combusted completely**, or the **conditions** might not have been standard.

## Practice Questions

Q1 Briefly describe an experiment that could be carried out to find the enthalpy of combustion of a reaction between a solid and a liquid.

Q2 What equation is used to calculate the enthalpy change in a calorimetry experiment?

Q3 Why might the enthalpy of combustion calculated from an experiment be different from the real value?

**Exam Questions**

Q1 The initial temperature of 25.0 cm$^3$ of 1.00 mol dm$^{-3}$ hydrochloric acid in a polystyrene cup was measured as 19.0 °C. This acid was exactly neutralised by 25.0 cm$^3$ of 1.00 mol dm$^{-3}$ sodium hydroxide solution. The maximum temperature of the resulting solution was measured as 25.8 °C.

Calculate the standard enthalpy change of neutralisation for the reaction. (You may assume the neutral solution formed has a specific heat capacity of 4.18 J g$^{-1}$ K$^{-1}$, and a density of 1.00 g cm$^{-3}$.) [3 marks]

Q2 A 50.0 cm$^3$ sample of 0.200 mol dm$^{-3}$ copper(II) sulfate solution placed in a polystyrene beaker gave a temperature increase of 2.00 K when excess zinc powder was added and stirred. (Ignore the increase in volume due to the zinc.) Calculate the enthalpy change when 1 mol of zinc reacts. Assume the solution's specific heat capacity is 4.18 J g$^{-1}$ K$^{-1}$. The equation for the reaction is: $Zn_{(s)} + CuSO_{4(aq)} \rightarrow Cu_{(s)} + ZnSO_{4(aq)}$ [3 marks]

## *If you can't stand the heat, get out of the calorimeter...*

*There's quite a lot to wrap your noggin round on these pages. Not only are there some fiddly calorimetry experiments, but you need to know how to calculate enthalpy changes from your results. You need to know the limitations of the experiments, too. You'll often assume that no heat is lost (or gained) from the surroundings, but this isn't always true...*

# Hess's Law

*You can't always work out an enthalpy change by measuring a single temperature change. But there are other ways...*

## Hess's Law — the Total Enthalpy Change is **Independent** of the Route Taken

Hess's Law says that: | The **total enthalpy change** of a reaction is always **the same**, no matter **which route** is taken.

This law is handy for working out enthalpy changes that you **can't find directly** by doing an experiment.

Here's an example:
The **total enthalpy change** for route 1 is the **same as for route 2**.
So, $\Delta_r H^\ominus = +114.4 + (-180.8) = \mathbf{-66.4 \; kJ \; mol^{-1}}$.

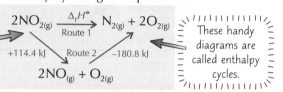

$$2NO_{2(g)} \xrightarrow[\text{Route 1}]{\Delta_r H^\ominus} N_{2(g)} + 2O_{2(g)}$$
$+114.4 \text{ kJ}$ — Route 2 — $-180.8 \text{ kJ}$
$$2NO_{(g)} + O_{2(g)}$$

*These handy diagrams are called enthalpy cycles.*

## Enthalpy Changes Can be Worked Out From **Enthalpies of Formation**

**Enthalpy changes of formation** are useful for calculating enthalpy changes you can't find directly.
You need to know $\Delta_f H^\ominus$ for **all** the reactants and products that are **compounds** — $\Delta_f H^\ominus$ for elements is **zero**.

**Example:** Use the enthalpy cycle on the right to calculate $\Delta_r H^\ominus$
for the reaction: $SO_{2(g)} + 2H_2S_{(g)} \rightarrow 3S_{(s)} + 2H_2O_{(l)}$

Using **Hess's Law:** Route 1 = Route 2

$\Delta_r H^\ominus$ + the sum of $\Delta_f H^\ominus$(reactants) = the sum of $\Delta_f H^\ominus$(products)

So, $\Delta_r H^\ominus$ = the sum of $\Delta_f H^\ominus$(products) – the sum of $\Delta_f H^\ominus$(reactants)

Just plug the numbers given on the right into the equation above:

$\Delta_r H^\ominus = [0 + (2 \times -286)] - [-297 + (2 \times -20.2)] = \mathbf{-235 \; kJ \; mol^{-1}}$

$\Delta_f H^\ominus$ of sulfur is zero
— it's an element.
There are 2 moles of $H_2O$
and 2 moles of $H_2S$.

REACTANTS $\xrightarrow{\Delta_r H^\ominus}$ PRODUCTS
$SO_{2(g)} + 2H_2S_{(g)} \longrightarrow 3S_{(s)} + 2H_2O_{(l)}$
Route 1
$\Delta_f H^\ominus_{\text{(reactants)}}$ Route 2 $\Delta_f H^\ominus_{\text{(products)}}$
$$3S_{(s)} + 2H_{2(g)} + O_{2(g)}$$
ELEMENTS
$\Delta_f H^\ominus[SO_{2(g)}] = -297 \text{ kJ mol}^{-1}$
$\Delta_f H^\ominus[H_2S_{(g)}] = -20.2 \text{ kJ mol}^{-1}$
$\Delta_f H^\ominus[H_2O_{(l)}] = -286 \text{ kJ mol}^{-1}$

It **always** works, no matter how complicated the reaction...

**Example:** Use the enthalpy cycle on the right to
calculate $\Delta_r H^\ominus$ for the reaction:
$2NH_4NO_{3(s)} + C_{(s)} \rightarrow 2N_{2(g)} + CO_{2(g)} + 4H_2O_{(l)}$

Using Hess's Law: Route 1 = Route 2

$\Delta_f H^\ominus$(reactants) + $\Delta_r H^\ominus$ = $\Delta_f H^\ominus$(products)

$(2 \times -365) + 0 + \Delta_r H^\ominus = 0 + -394 + (4 \times -286)$

$\Delta_r H^\ominus = -394 + (-1144) - (-730)$

$= \mathbf{-808 \; kJ \; mol^{-1}}$

REACTANTS $\xrightarrow{\Delta_r H^\ominus}$ PRODUCTS
$2NH_4NO_{3(s)} + C_{(s)} \longrightarrow 2N_{2(g)} + CO_{2(g)} + 4H_2O_{(l)}$
Route 1
$\Delta_f H^\ominus_{\text{(reactants)}}$ Route 2 $\Delta_f H^\ominus_{\text{(products)}}$
$$C_{(s)} + 2N_{2(g)} + 4H_{2(g)} + 3O_{2(g)}$$
ELEMENTS
$\Delta_f H^\ominus[NH_4NO_{3(s)}] = -365 \text{ kJ mol}^{-1}$
$\Delta_f H^\ominus[CO_{2(g)}] = -394 \text{ kJ mol}^{-1}$
$\Delta_f H^\ominus[H_2O_{(l)}] = -286 \text{ kJ mol}^{-1}$

## Enthalpy Changes Can be Worked Out From **Enthalpies of Combustion**

You can use a similar method to find an enthalpy change from **enthalpy changes of combustion**.

**Example:** Use the enthalpy cycle on the right
to calculate $\Delta_f H^\ominus$ for $C_2H_5OH$.

*You need to add enough oxygen to balance the equations.*

Using Hess's Law: Route 1 = Route 2

$\Delta_f H^\ominus[C_2H_5OH] + \Delta_c H^\ominus[C_2H_5OH] = 2\Delta_c H^\ominus[C] + 3\Delta_c H^\ominus[H_2]$

$\Delta_f H^\ominus[C_2H_5OH] + (-1367) = (2 \times -394) + (3 \times -286)$

$\Delta_f H^\ominus[C_2H_5OH] = -788 + -858 - (-1367) = \mathbf{-279 \; kJ \; mol^{-1}}$

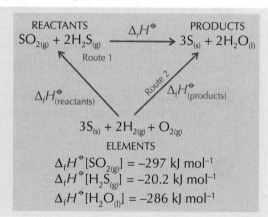

REACTANTS $\xrightarrow{\Delta_f H^\ominus}$ PRODUCTS
$2C_{(s)} + 3H_{2(g)} + \frac{1}{2}O_{2(g)} \longrightarrow C_2H_5OH_{(l)}$
Route 1
$3O_{2(g)}$ Route 2 $3O_{2(g)}$
$$2CO_{2(g)} + 3H_2O_{(l)}$$
COMBUSTION PRODUCTS
$\Delta_c H^\ominus[C_{(s)}] = -394 \text{ kJ mol}^{-1}$
$\Delta_c H^\ominus[H_{2(g)}] = -286 \text{ kJ mol}^{-1}$
$\Delta_c H^\ominus[C_2H_5OH_{(l)}] = -1367 \text{ kJ mol}^{-1}$

# Hess's Law

## Hess's Law Lets You Find Enthalpy Changes Indirectly From Experiments

On pages 106-107 you saw how you could find the enthalpy change of a reaction using calorimetry. Sometimes you can **combine** the enthalpy change results from these experiments (neutralisation reactions, for example) to work out an enthalpy change that you **can't find directly**. It's clever stuff... read on.

You **can't** find the enthalpy change of the thermal decomposition of calcium carbonate by measuring a temperature change.

$$CaCO_{3(s)} \rightarrow CaO_{(s)} + CO_{2(g)} \quad \text{Enthalpy change = ?}$$

(It's an endothermic reaction, so you'd expect the temperature to fall. But you need to heat it up for the reaction to happen at all). But you can find it in a more **indirect** way.

The aim is to make one of those **Hess cycles** (the technical name for a "Hess's Law triangle diagram thing").

1) Write the reaction you want to find the enthalpy change for at the top of the triangle — include your **reactants** and **products**:

$$CaCO_3 \xrightarrow{\Delta_r H^\ominus} CaO + CO_2$$

2) Next, you're going to carry out two **neutralisation** reactions involving **hydrochloric acid**, and use the results to complete your Hess cycle. You **can** find the enthalpy changes of these reactions (using calorimetry — see pages 106-107). Call them $\Delta H_1$ and $\Delta H_2$.

   **Reaction 1**: $CaCO_3 + 2HCl \rightarrow CaCl_2 + CO_2 + H_2O \quad \Delta H_1$
   **Reaction 2**: $CaO + 2HCl \rightarrow CaCl_2 + H_2O \quad \Delta H_2$

3) Now you can build the other two sides of your Hess cycle. Add **2 moles of HCl** to both sides of your triangle's top (representing the 2 moles of HCl in the above equations).

   $$CaCO_3 + 2HCl \xrightarrow{\Delta_r H^\ominus} CaO + CO_2 + 2HCl$$

   Add the **products** of the neutralisation reactions to the bottom of the triangle. Notice how all three corners 'balance'.

   $$CaCO_3 + 2HCl \xrightarrow{\Delta_r H^\ominus} CaO + 2HCl + CO_2$$
   $$\Delta H_1 \text{ (Reaction 1)} \qquad \Delta H_2 \text{ (Reaction 2)}$$
   $$CaCl_2 + H_2O + CO_2$$

4) Add the enthalpy changes you found to your diagram.

5) And do the maths... the enthalpy change you want to find is just: $\quad \Delta H_1 - \Delta H_2$

## Practice Questions

Q1 What does Hess's Law state?

Q2 What is the standard enthalpy change of formation of any element?

Q3 Describe how you can make a Hess cycle to find the standard enthalpy change of a reaction using standard enthalpy changes of formation.

**Exam Questions**

Q1 Using the facts that the standard enthalpy change of formation of $Al_2O_{3(s)}$ is $-1676$ kJ mol$^{-1}$ and the standard enthalpy change of formation of $MgO_{(s)}$ is $-602$ kJ mol$^{-1}$, calculate the enthalpy change of the following reaction.

$$Al_2O_{3(s)} + 3Mg_{(s)} \rightarrow 2Al_{(s)} + 3MgO_{(s)} \qquad \text{[2 marks]}$$

Q2 Calculate the enthalpy change for the reaction below (the fermentation of glucose).

$$C_6H_{12}O_{6(s)} \rightarrow 2C_2H_5OH_{(l)} + 2CO_{2(g)}$$

Use the following standard enthalpies of combustion in your calculations:

$$\Delta_c H^\ominus (\text{glucose}) = -2820 \text{ kJ mol}^{-1} \qquad \Delta_c H^\ominus (\text{ethanol}) = -1367 \text{ kJ mol}^{-1} \qquad \text{[2 marks]}$$

## Meet Hessie. She's the Lawch Hess Monster...

*To get your head around those enthalpy cycles, you're going to have to do more than skim read them. It'll also help if you know the definitions for those standard enthalpy thingumabobs. I'd read those enthalpy cycle examples again and make sure you understand how the elements/compounds at each corner were chosen to be there.*

# Bond Enthalpy

*During chemical reactions, some bonds are broken, whilst others are made. By working out the total energy needed to break all the bonds, and the energy given out as new bonds form, you can find the enthalpy change of a reaction.*

## Reactions are all about Breaking and Making Bonds

When reactions happen, **reactant bonds** are **broken** and **product bonds** are **formed**.

1) You **need** energy to break bonds, so bond breaking is **endothermic** ($\Delta H$ is **positive**).

2) Energy is **released** when bonds are formed, so this is **exothermic** ($\Delta H$ is **negative**).

3) The **enthalpy change** for a reaction is the **overall effect** of these two changes. If you need **more** energy to **break** bonds than is released when bonds are made, $\Delta H$ is **positive**. If it's **less**, $\Delta H$ is **negative**.

## You Need Energy to Break the Attraction Between Atoms or Ions

1) In ionic bonding, **positive** and **negative ions** are attracted to each other. In covalent molecules, the **positive nuclei** are attracted to the **negative** charge of the shared electrons in a covalent bond.

2) You need energy to **break** this attraction — **stronger** bonds take more energy to break.

> **Bond enthalpy** is the amount of energy required to **break** 1 mole of a type of bond in a molecule in the **gas phase**.

*Breaking bonds is always an endothermic process, so bond enthalpies are always positive.*

## Mean Bond Enthalpies are Not Exact

1) Water ($H_2O$) has **two O–H bonds**. You'd think it'd take the same amount of energy to break them both... but it **doesn't**.

> The **first** bond, $H–OH_{(g)}$:    $E(H–OH) = +492$ kJ mol$^{-1}$
> The **second** bond, $H–O_{(g)}$:    $E(H–O) = +428$ kJ mol$^{-1}$
> (O–H is a bit easier to break apart because of the extra electron repulsion.)
> So the **mean** bond enthalpy is $(492 + 428) \div 2 = \mathbf{+460}$ **kJ mol**$^{-1}$.

2) The **data book** says the mean bond enthalpy for O–H is +463 kJ mol$^{-1}$. It's a bit different because it's the average for a **much bigger range** of molecules, not just water. For example, it includes the O–H bonds in alcohols and carboxylic acids too.

3) So when you look up a **mean bond enthalpy**, what you get is:

> The energy needed to break **one mole** of bonds in the **gas phase**, averaged over **many different** compounds.

## Enthalpy Changes Can Be Calculated Using Mean Bond Enthalpies

In any chemical reaction, energy is **absorbed** to **break bonds** and **given out** during **bond formation**. The difference between the energy absorbed and released is the overall **enthalpy change of reaction**:

This is the total energy absorbed to break bonds.

$$\text{Enthalpy Change of Reaction} = \text{Sum of bond enthalpies of reactants} - \text{Sum of bond enthalpies of products}$$

This is the total energy released in making bonds

**Example:** Calculate the overall enthalpy change for this reaction: $N_{2(g)} + 3H_{2(g)} \rightarrow 2NH_{3(g)}$
Use the mean bond enthalpy values in the table.

**Bonds broken:**   1 mole of N≡N bond broken    $= 1 \times 945 = 945$ kJ mol$^{-1}$
                 3 moles of H–H bonds broken   $= 3 \times 436 = 1308$ kJ mol$^{-1}$

Sum of bond enthalpies = 945 + 1308 = **2253 kJ mol**$^{-1}$

**Bonds formed:**   6 moles of N–H bonds formed    $= 6 \times 391 = 2346$ kJ mol$^{-1}$

Sum of bond enthalpies = **2346 kJ mol**$^{-1}$

| Bond | Average Bond Enthalpy |
|------|----------------------|
| N≡N | 945 kJ mol$^{-1}$ |
| H–H | 436 kJ mol$^{-1}$ |
| N–H | 391 kJ mol$^{-1}$ |

Now you just subtract the bond enthalpies of the products from the bond enthalpies of the reactants.

**Enthalpy Change of Reaction = 2253 – 2346 = –93 kJ mol**$^{-1}$

There might be a small amount of **variation** between the enthalpy change of reaction calculated from **mean bond enthalpies** and the **true** enthalpy change of reaction. This is because the **specific** bond enthalpies of the molecules in the reaction will be **slightly different** from the **average** values.

# Bond Enthalpy

## You Can Calculate *Mean Bond Enthalpies* Using *Reaction Enthalpies*

If you're given the enthalpy change of a reaction along with all but **one** of the bond enthalpies of the reactants and products, you can **rearrange** the equation on the previous page to find the **remaining** mean bond enthalpy.

**Example:** The enthalpy change of the reaction between nitrogen and fluorine to form nitrogen trifluoride is –264.2 kJ mol⁻¹: $N_{2(g)} + 3F_{2(g)} \rightarrow 2NF_{3(g)}$
Find the mean N–F bond enthalpy in $NF_3$.

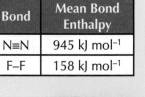

| Bond | Mean Bond Enthalpy |
|------|--------------------|
| N≡N | 945 kJ mol⁻¹ |
| F–F | 158 kJ mol⁻¹ |

**Bonds broken:** 1 mole N≡N bonds broken = 1 × 945 = 945 kJ mol⁻¹
3 moles F–F bonds broken = 3 × 158 = 474 kJ mol⁻¹

Sum of bond enthalpies = 945 + 474 = **1419 kJ mol⁻¹**

**Bonds formed:** 6 N–F bonds formed = 6 × $E$(N–F) ← '$E$(X)' is just a quick way of writing the mean bond enthalpy of bond X.

**Enthalpy change of reaction** = –246.2 kJ mol⁻¹

You know that: $\dfrac{\text{Enthalpy Change}}{\text{of Reaction}} = \dfrac{\text{Sum of bond}}{\text{enthalpies of reactants}} - \dfrac{\text{Sum of bond}}{\text{enthalpies of products}}$

*Jack preferred bones to bonds.*

Substituting in the values given in the question gives: $-264.2 = (945 + 474) - (6 \times E(\text{N–F}))$
Rearranging this gives: $E(\text{N–F}) = [945 + 474 - (-264.2)] \div 6 = \textbf{+281 kJ mol}^{-1}$

## Practice Questions

Q1 Is energy taken in or released when bonds are broken?
Q2 Define bond enthalpy.
Q3 What state must compounds be in when bond dissociation enthalpies are measured?
Q4 Define mean bond enthalpy.

### Exam Questions

Q1 The table below shows some mean bond enthalpy values.

| Bond | C–H | C=O | O=O | O–H |
|------|-----|-----|-----|-----|
| Mean Bond Enthalpy (kJ mol⁻¹) | 435 | 805 | 498 | 464 |

The complete combustion of methane can be represented by the equation: $CH_{4(g)} + 2O_{2(g)} \rightarrow CO_{2(g)} + 2H_2O_{(l)}$

Use the table of bond enthalpies above to calculate the enthalpy change for the reaction. [2 marks]

Q2 Use the following bond enthalpy data to calculate the standard enthalpy change for the formation of water: $\frac{1}{2}O_{2(g)} + H_{2(g)} \rightarrow H_2O_{(l)}$.

$E$(H–O) in water = +460 kJ mol⁻¹
$E$(O=O) in oxygen = +498 kJ mol⁻¹
$E$(H–H) in hydrogen = +436 kJ mol⁻¹ [2 marks]

Q3 Methane and chlorine gas will react together under certain conditions to form chloromethane:

$$CH_{4(g)} + Cl_{2(g)} \rightarrow CH_3Cl_{(g)} + HCl_{(g)} \quad \Delta_r H = -101 \text{ kJ mol}^{-1}$$

$E$(C–H) in methane = +435 kJ mol⁻¹    $E$(C–H) in chloromethane = +397 kJ mol⁻¹
$E$(Cl–Cl) = +243 kJ mol⁻¹    $E$(H–Cl) = +432 kJ mol⁻¹

a) Calculate the C–Cl bond enthalpy in chloromethane. [2 marks]

b) The data book value for the mean bond enthalpy of C–Cl is +346 kJ mol⁻¹.
Comment on this value with reference to your answer to part a). [1 mark]

---

## *Do you expect me to react? No, Mr Bond, I expect you to break...*

*Reactions are like pulling plastic building bricks apart and building something new. Sometimes bits get stuck together and you need lots of energy to pull 'em apart. Okay, so energy's not really released when you stick them together, but you can't have everything — it wasn't that bad an analogy up till now. Ah, well...you best get on and learn this stuff.*

# Collision Theory

*The rate of a reaction is just how quickly it happens. Lots of things can make it go faster or slower.*

## Particles **Must** Collide to **React**

1) Particles in liquids and gases are **always moving** and **colliding** with **each other**. They **don't** react every time though — only when the **conditions** are right. A reaction **won't** take place between two particles **unless** —

> - They collide in the **right direction**. They need to be **facing** each other the right way.
> - They collide with at least a certain **minimum** amount of kinetic (movement) **energy**.

This stuff's called **Collision Theory**.

2) The **minimum amount of kinetic energy** particles need to react is called the **activation energy**. The particles need this much energy to **break the bonds** to start the reaction.

3) Reactions with **low activation energies** often happen **pretty easily**. But reactions with **high activation energies** don't. You need to give the particles extra energy by **heating** them.

To make this a bit clearer, here's a **reaction profile diagram**.

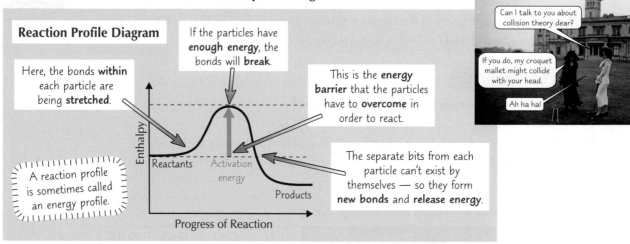

**Reaction Profile Diagram**

Here, the bonds **within** each particle are being **stretched**.

If the particles have **enough energy**, the bonds will **break**.

This is the **energy barrier** that the particles have to **overcome** in order to react.

A reaction profile is sometimes called an energy profile.

The separate bits from each particle can't exist by themselves — so they form **new bonds** and **release energy**.

Reactants — Activation energy — Products

Enthalpy / Progress of Reaction

Can I talk to you about collision theory dear?

If you do, my croquet mallet might collide with your head.

Ah ha ha!

## Molecules **Don't** all have the **Same Amount of Energy**

Imagine looking down on Oxford Street when it's teeming with people. You'll see some people ambling along **slowly**, some hurrying **quickly**, but most of them will be walking with a **moderate speed**. It's the same with the **molecules** in a liquid or gas. Some **don't have much kinetic energy** and move **slowly**. Others have **loads** of **kinetic energy** and **whizz** along. But most molecules are somewhere **in between**.

If you plot a **graph** of the **numbers of molecules** in a substance with different **kinetic energies** you get a **Maxwell-Boltzmann distribution**. It looks like this —

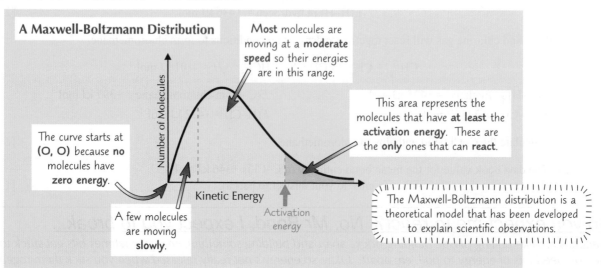

**A Maxwell-Boltzmann Distribution**

Most molecules are moving at a **moderate speed** so their energies are in this range.

This area represents the molecules that have **at least** the **activation energy**. These are the **only** ones that can **react**.

The curve starts at (O, O) because **no** molecules have **zero energy**.

A few molecules are moving **slowly**.

Number of Molecules / Kinetic Energy / Activation energy

The Maxwell-Boltzmann distribution is a theoretical model that has been developed to explain scientific observations.

# Collision Theory

## Increasing the Temperature makes Reactions Faster

1) If you increase the **temperature**, the particles will, on average, have more **kinetic energy** and will move **faster**.

2) So, a **greater proportion** of molecules will have at least the **activation energy** and be able to **react**. This changes the **shape** of the **Maxwell-Boltzmann distribution curve** — it pushes it over to the **right**.

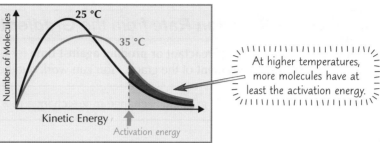

⧽ The total number of molecules is still the same, which means the area under each curve must be the same. ⧼

⧽ At higher temperatures, more molecules have at least the activation energy. ⧼

3) Because the molecules are flying about **faster**, they'll **collide more often**. This is **another reason** why increasing the temperature makes a reaction faster, i.e. the reaction rate increases (see the next page for more on reaction rates).

## Concentration, Pressure and Catalysts also Affect the Reaction Rate

### Increasing Concentration Speeds Up Reactions

If you increase the **concentration** of reactants in a **solution**, there'll be **more particles** in a **given volume** of the solution, so particles will **collide more frequently**. If there are **more collisions**, they'll have **more chances** to react.

### Increasing Pressure Speeds Up Reactions

If any of your reactants are **gases**, increasing the **pressure** will increase the rate of reaction. It's pretty much the same as increasing the **concentration** of a solution — at higher pressures, there are more particles in a **given volume** of gas, which increases the frequency of **successful collisions**.

### Catalysts Can Speed Up Reactions

**Catalysts** are really useful. They **lower the activation energy** by providing a **different way** for the bonds to be broken and remade. If the activation energy's **lower**, more particles will have **enough energy** to react. There's heaps of information about catalysts on pages 116-117.

⧽ Increasing the surface area of a solid reactant(s) also makes the reaction faster as it increases the surface where collisions can happen. ⧼

## Practice Questions

Q1 Explain the term 'activation energy'.

Q2 Name four factors that affect the rate of a reaction.

**Exam Questions**

Q1 Nitrogen oxide (NO) and ozone ($O_3$) sometimes react to produce nitrogen dioxide ($NO_2$) and oxygen ($O_2$). How would increasing the pressure affect the rate of this reaction? Explain your answer.     [2 marks]

Q2 Use the collision theory to explain why the reaction between a solid and a liquid is generally faster than that between two solids.     [2 marks]

Q3 On the right is a Maxwell-Boltzmann distribution curve for a sample of a gas at 25 °C.

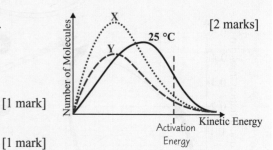

a) Which of the curves, X or Y, shows the Maxwell-Boltzmann distribution curve for the same sample at 15 °C ?     [1 mark]

b) Explain how this curve shows that the reaction rate will be lower at 15 °C than at 25 °C.     [1 mark]

## Clap along if you feel like reaction rates are what you wanna do...

*No equations, no formulae... What more could you ask for. Remember, increasing concentration and pressure do exactly the same thing. The only difference is, you increase the concentration of a solution and the pressure of a gas.*

# Reaction Rates

*Sorry — this section gets a bit mathsy. Just take a deep breath, dive in, and don't bash your head on the bottom.*

## Reaction Rate tells you How Fast Reactants are Converted to Products

**Reaction rate** is the **change in amount** of reactant or product **per unit time** (usually seconds).
E.g. if the reactants are in solution, the rate will be **change in concentration per second**. The units will be **mol dm$^{-3}$ s$^{-1}$**.

## You can Work out Reaction Rate from the Gradient of a Graph

If you draw a graph of the **amount of reactant or product against time** for a reaction (with time on the x-axis), then the reaction rate is just the **gradient** of the graph. You can work out the gradient using the equation...

gradient = change in y ÷ change in x

The data on the graph came from measuring the volume of gas given off during a chemical reaction.

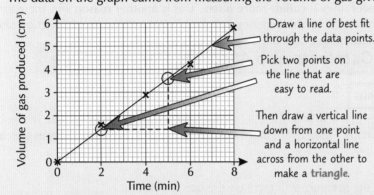

Draw a line of best fit through the data points.

Pick two points on the line that are easy to read.

Then draw a vertical line down from one point and a horizontal line across from the other to make a triangle.

change in y = 3.6 – 1.4 = 2.2 cm$^3$
change in x = 5.0 – 2.0 = 3.0 minutes
gradient = 2.2 ÷ 3.0 = 0.73 cm$^3$ min$^{-1}$

So the rate of reaction = **0.73 cm$^3$ min$^{-1}$**

## You May Need to Work Out the Gradient from a Curved Graph

When the points on a graph lie in a **curve**, you can't draw a straight line of best fit through them. But you can still work out the gradient, and so the rate, at a **particular point** in the reaction by working out the **gradient of a tangent**. The gradient at **time = 0** is called the **initial rate**.

*A tangent is a line that just touches a curve and has the same gradient as the curve does at that point.*

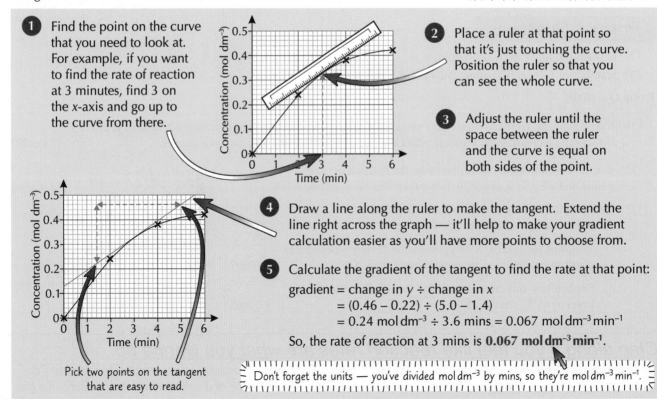

**1** Find the point on the curve that you need to look at. For example, if you want to find the rate of reaction at 3 minutes, find 3 on the x-axis and go up to the curve from there.

**2** Place a ruler at that point so that it's just touching the curve. Position the ruler so that you can see the whole curve.

**3** Adjust the ruler until the space between the ruler and the curve is equal on both sides of the point.

**4** Draw a line along the ruler to make the tangent. Extend the line right across the graph — it'll help to make your gradient calculation easier as you'll have more points to choose from.

**5** Calculate the gradient of the tangent to find the rate at that point:
gradient = change in y ÷ change in x
= (0.46 – 0.22) ÷ (5.0 – 1.4)
= 0.24 mol dm$^{-3}$ ÷ 3.6 mins = 0.067 mol dm$^{-3}$ min$^{-1}$
So, the rate of reaction at 3 mins is **0.067 mol dm$^{-3}$ min$^{-1}$**.

Pick two points on the tangent that are easy to read.

*Don't forget the units — you've divided mol dm$^{-3}$ by mins, so they're mol dm$^{-3}$ min$^{-1}$.*

# Reaction Rates

## You Can Work out the *Initial Rate* of a Reaction

The **initial rate of a reaction** is the rate at the **start** of the reaction. You can find this from a **concentration-time** graph by calculating the **gradient** of the **tangent** at **time = 0**.

**Example:** The graph on the right shows the change in concentration of $H^+$ ions over time in a reaction. Calculate the initial rate of reaction.

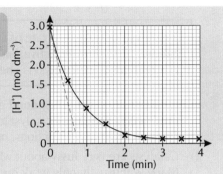

- Draw a **tangent** to the curve at **time = 0**.
- Work out the **gradient** of the tangent.
  gradient = change in y ÷ change in x
  $= (0.3 - 3.0) \div (0.7 - 0.0) = -2.7 \ mol\,dm^{-3} \div 0.7 \ mins$
  $= -3.875... \ mol\,dm^{-3}\,min^{-1}$
- So the initial rate of reaction was **3.9 mol dm$^{-3}$ min$^{-1}$**.

## You Can Work Out *Rates* From *Experimental Data*

1) In some reactions, you'll measure the time taken for something to happen, e.g. a **colour change** to occur.

2) If you're waiting for a set amount of **product to form**, or a set amount of **reactant to be used up**, you can use this equation to work out the rate:

$$\text{rate of reaction} = \frac{\text{amount of reactant used or amount of product formed}}{\text{time taken}}$$

So, for example, if during a reaction, it took **16 seconds** for **10 cm$^3$** of a gas to form, the rate of reaction would be: $10 \div 16 = \textbf{0.625 cm}^3 \ \textbf{s}^{-1}$

3) The rate of reaction is proportional to **1 ÷ time**, so you can use **1/time** as a measure of the relative **rate** of reaction.

**Example:** A student measures the time taken for a **colour change** to occur in a reaction as he varies the **concentration** of a reactant, **A**. His results are shown in the table. Calculate the relative rates of reaction.

1) First calculate the relative rate of **each reaction** in s$^{-1}$.
   When [A] = 0.10 mol dm$^{-3}$, $1 \div 124 = 0.00806... \ s^{-1}$
   When [A] = 0.15 mol dm$^{-3}$, $1 \div 62 = 0.0161... \ s^{-1}$
   When [A] = 0.20 mol dm$^{-3}$, $1 \div 25 = 0.0400 \ s^{-1}$

| [A] / mol dm$^{-3}$ | Time taken until colour change (s) |
|---|---|
| 0.10 | 124 |
| 0.15 | 62 |
| 0.20 | 25 |

2) You should report the relative rate as a **ratio**.
   **Divide** by the **smallest** relative rate to get the rates as the smallest whole number ratio possible.
   $$0.0081 : 0.016 : 0.040 = \textbf{1} : \textbf{2} : \textbf{5}$$

## Practice Questions

Q1 What is meant by the term 'reaction rate'?

Q2 What is the formula to find the gradient of a line?

**Exam Question**

Q1 Compounds X and Y react as in the equation below.

$$X + Y \rightarrow Z$$

From the graph on the right, work out the rate of reaction at 3 minutes.

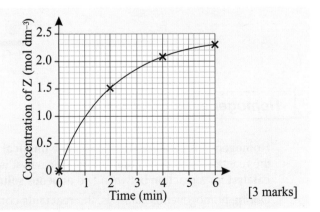

[3 marks]

## *Calculate your reaction to this page. Boredom? How dare you...*

*Plenty to learn on this page, but first things first — make sure you've got a ruler in the exam in case you need to draw a tangent to find the gradient from a curved graph. Then, make sure you know what you actually need to do with it. Finally, make sure you know how to deal with any calculations that might come your way, not forgetting any units.*

# Catalysts

*Catalysts were tantalisingly mentioned a couple of pages ago — here's the full story...*

## Catalysts *Increase* the *Rate* of *Reactions*

You can use **catalysts** to make chemical reactions happen **faster**. Learn this definition:

> A **catalyst** increases the **rate** of a reaction by providing an **alternative reaction pathway** with a **lower activation energy**, so a greater proportion of **collisions** result in a **reaction**. The catalyst is **chemically unchanged** at the end of the reaction.

1) Catalysts are **great**. They **don't** get used up in reactions, so you only need a **tiny bit** of catalyst to catalyse a **huge** amount of stuff. They **do** take part in reactions, but they're **remade** at the end.

2) Catalysts are **very fussy** about which reactions they catalyse. Many will usually **only** work on a single reaction.

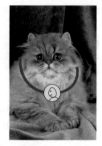
The 1985 Nobel Prize in Chemistry was awarded to Mr Tiddles for discovering catalysis.

## Reaction Profiles *Show Why* Catalysts *Work...*

### *Heterogeneous* Catalysis

A heterogeneous catalyst is one that is in a **different phase** from the reactants — i.e. in a different **physical state**. For example, in the Haber Process (see below), **gases** are passed over a **solid iron catalyst**.

The **reaction** happens on the **surface** of the **heterogeneous catalyst**. So, **increasing the surface area** of the catalyst increases the number of molecules that can **react** at the same time, **increasing the rate** of the reaction. The heterogeneous catalyst works by **lowering the activation energy** of the reaction — you can see this on a reaction profile diagram.

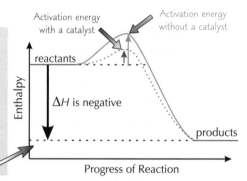

**Solid** heterogeneous catalysts can provide a **surface** for a reaction to take place on. Here's how it works —

1) **Reactant molecules** arrive at the **surface** and **bond** with the solid catalyst. This is called **a**d**sorption**.

2) The bonds between the **reactant's** atoms are **weakened** and **break up**. This forms **radicals** — atoms or molecules with **unpaired** electrons. These radicals then **get together** and make **new molecules**.

3) The new molecules are then detached from the catalyst. This is called **desorption**.

This example shows you how an iron catalyst provides a surface for the atoms to react on in the **Haber Process** to produce ammonia.

$$N_{2(g)} + 3H_{2(g)} \xrightleftharpoons{Fe_{(s)}} NH_{3(g)}$$

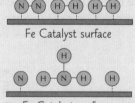

Adsorption of $N_2$ and $H_2$ to the catalyst.

↓

Chemical reaction — $NH_3$ is formed.

↓

Desorption of $NH_3$ from the catalyst.

### *Homogeneous* Catalysis

**Homogeneous catalysts** are in the **same physical state** as the reactants. Usually a **homogeneous** catalyst is an **aqueous catalyst** for a reaction between two **aqueous solutions**.

During homogeneous catalysis, the **reactants** combine with the **catalyst** to make an **intermediate species**, which then reacts to form the **products** and **reform the catalyst**.

E' = the activation energy of the **first** step in the catalysed reaction.
E" = the activation energy of the **second** step in the catalysed reaction.

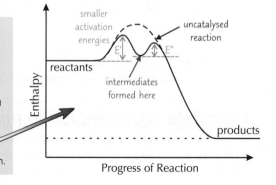

# Catalysts

## ...as do *Maxwell-Boltzmann* Distributions

As you've seen in the graphs on the previous page, in both homogeneous and heterogeneous catalysis, the catalyst **lowers the activation energy**.
This means there are **more particles** with **enough energy** to react when they collide. This is shown by the Maxwell-Boltzmann distribution on the right.
So, in a certain amount of time, **more particles react**.

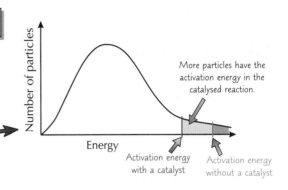

## *Catalysts* Have Economic Benefits

Loads of industries rely on **catalysts**. They can dramatically lower production costs, give you more product in a shorter time and help make better products. Here are a few examples:

1)  Iron is used as a catalyst in **ammonia** production. If it wasn't for the catalyst, the **temperature** would have to be raised loads to make the reaction happen **quick enough**. Not only would this be bad for the fuel bills, it'd **reduce the amount of ammonia** produced since the reaction is reversible, and exothermic in the direction of ammonia production.

*See pages 120-121 for more on reversible reactions and changing conditions.*

2)  Using a catalyst can change the properties of a product to make it more useful, e.g. **poly(ethene)**.

|  | Made without a catalyst | Made with a catalyst (a Ziegler-Natta catalyst, to be precise) |
|---|---|---|
| Properties of poly(ethene) | less dense, less rigid | more dense, more rigid, higher melting point |

## Practice Questions

Q1 Explain what a catalyst is.

Q2 Explain what the difference between a heterogeneous and a homogeneous catalyst is.

Q3 Describe two reasons why catalysts are useful for industry.

**Exam Question**

Q1 Sulfuric acid is manufactured by the contact process. In one of the stages, sulfur dioxide gas is mixed with oxygen gas and converted into sulfur trioxide gas. A solid vanadium(V) oxide ($V_2O_5$) catalyst is used. The enthalpy change for the uncatalysed reaction is $-197$ kJ mol$^{-1}$.

a)  Which of the following reaction profile diagrams is correct for the catalysed reaction? [1 mark]

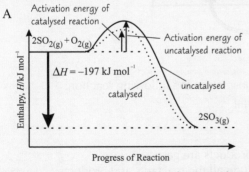

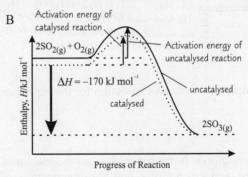

b)  Describe how a catalyst works to increase the rate of the reaction. [3 marks]

c)  Is the vanadium(V) oxide catalyst heterogeneous or homogeneous? Explain your answer. [1 mark]

---

## *Catalysts and walking past bad buskers — increased speed but no change...*

*Whatever you do, don't confuse the Maxwell-Boltzmann diagram for catalysts with the one for a temperature change. Catalysts lower the activation energy without changing the shape of the curve. BUT, the shape of the curve does change with temperature. Get these mixed up and you'll be the laughing stock of the Examiners' tea room.*

# Dynamic Equilibrium

*There's a lot of to-ing and fro-ing on this page. Mind your head doesn't start spinning.*

## Reversible Reactions Can Reach Dynamic Equilibrium

1) Lots of chemical reactions are **reversible** — they go **both ways**. To show a reaction's reversible, you stick in a $\rightleftharpoons$. Here's an example:

$$H_{2(g)} + I_{2(g)} \rightleftharpoons 2HI_{(g)}$$

This reaction can go in **either direction** —

forwards $H_{2(g)} + I_{2(g)} \rightleftharpoons 2HI_{(g)}$ ...or backwards $2HI_{(g)} \rightleftharpoons H_{2(g)} + I_{2(g)}$

2) As the **reactants** get used up, the **forward** reaction **slows down** — and as more **product** is formed, the **reverse** reaction **speeds up**.

3) After a while, the forward reaction will be going at exactly the **same rate** as the backward reaction, so the amounts of reactants and products **won't be changing** any more — it'll seem like **nothing's happening**.

4) This is called **dynamic equilibrium**. At equilibrium the **concentrations** of **reactants** and **products** stay **constant**.

5) A **dynamic equilibrium** can only happen in a **closed system**. This just means nothing can get in or out.

Although it appeared that the Smiths were doing nothing, they were actually in a state of dynamic equilibrium.

## $K_c$ is the Equilibrium Constant

The equilibrium constant, or $K_c$, gives you an idea of **how far** to the **left or right** the equilibrium is. It's calculated using the equilibrium concentrations of the reactants and products in a system.

*In Chemistry, the word system is used to refer to a particular thing being studied.*

### Homogeneous Equilibria and $K_c$

1) A **homogeneous system** is a **system** in which everything is in the **same physical state**.

2) When you have a **homogeneous reaction** that's reached **dynamic equilibrium**, you can work out the **equilibrium constant, $K_c$,** using the concentrations of the products and reactants at equilibrium.

3) For homogeneous equilibria, all the products and reactants are included in the expression for $K_c$.

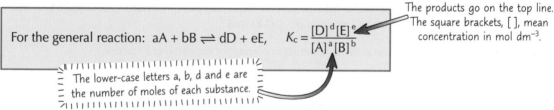

For the general reaction: $aA + bB \rightleftharpoons dD + eE$,    $K_c = \dfrac{[D]^d[E]^e}{[A]^a[B]^b}$

*The products go on the top line. The square brackets, [ ], mean concentration in mol dm$^{-3}$.*

*The lower-case letters a, b, d and e are the number of moles of each substance.*

**Example:** Write an expression for the equilibrium constant for the following reaction:

$$H_{2(g)} + I_{2(g)} \rightleftharpoons 2HI_{(g)}$$

The reaction is **homogeneous** — all the reactants and products are gases.
So the expression for the equilibrium constant will include **all** the reactants and products.

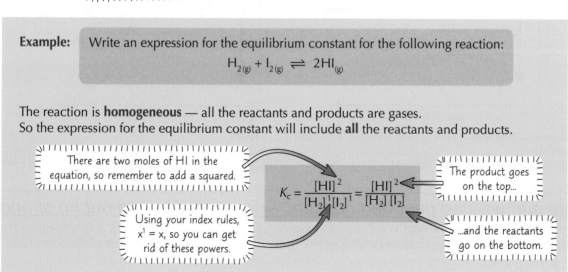

*There are two moles of HI in the equation, so remember to add a squared.*

$$K_c = \frac{[HI]^2}{[H_2]^1[I_2]^1} = \frac{[HI]^2}{[H_2][I_2]}$$

*The product goes on the top...*

*Using your index rules, $x^1 = x$, so you can get rid of these powers.*

*...and the reactants go on the bottom.*

# Dynamic Equilibrium

## Heterogeneous Equilibria and $K_c$

1) In a **heterogeneous system**, **not everything's** in the same **physical state**.

2) Writing the expression for $K_c$ for a **heterogeneous reaction** (a reaction where not all the reactants and products are in the same physical state) that's reached **dynamic equilibrium** can be a bit tricky.

3) Unlike with **homogeneous equilibria**, not everything is included in the expression for $K_c$.

4) You don't include **solids** or **pure liquids** in the expression for $K_c$ when you're dealing with heterogeneous equilibria. This is because their concentrations **stay constant** throughout the reaction.

> **Example:**  Write an expression for the equilibrium constant for the following reaction:
>
> $$H_2O_{(g)} + C_{(s)} \rightleftharpoons H_{2(g)} + CO_{(g)}$$
>
> The reaction is **heterogeneous**, so don't include any solids or pure liquids in your expression for $K_c$.
> In this reaction, carbon is a **solid** and everything else is a **gas**.
> Therefore, **carbon** is the only thing you **exclude** from your expression for $K_c$.
>
> $$K_c = \frac{[H_2]^1[CO]^1}{[H_2O]^1} = \frac{[H_2][CO]}{[H_2O]}$$

## Catalysts Don't Affect the Equilibrium Constant

You **don't** include **catalysts** in **expressions** for the **equilibrium constant**. Catalysts **don't affect** the equilibrium **concentrations** of the products or reactants — they just **speed up** the **rate** at which **dynamic equilibrium** is **reached**.

## Practice Questions

Q1 Using an example, explain the term 'reversible reaction'.

Q2 What is a meant by a homogeneous system?

Q3 Write an expression for the equilibrium constant of the reaction, $aA + bB \rightleftharpoons dD + eE$.

Q4 What shouldn't you include in the expression for $K_c$ for a heterogeneous system at dynamic equilibrium?

**Exam Questions**

Q1 In the Haber Process, nitrogen and hydrogen gases react to form ammonia:  $N_{2(g)} + 3H_{2(g)} \rightleftharpoons 2NH_{3(g)}$

    a)  At a certain point, the reaction reaches 'dynamic equilibrium'. Explain what is meant by this. [2 marks]

    b)  Write an expression for the equilibrium constant, $K_c$, for the Haber Process. [1 mark]

Q2 A student is investigating the equilibrium constant for the following reaction: $NH_{3(g)} + H_2O_{(l)} \rightleftharpoons NH_4^+{}_{(aq)} + OH^-{}_{(aq)}$

    He states that the expression for the equilibrium constant, $K_c$, is: $K_c = \dfrac{[NH_3][H_2O]}{[NH_4^+][OH^-]}$.

    Explain what mistakes the student has made in his expression for $K_c$. [2 marks]

Q3 Which of the reactions below can be represented by the following expression for the equilibrium constant? $K_c = [CO_2]$

    **A**  $C_{(s)} + O_{2(g)} \rightleftharpoons CO_{2(g)}$                     **B**  $CaCO_{3(s)} \rightleftharpoons CaO_{(s)} + CO_{2(g)}$

    **C**  $2NaOH_{(aq)} + CO_{2(g)} \rightleftharpoons Na_2CO_{3(aq)} + H_2O_{(l)}$     **D**  $CH_{4(g)} + 2O_{2(g)} \rightleftharpoons CO_{2(g)} + 2H_2O_{(g)}$     [1 mark]

---

### *I'm constantly going on about equilibrium — that's what it feels like anyway...*

*Working out the expression for $K_c$ for both homogeneous and heterogeneous systems is pretty straightforward once you've got the hang of it. If you've not quite got it yet go back through these two pages until it all makes perfect sense. Once you've done that, keep going. You're halfway through the section already — just 2 more pages on equilibrium to go.*

# Le Chatelier's Principle

*'Oh no, not another page on equilibria', I hear you cry... Fair enough really.*

## Le Chatelier's Principle *Predicts what will Happen if* Conditions are Changed

If you **change** the **concentration**, **pressure** or **temperature** of a reversible reaction, you tend to **alter** the **position of equilibrium**. This just means you'll end up with **different amounts** of reactants and products at equilibrium.

> If the position of equilibrium moves to the **left**, you'll get more **reactants**.
>
> $$H_{2(g)} + I_{2(g)} \rightleftharpoons 2HI_{(g)}$$

> If the position of equilibrium moves to the **right**, you'll get more **products**.
>
> $$H_{2(g)} + I_{2(g)} \rightleftharpoons 2HI_{(g)}$$

Le Chatelier's principle tells you how the **position of equilibrium** will change if a **condition changes**:

> If there's a change in **concentration**, **pressure** or **temperature**, the equilibrium will move to help **counteract** the change.

So, basically, if you **raise the temperature**, the position of equilibrium will shift to try to **cool things down**. And, if you **raise the pressure or concentration**, the position of equilibrium will shift to try to **reduce it again**.

## Here Are Some Handy Rules *for Using* Le Chatelier's Principle

You need to know how **temperature**, **concentration** and **pressure** affect equilibrium. So, here goes...

### Concentration

$$2SO_{2(g)} + O_{2(g)} \rightleftharpoons 2SO_{3(g)}$$

1) If you **increase** the **concentration** of a **reactant** ($SO_2$ or $O_2$), the equilibrium tries to **get rid** of the extra reactant. It does this by making **more product** ($SO_3$). So the equilibrium's shifted to the **right**.

2) If you **increase** the **concentration** of the **product** ($SO_3$), the equilibrium tries to remove the extra product. This makes the **reverse reaction** go faster. So the equilibrium shifts to the **left**.

3) **Decreasing** the concentrations has the **opposite effect**.

### Pressure *(this only affects* gases*)*

$$2SO_{2(g)} + O_{2(g)} \rightleftharpoons 2SO_{3(g)}$$

There are 3 moles on the left, but only 2 on the right. So, increasing the pressure shifts the equilibrium to the right.

1) **Increasing** the pressure shifts the equilibrium to the side with **fewer** gas molecules. This **reduces** the pressure.

2) **Decreasing** the pressure shifts the equilibrium to the side with **more** gas molecules. This **raises** the pressure again.

### Temperature

1) **Increasing** the temperature means **adding heat**. The equilibrium shifts in the **endothermic (positive $\Delta H$) direction** to absorb this heat.

2) **Decreasing** the temperature **removes heat**. The equilibrium shifts in the **exothermic (negative $\Delta H$) direction** to try to replace the heat.

3) If the forward reaction's **endothermic**, the reverse reaction will be **exothermic**, and vice versa.

This reaction's exothermic in the forward direction ($\Delta H = -197$ kJ mol$^{-1}$). If you increase the temperature, the equilibrium shifts to the left to absorb the extra heat.

$$\text{Exothermic} \Longrightarrow$$
$$2SO_{2(g)} + O_{2(g)} \rightleftharpoons 2SO_{3(g)}$$
$$\Longleftarrow \text{Endothermic}$$

# Le Chatelier's Principle

## In *Industry*, the *Conditions* Chosen are a *Compromise*

In the exam, you may be asked to look at an **industrial process** and work out what **conditions** should be used to give the best **balance** between a **high rate** and a **high yield**. If you're asked to do this, you'll need to look at any **data** given, e.g. the **enthalpy change** of reaction, and use Le Chatelier's principle to work out what the **optimum conditions** are. Let's have a look at an example...

### *Ethanol* can be Formed From *Ethene* and *Steam*

1) The industrial production of **ethanol** is a good example of why Le Chatelier's principle is important in **real life**.

2) Ethanol is produced via a **reversible exothermic reaction** between **ethene** and **steam**:

*Mr and Mrs Le Chatelier celebrate another successful year in the principle business*

$$C_2H_{4(g)} + H_2O_{(g)} \rightleftharpoons C_2H_5OH_{(g)} \qquad \Delta H = -46 \text{ kJ mol}^{-1}$$

3) The reaction is carried out at a pressure of **60-70 atmospheres** and a temperature of **300 °C**, with a **phosphoric(V) acid** catalyst.

- Because it's an **exothermic reaction**, **lower** temperatures favour the forward reaction. This means **more** ethene and steam are converted to ethanol at lower temperatures — you get a better **yield**.

- But **lower temperatures** mean a **slower rate of reaction**. You'd be **daft** to try to get a **really high yield** of ethanol if it's going to take you 10 years. So the 300 °C is a **compromise** between **maximum yield** and **a faster reaction**.

- **Higher pressures** favour the **forward reaction**, so a pressure of **60-70 atmospheres** is used — **high pressure** moves the reaction to the side with **fewer molecules of gas**. **Increasing the pressure** also increases the **rate** of reaction.

  *In the end, it all comes down to minimising costs.*

- Cranking up the pressure as high as you can sounds like a great idea so far. But **high pressures** are **expensive** to produce. You need **stronger pipes** and **containers** to withstand high pressure. In this process, increasing the pressure can also cause **side reactions** to occur.

- So the **60-70 atmospheres** is a **compromise** between **maximum yield** and **expense**.

## Practice Questions

Q1 If the equilibrium moves to the right, do you get more products or reactants?

Q2 A reaction at equilibrium is endothermic in the forward direction. What happens to the position of equilibrium as the temperature is increased?

**Exam Questions**

Q1 Nitrogen and oxygen gases were reacted together in a closed flask and allowed to reach equilibrium, with nitrogen monoxide being formed. The forward reaction is endothermic.

$$N_{2(g)} + O_{2(g)} \rightleftharpoons 2NO_{(g)}$$

a) Explain how the following changes would affect the position of equilibrium of the above reaction:

   i) Pressure is increased. [1 mark]

   ii) Temperature is reduced. [1 mark]

   iii) Nitrogen monoxide is removed. [1 mark]

Q2 Explain why moderate reaction temperatures are a compromise for exothermic reactions. [2 marks]

---

## *If it looks like I'm not doing anything, I'm just being dynamic... honest...*

*Equilibria never do what you want them to do. They always oppose you. Be sure you know what happens to an equilibrium if you change the conditions. About pressure — if there's the same number of gas moles on each side of the equation, you can raise the pressure as high as you like and it won't make a difference to the position of equilibrium.*

# Planning Experiments

*As well as doing practical work in class, you can get asked about it in your exams too. Harsh I know, but that's how it goes. You need to be able to plan the perfect experiment and make improvements to ones other people have planned.*

## Make Sure You **Plan** Your **Experiment Carefully**

It's really important to plan an experiment well if you want to get accurate and precise results. Here's how to go about it...

*Have a peek at page 130 to find out more about accurate and precise results.*

1) Work out the **aim** of the experiment — what are you trying to find out?
2) Identify the **independent**, **dependent** and other **variables** (see below).
3) Decide what **data** to collect.
4) Select **appropriate equipment** which will give you accurate results.
5) Make a **risk assessment** and plan any safety precautions.
6) Write out a **detailed method**.
7) Carry out **tests** — to gather **evidence** to address the aim of your experiment.

## Make it a **Fair Test** — Control your **Variables**

You probably know this all off by heart but it's easy to get mixed up sometimes. So here's a quick recap:

**Variable** — A variable is a **quantity** that has the **potential to change**, e.g. mass. There are two types of variable commonly referred to in experiments:

- **Independent variable** — the thing that you **change** in an experiment.
- **Dependent variable** — the thing that you **measure** in an experiment.

As well as the independent and dependent variables, you need to think of all the other variables in your experiment and plan ways to keep each of those the same.

For example, if you're investigating the effect of **temperature** on rate of reaction using the apparatus on the right, the variables will be:

| Independent variable | Temperature |
|---|---|
| Dependent variable | Volume of gas produced — you can measure this by collecting it in a gas syringe. |
| Other variables | E.g. concentration and volume of solutions, mass of solids, pressure, the presence of a catalyst and the surface area of any solid reactants. |

*You MUST control your other variables so they're always the same.*

## Collect the Appropriate **Data**

Experiments often involve collecting **data** and you need to decide what data to collect.

1) There are different types of data, so it helps to know what they are:

- **Discrete** — you get discrete data by **counting**. E.g. the number of bubbles produced in a reaction.
- **Continuous** — a continuous variable can have **any value** on a scale. For example, the volume of gas produced. You can never measure the exact value of a continuous variable.
- **Categoric** — a categoric variable has values that can be sorted into **categories**. For example, the colours of solutions might be blue, red and green.

2) You need to make sure the data you collect is appropriate for your experiment.

**Example:** A student suggests measuring the rate of the following reaction by observing how conductivity changes over the course of the reaction:

$$NaOH_{(aq)} + CH_3CH_2Br_{(l)} \rightarrow CH_3CH_2OH_{(l)} + NaBr_{(aq)}$$

Suggest what is wrong with the student's method, and how it could be improved.

You couldn't collect data about how the **conductivity changes** over the course of the reaction, because there are **salts** in both the reactants and the products.

Instead you could use a **pH meter** to measure how the **pH changes** from basic (due to sodium hydroxide) to neutral.

# Planning Experiments

## Choose *Appropriate* Equipment — *Think about Size and Precision*

Selecting the right apparatus may sound easy but it's something you need to think carefully about.

1) The equipment has to be **appropriate** for the specific experiment.

   For example, if you want to measure the volume of gas produced in a reaction, you need to make sure you use apparatus which will collect the gas, without letting any escape.

2) The equipment needs to be the right **size**.

   For example, if you're using a gas syringe to collect a gas, it needs to be big enough to collect **all** the gas produced during the experiment, or the plunger will just fall out the end. You might need to do some **calculations** to work out what size of syringe to use.

3) The equipment needs to be the right level of **precision**.

   If you want to measure 10 cm³ of a liquid, it will be more precise to use a measuring cylinder that is graduated to the nearest 0.5 cm³ than to the nearest 1 cm³. A burette would be most precise though (they can measure to the nearest 0.1 cm³).

## *Risk Assessments* Help You to Work *Safely*

1) When you're planning an experiment, you need to carry out a **risk assessment**. To do this, you need to identify:
   - All the **dangers** in the experiment, e.g. any hazardous compounds or naked flames.
   - **Who** is at **risk** from these dangers.
   - What can be done to **reduce the risk**, such as wearing goggles or working in a fume cupboard.

2) You need to make sure you're working **ethically** too. This is most important if there are other people or animals involved. You have to put their welfare first.

There's more about risks and hazards on page 62.

## Methods Must be *Clear* and *Detailed*

When **writing** or **evaluating** a method, you need to think about all of the things on these two pages. The method must be **clear** and **detailed** enough for anyone to follow — it's important that **other people** can recreate your experiment and get the **same** results. Make sure your method includes:

1) All **substances** and **quantities** to be used.
2) How to **control** variables.
3) The exact **apparatus** needed (a diagram is usually helpful to show the set up).
4) Any **safety precautions** that should be taken.
5) What **data** to collect and **how** to collect it.

## Practice Questions

Q1 Briefly outline the steps involved in planning an experiment.

Q2 What three things should you consider when choosing the best apparatus for your experiment?

**Exam Question**

Q1 A student carries out an experiment to investigate how the rate of the following reaction changes with the concentration of hydrochloric acid: $Mg_{(s)} + 2HCl_{(aq)} \rightarrow MgCl_{2\,(aq)} + H_{2\,(g)}$

The student decides to measure how the pH changes over time using litmus paper.
Explain why this method of measuring pH is unsuitable, and suggest an alternative method. [2 marks]

---

*Revision time — independent variable. Exam mark — dependent variable...*

I wouldn't advise you to investigate the effect of revision on exam marks. Just trust me — more revision = better marks. But if you were to investigate it, there are all manner of variables that you'd need to control. The amount of sleep you had the night before, how much coffee you drank in the morning, your level of panic on entering the exam hall...

# Practical Techniques

*The way you carry out your experiment is important, so here's a nice round up of some of the techniques chemists use all the time. You've probably met some of them before, which should hopefully make it all a bit easier. Hopefully... :-)*

## Results Should be **Repeatable** and **Reproducible**

1) **Repeatable** means that if the **same** person does the experiment again using the same methods and equipment, they'll get the same results. **Reproducible** means that if someone **else** does the experiment, or a different **method** or piece of **equipment** is used, the results will still be the same.

2) To make sure your results can be consistently repeated and reproduced, you need to **minimise** any **errors** that might sneak into your data. This includes:
   - using **apparatus** and **techniques** correctly,
   - taking **measurements** correctly,
   - **repeating** your experiments and calculating a **mean**.

## Make Sure You **Measure** Substances **Correctly**

The **state** (solid, liquid or gas) that your substance is in will determine **how** you decide to measure it.

1) You weigh **solids** using a **balance**. Here are a couple of things to look out for:
   - Put the container you are weighing your substance into on the balance, and make sure the balance is set to exactly zero before you start weighing out your substance.
   - If you need to **transfer** the solid into another container, make sure that it's **all** transferred. For example, if you're making up a standard solution you could wash any remaining solid into the new container using the solvent. Or, you could **reweigh** the weighing container after you've transferred the solid so you can work out **exactly** how much you added to your experiment.

2) There are a few methods you might use to measure the volume of a liquid. Whichever method you use, always read the volume from the **bottom** of the **meniscus** (the curved upper surface of the liquid) when it's at **eye level**.

Read volume from here — the bottom of the meniscus.

**Pipettes** are long, narrow tubes that are used to **suck up** an **accurate volume** of liquid and transfer it to another container. They are often **calibrated** to allow for the fact that the last drop of liquid stays in the pipette when the liquid is ejected. This reduces transfer errors.

**Burettes** measure from **top** to **bottom** (so when they are **full**, the scale reads **zero**). They have a **tap** at the bottom which you can use to release the liquid into another container (you can even release it drop by drop). To use a burette, take an **initial reading**, and once you've released as much liquid as you want, take a **final reading**. The **difference** between the readings tells you how much liquid you used.

*Burettes are used a lot for titrations. There's loads more about titrations on pages 62-65.*

**Volumetric flasks** allow you to **accurately** measure a very **specific** volume of liquid. They come in various **sizes** (e.g. 100 cm³, 250 cm³) and there's a **line** on the neck that marks the volume that they measure. They're used to make **accurate dilutions** and **standard solutions**. To use them, first measure out and add the liquid or solid that is being diluted or dissolved. Rinse out the measuring vessel into the volumetric flask with a little solvent to make sure everything's been transferred. Then fill the flask with solvent to the **bottom** of the neck. Fill the neck **drop by drop** until the bottom of the meniscus is **level** with the line.

*A standard solution is a solution with a precisely known concentration. You can find out how they're made on page 62.*

**500 cm³**

3) Gases can be measured with a **gas syringe**. They should be measured at **room temperature** and **pressure** as the **volume** of a gas **changes** with temperature and pressure. Before you use the syringe, you should make sure it's completely **sealed** and that the **plunger** moves **smoothly**.

Once you've measured a quantity of a substance you need to be careful you don't **lose** any. In particular, think about how to minimise losses as you transfer it from the measuring equipment to the reaction container.

# Practical Techniques

## Measure **Temperature** Accurately

I'm sure you've heard this before, so I'll be quick...   You can use a **thermometer** or a **temperature probe** to measure the temperature of a substance (a temperature probe is like a thermometer but it will always have a **digital display**).

- Make sure the **bulb** of your thermometer or temperature probe is **completely submerged** in any mixture you're measuring.
- Wait for the temperature to **stabilise** before you take an initial reading
- If you're using a thermometer with a scale, read off your measurement at **eye level** to make sure it's accurate.

## **Qualitative** Tests Can be Harder to **Reproduce**

**Qualitative** tests measure **physical qualities** (e.g. colour) while **quantitative** tests measure numerical data, (e.g. mass).

So if you carried out a reaction and noticed that heat was produced, this would be a **qualitative** observation. If you **measured** the temperature change with a thermometer, this would be **quantitative**.

Qualitative tests can be harder to **reproduce** because they're often **subjective** (based on **opinion**), such as describing the **colour** or **cloudiness** of a solution.  There are ways to **reduce** the subjectivity of qualitative results though.
For example:

- If you're looking for a **colour change**, put a **white background** behind your reaction container.
- If you're looking for a **precipitate** to form, mark an **X** on a piece of paper and place it under the reaction container.  Your solution is 'cloudy' when you can **no longer see** the X.

## There are Specific Techniques for Synthesising **Organic Compounds**

**Synthesis** is used to **make** one **organic compound** from another.  There are a number of techniques that chemists use to help them make and purify their products:

*These techniques are covered in more detail on pages 98-99.*

1) **Reflux** — heating a reaction mixture in a flask fitted with a **condenser** so that any materials that **evaporate**, condense and drip back into the mixture.

2) **Distillation** — gently heating a mixture so that the compounds evaporate off in order of **increasing boiling point** and can be collected separately.  This can be done **during** a reaction to collect a product as it forms, or **after** the reaction is **finished** to purify the mixture.

3) **Removing water soluble impurities** — adding **water** to an organic mixture in a separating funnel.  Any **water soluble impurities** move out of the organic layer and dissolve in the aqueous layer.  The layers have different **densities** so are easy to separate.

## Practice Questions

Q1  Give three ways that you could ensure your experiment is repeatable and reproducible.

Q2  How would you measure out a desired quantity of a solid?  And a gas?

Q3  How could you make the results of an experiment measuring time taken for a precipitate to form less subjective?

**Exam Question**

Q1  A student dilutes a 1 mol dm$^{-3}$ solution of sodium chloride to 0.1 mol dm$^{-3}$ as follows:

He measures 10 cm$^3$ of 1 mol dm$^{-3}$ sodium chloride solution in a pipette and puts this into a 100 cm$^3$ volumetric flask.  He then tops up the volumetric flask with distilled water until the top of the meniscus is at 100 cm$^3$.

a)  What has the student done incorrectly?  What should he have done instead?          [1 mark]

b)  Which of the arrows in the diagram on the right indicates the level to which you should fill a volumetric flask?          [1 mark]

## *Reflux, take it easy...*

*It might seem like there's a lot to do to make sure your results are accurate, but you should get lots of practice in practicals.  Before long you'll be measuring temperatures and volumes with your eyes shut (metaphorically speaking).*

# Presenting Results

*Once you've collected the data from your experiment, it's not time to stop, put your feet up and have a cup of tea —*
*you've got some presenting to do. Results tables need converting into graphs and other pretty pictures.*

## Organise Your Results in a **Table**

It's a good idea to set up a table to **record** the **results** of your experiment in. When you draw a table, make sure you
**include** enough **rows** and **columns** to **record all of the data** you need. You might also need to include a column for
**processing** your data (e.g. working out an average).

Make sure each **column** has a **heading** so you
know what's going to be recorded where.

The **units** should be in the
**column heading**, not the table itself.

| Temperature (°C) | Time (s) | Volume of gas evolved (cm³) | | | Average volume of gas evolved (cm³) |
|---|---|---|---|---|---|
| | | Run 1 | Run 2 | Run 3 | |
| 20 | 10 | 8.1 | 7.6 | 8.5 | (8.1 + 7.6 + 8.5) ÷ 3 = 8.1 |
| | 20 | 17.7 | 19.0 | 20.1 | (17.7 + 19.0 + 20.1) ÷ 3 = 18.9 |
| | 30 | 28.5 | 29.9 | 30.0 | (28.5 + 29.9 + 30.0) ÷ 3 = 29.5 |

You'll need to repeat each test **at least three**
times to check your results are **repeatable**.

You can find the **mean result** by
**adding up** the data from each repeat
and **dividing** by the number of repeats.

## Graphs: **Scatter** or **Bar** — Use the **Best Type**

When drawing graphs, the
dependent variable should
go on the *y*-axis, the
independent on the *x*-axis.

You'll often need to make a **graph** of your results.
Graphs make your data **easier to understand** — so long as you choose the right type.

**Scatter plots** are great for showing how two sets of continuous data are related (or **correlated** — see page 128).
Don't try to join all the points on a scatter plot — draw a straight or curved **line of best fit** to show the **trend**.

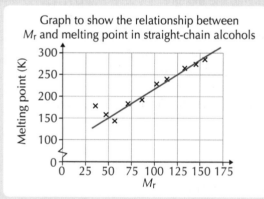

Graph to show the relationship between
$M_r$ and melting point in straight-chain alcohols

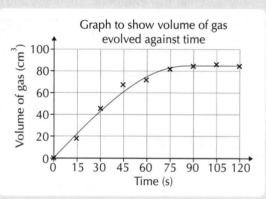

Graph to show volume of gas
evolved against time

You should use a **bar chart** when one of
your data sets is **categoric**. For example:

Apple and blackberry
was number one on
Jane's pie chart

**Whatever type of graph you make,**
**you'll ONLY get full marks if you:**

- Choose a sensible **scale** — don't do a tiny graph
  in the corner of the paper, or massive axes where
  the data only takes up a tiny part of the graph.

- **Label** both **axes** — including units.

- Plot your points accurately — use a **sharp pencil**.

Sometimes you might need to work out the gradient
of a graph, e.g. to work out the rate of a reaction.
There are details of how to do this on page 114.

Pie charts are also used to display categoric data.

# Presenting Results

## Don't Forget About *Units*

**Units** are really important — 10 g is a bit different from 10 kg, so make sure you don't forget to add them to your **tables** and **graphs**. It's often a good idea to write down the units on each line of any **calculations** you do — it makes things less confusing, particularly if you need to convert between two different units.

Here are some useful examples:

**Concentration** can be measured in **mol dm$^{-3}$** and **mol cm$^{-3}$**.

$$mol\ dm^{-3} \underset{\times\ 1000}{\overset{\div\ 1000}{\rightleftarrows}} mol\ cm^{-3}$$

**Example:** Write 0.2 mol dm$^{-3}$ in mol cm$^{-3}$.

To convert 0.2 mol dm$^{-3}$ into mol cm$^{-3}$ you divide by 1000.

0.2 mol dm$^{-3}$ ÷ 1000 = $2 \times 10^{-4}$ mol cm$^{-3}$

*Standard form is useful for writing very big or very small numbers.*

**Volume** can be measured in **m$^3$**, **dm$^3$** and **cm$^3$**.

$$m^3 \underset{\div\ 1000}{\overset{\times\ 1000}{\rightleftarrows}} dm^3 \underset{\div\ 1000}{\overset{\times\ 1000}{\rightleftarrows}} cm^3$$

**Example:** Write 6 dm$^3$ in m$^3$ and cm$^3$.

To convert 6 dm$^3$ into m$^3$ you divide by 1000.
6 dm$^3$ ÷ 1000 = 0.006 m$^3$ = $6 \times 10^{-3}$ m$^3$
To convert 6 dm$^3$ into cm$^3$ you multiply by 1000.
6 dm$^3$ × 1000 = 6000 cm$^3$ = $6 \times 10^3$ cm$^3$

## Round to the *Lowest Number* of *Significant Figures*

You always need to be aware of **significant figures** when working with data.

1) The rule is the same for when doing calculations with the results from your experiment, or when doing calculations in the exam — you have to round your answer to the **lowest number of significant figures** (s.f.) given in the question.

2) It always helps to write down the number of significant figures you've rounded to after your answer — it shows you really know what you're talking about.

3) If you're converting between **standard** and **ordinary form**, you have to keep the **same number** of significant figures. For example, 0.0060 mol dm$^{-3}$ is the same as $6.0 \times 10^{-3}$ mol dm$^{-3}$ — they're both given to 2 s.f..

*The first significant figure of a number is the first digit that isn't a zero. The second, third and fourth significant figures follow on immediately after the first (even if they're zeros).*

**Example:** 13.5 cm$^3$ of a 0.51 mol dm$^{-3}$ solution of sodium hydroxide reacts with 1.5 mol dm$^{-3}$ hydrochloric acid. Calculate the volume of hydrochloric acid required to neutralise the sodium hydroxide

*3 s.f.* *2 s.f.*

No. of moles of NaOH: (13.5 cm$^3$ × 0.51 mol dm$^{-3}$) ÷ 1000 = $6.885 \times 10^{-3}$ mol

*You don't need to round intermediate answers. Rounding too early will make your final answer less accurate.*

Volume of HCl: ($6.885 \times 10^{-3}$) mol × 1000 ÷ 1.5 mol dm$^{-3}$ = 4.59 cm$^3$ = **4.6 cm$^3$ (2 s.f.)**

Final answer should be rounded to 2 s.f.

*Make sure all your units match when you're doing calculations.*

## Practice Questions

Q1 Why is it always a good idea to repeat your experiments?

Q2 How would you convert an answer from m$^3$ to dm$^3$?

Q3 How do you decide how many significant figures you should round your answer to?

**Exam Question**

Q1 10 cm$^3$ sodium hydroxide solution is titrated with 0.50 mol dm$^{-3}$ hydrochloric acid to find its concentration. The titration is repeated three times and the volumes of hydrochloric acid used are: 7.30 cm$^3$, 7.25 cm$^3$, 7.25 cm$^3$.

a) What is the mean volume of hydrochloric acid recorded in dm$^3$? [1 mark]

b) What is the concentration of hydrochloric acid in mol cm$^{-3}$? [1 mark]

## *Significant figures — a result of far too many cream cakes...*

*When you draw graphs, always be careful to get your axes round the right way. The thing you've been changing (the independent variable) goes on the x-axis, and the thing you've been measuring (the dependent variable) is on the y-axis.*

# Analysing Results

*You're not quite finished yet... there's still time to look at your results and try and make sense of them. Graphs can help you to see patterns but don't try and read too much in to them — they won't tell you what grade you're going to get.*

## Watch Out For **Anomalous** Results

1) Anomalous results are ones that **don't fit** in with the other values and are likely to be wrong.

2) They're often due to **random errors**, e.g. if a drop in a titration is too big and shoots past the end point, or if a syringe plunger gets stuck whilst collecting gas produced in a reaction.

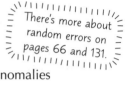
There's more about random errors on pages 66 and 131.

3) When looking at results in tables or graphs, you always need to look to see if there are any anomalies — you need to **ignore** these results when calculating means or drawing lines of best fit.

**Example:** Calculate the mean volume from the results in the table below.

| Titration Number | 1 | 2 | 3 | 4 |
|---|---|---|---|---|
| Titre Volume (cm³) | 15.20 | 15.30 | 15.25 | 15.50 |

Titre **4** isn't **concordant** (doesn't match) the other results so you need to ignore it and just use the other three:
$$\frac{15.20 + 15.30 + 15.25}{3} = \textbf{15.25 cm}^3$$

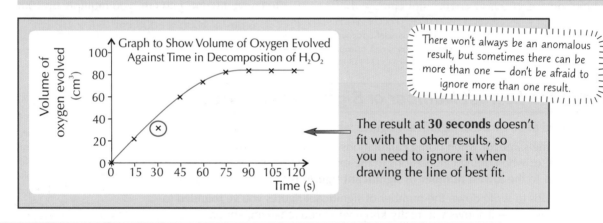

There won't always be an anomalous result, but sometimes there can be more than one — don't be afraid to ignore more than one result.

The result at **30 seconds** doesn't fit with the other results, so you need to ignore it when drawing the line of best fit.

## Scatter Graphs Show The **Relationship** Between Variables

Correlation describes the **relationship** between two variables — the independent one and the dependent one. Data can show:

**(1) Positive correlation**
As one variable **increases** the other **increases**.

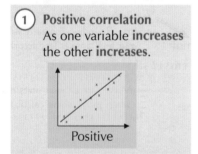
Positive

**(2) Negative correlation**
As one variable **increases** the other **decreases**.

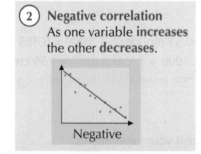
Negative

**(3) No correlation**
There is **no relationship** between the two variables.

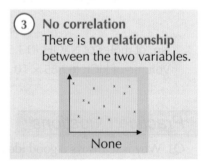
None

## Correlation **Doesn't** Mean **Cause** — Don't Jump to Conclusions

1) Ideally, only **two** quantities would **ever** change in any experiment — everything else would remain **constant**.

2) But in experiments or studies outside the lab, you **can't** usually control all the variables. So even if two variables are correlated, the change in one may **not** be causing the change in the other. Both changes might be caused by a **third variable**.

**Example:**
Some studies have found a correlation between **drinking chlorinated tap water** and the risk of developing certain cancers. So some people argue that water shouldn't have chlorine added.

**BUT** it's hard to control all the **variables** between people who drink tap water and people who don't. It could be due to other lifestyle factors.

Or, the cancer risk could be affected by something else in tap water — or by whatever the non-tap water drinkers drink instead...

# Analysing Results

## Don't Get **Carried Away** When Drawing Conclusions

The **data** should always **support** the conclusion. This may sound obvious but it's easy to **jump** to conclusions. Conclusions have to be **specific** — not make sweeping generalisations.

**Example:**

1) The rate of an enzyme-controlled reaction was measured at **10 °C, 20 °C, 30 °C, 40 °C, 50 °C** and **60 °C**. All other variables were kept constant, and the results are shown in the graph below.

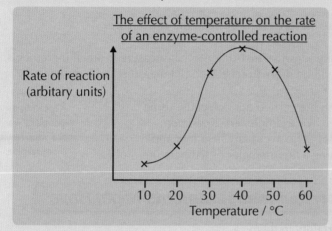

The effect of temperature on the rate of an enzyme-controlled reaction

2) A science magazine **concluded** from this data that this enzyme works best at **40 °C**.

3) The data **doesn't** support this. The enzyme **could** work best at 42 °C or 47 °C but you can't tell from the data because **increases** of **10 °C** at a time were used. The rate of reaction at in-between temperatures **wasn't** measured.

4) All you know is that it's faster at **40 °C** than at any of the other temperatures tested.

5) The experiment **ONLY** gives information about this particular enzyme-controlled reaction. You can't conclude that **all** enzyme-controlled reactions happen faster at a particular temperature — only this one. And you can't say for sure that doing the experiment at, say, a different constant pressure, wouldn't give a different optimum temperature.

## Practice Questions

Q1 How do you treat anomalous results when calculating averages? And when drawing lines of best fit?

Q2 What is negative correlation?

**Exam Question**

Q1 A student carried out an investigation to study how the rate of a reaction changed with temperature. He plotted his results on the graph shown on the right.

a) Give the temperatures at which any anomalous results occurred. [1 mark]

b) What type of correlation is there between temperature and rate of reaction? [1 mark]

c) Which of the following statements are appropriate conclusions to draw from this experiment?

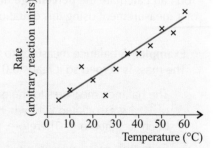

1. The rate of the reaction is highest at 60 °C.
2. Increasing the temperature causes the rate of the reaction to increase.
3. Between 5 °C and 60 °C, the rate of the reaction increased as temperature increased.

A   Statements 1, 2 and 3.     B   Statements 2 and 3 only.

C   Statement 3 only.     D   Statement 2 only. [1 mark]

## Correlation Street — my favourite programme...

*Watch out for bias when you're reading about the results of scientific studies. People often tell you what they want you to know. So a bottled water company might say that studies have shown that chlorinated tap water can cause cancer, without mentioning any of the doubts in the results. After all, they want to persuade you to buy their drinks.*

# Evaluating Experiments

*So you've planned an experiment, collected your data (no less than three times, mind you) and put it all onto a lovely graph. Now it's time to sit back, relax and... work out everything you did wrong. That's science, I'm afraid.*

## You Need to Look **Critically** at Your Experiment

There are a few terms that'll come in handy when you're evaluating how convincing your results are...

1) **Valid results** — Valid results answer the **original question**. For example, if you haven't **controlled all the variables** your results won't be valid, because you won't be testing just the thing you wanted to.

2) **Accurate results** — Accurate results are those that are **really close** to the **true** answer.

3) **Precise results** — These are results taken using **sensitive instruments** that measure in **small increments**, e.g. pH measured with a meter (pH 7.692) will be **more precise** than pH measured with paper (pH 7).

4) **Reliable experiments** — Reliable experiments are carried out **correctly**, using **suitable equipment** and with **minimal errors**. For example, an experiment measuring a temperature change would be set up to avoid any heat loss and temperature changes would be measured using a thermometer or temperature probe.

*Repeating an experiment won't make your results more reliable.*

## *Uncertainty* is the Amount of *Error* Your *Measurements* Might Have

1) Any measurements you make will have **uncertainty** in them due to the limits to the **precision** of the equipment you used.

2) If you use a weighing scale that measures to the nearest 0.1 g, then the **true** weight of any substance you weigh could be up to 0.05 g **more than** or **less than** your reading. Your measurement has an **uncertainty** (or error) of ±0.05 g in either direction.

3) The ± sign tells you the **range** in which the true value could lie. The range can also be called the **margin of error**.

4) For any piece of equipment you use, the uncertainty will be **half** the **smallest increment** the equipment can measure, in either direction.

5) If you're **combining measurements**, you'll need to combine their **uncertainties**. For example, if you're calculating a temperature change by measuring an initial and a final temperature, the **total** uncertainty for the temperature change will be the uncertainties for both measurements added together.

## The **Percentage Uncertainty** in a Result Should be Calculated

You can calculate the **percentage uncertainty** of a measurement using this equation:

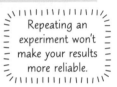

$$\text{percentage uncertainty} = \frac{\text{uncertainty}}{\text{reading}} \times 100$$

*You may see percentage uncertainty called percentage error.*

**Example:** A balance measures to the nearest 0.2 g, and is used to measure the **mass** of a substance. The mass is zeroed so it reads 0.0 g. Then, 18.4 g of a solid are weighed. Calculate the percentage uncertainty.

The balance measures to the nearest 0.2 g, so **each reading** has an uncertainty of ±0.1 g. There is an error of ±0.1 g associated with when the balance reads 0.0 g (when it's zeroed), and when the mass of solid has been weighed out. Therefore, there are two sources of error, so the **total uncertainty** is 0.1 × 2 = 0.2 g.

So for this mass measurement, percentage uncertainty $= \frac{0.2}{18.4} \times 100 = \mathbf{1.1\%}$

*This stuff's really important, so there are more examples on pages 66 and 67.*

## You Can **Minimise** the **Percentage Uncertainty**

1) One obvious way to **reduce errors** in your measurements is to use the most **precise equipment** available to you.

2) A bit of clever **planning** can also improve your results. If you measure out **5 cm³** of liquid in a measuring cylinder that has increments of 0.1 cm³ then the percentage uncertainty is (0.05 ÷ 5) × 100 = **1%**.
But if you measure **10 cm³** of liquid in the same measuring cylinder the percentage uncertainty is (0.05 ÷ 10) × 100 = **0.5%**. Hey presto — you've just halved the percentage uncertainty.
So the percentage uncertainty can be reduced by planning an experiment so you use a **larger volume** of liquid.

3) The general principle is that the **smaller** the measurement, the **larger** the percentage uncertainty.

# Evaluating Experiments

## Errors Can Be Systematic or Random

1) **Systematic errors** are the same every time you repeat the experiment. They may be caused by the **set-up** or **equipment** you used. For example, if the 10.00 cm$^3$ pipette you used to measure out a sample for titration actually only measured 9.95 cm$^3$, your sample would have been about 0.05 cm$^3$ too small **every time** you repeated the experiment.

2) **Random errors** vary — they're what make the results a bit **different** each time you repeat an experiment. The errors when you make a reading from a burette are random. You have to estimate or round the level when it's between two marks — so sometimes your figure will be **above** the real one, and sometimes it will be **below**.

3) **Repeating an experiment** and finding the mean of your results helps to deal with **random errors**. The results that are a bit high will be **cancelled out** by the ones that are a bit low. But repeating your results won't get rid of any **systematic errors**, so your results won't get more **accurate**.

This should be a photo of a scientist. I don't know what happened — it's a random error...

## Think About How the Experiment Could Be Improved

In your evaluation you need to think about anything that you could have done differently to improve your results. Here are some things to think about...

1) **Whether your method gives you valid results.**
   - Will the data you collected answer the question your experiment aimed to answer?
   - Did you control all your variables?

2) **How you could improve the accuracy of your results.**
   - Was the apparatus you used on an appropriate scale for your measurements?
   - Could you use more precise equipment to reduce the random errors and uncertainty of your results?

3) **Whether your results are repeatable and reproducible.**
   - Did you repeat the experiment, and were the results you got similar?

There's more about repeatable and reproducible results on page 124.

## Practice Questions

Q1 What's the difference between the accuracy and precision of results?

Q2 What's the uncertainty of a single reading on a balance that reads to the nearest 0.1 g?

Q3 How do you calculate percentage uncertainty?

Q4 Give two ways of reducing percentage uncertainty.

Q5 How can you reduce the random errors in your experiments?

**Exam Question**

Q1 A student carried out an experiment to determine the temperature change in the reaction between citric acid and sodium bicarbonate using the following method:

1. Measure out 25.0 cm$^3$ of 1.00 mol dm$^{-3}$ citric acid solution in a measuring cylinder and put it in a polystyrene cup.
2. Weigh out 2.10 g sodium bicarbonate and add it to the citric acid solution.
3. Place a thermometer in the solution and measure the temperature change over one minute.

a) The measuring cylinder the student uses measures to the nearest 0.5 cm$^3$.
   What is the percentage uncertainty of the student's measurement? [1 mark]

b) The student's result is different to the documented value. How could you change the method to give a more accurate measurement for the change in temperature of the complete reaction? [2 marks]

## Repeat your results: Your results, your results, your results, your results...

*So there you have it. All you need to know about planning, carrying out and analysing experiments. Watch out for errors creeping in to your experimental methods. It may not seem obvious that there's an error when you're taking a measurement that's zero (e.g. on a balance or a burette), so remember to include this when calculating errors.*

# Answers

## Topic 1 — Atomic Structure and the Periodic Table

### Page 5 — The Atom

1 a) Similarity — They've all got the same number of protons/electrons *[1 mark]*.
Difference — They all have different numbers of neutrons *[1 mark]*.
  b) 1 proton, 1 neutron (2 – 1), 1 electron *[1 mark]*.
  c) $^3_1$H *[1 mark]*

2 a) i) Same number of electrons. $^{32}S^{2-}$ has 16 + 2 = 18 electrons. $^{40}$Ar has 18 electrons too *[1 mark]*.
    ii) Same number of protons. Each has 16 protons *[1 mark]*.
    iii) Same number of neutrons. $^{40}$Ar has 40 – 18 = 22 neutrons. $^{42}$Ca has 42 – 20 = 22 neutrons *[1 mark]*.
  b) **A** and **C** *[1 mark]*. They have the same number of protons but different numbers of neutrons *[1 mark]*.
    *It doesn't matter that they have a different number of electrons because they are still the same element.*

3 H has 1 proton, O has 8 protons and C has 6 protons, so the total number of protons in $C_3H_7OH$ is (3 × 6) + (8 × 1) + 8 = **34**.
H has 1 electron, O has 8 electrons and C has 6 electrons, so the total number of electrons in $C_3H_7OH$ is (3 × 6) + (8 × 1) + 8 = **34** *[1 mark for correct numbers of protons and electrons]*.
*For neutral molecules, the number of electrons is equal to the number of protons.*
H has 1 – 1 = 0 neutrons, O has 16 – 8 = 8 neutrons and C has 12 – 6 = 6 neutrons.
So $C_3H_7OH$ has (3 × 6) + (8 × 0) + 8 = **26** neutrons *[1 mark]*.

### Page 7 — Relative Mass

1 a) First multiply each relative abundance by the relative mass —
120.8 × 63 = 7610.4, 54.0 × 65 = 3510.0
Next add up the products: 7610.4 + 3510.0 = 11 120.4 *[1 mark]*
Now divide by the total abundance (120.8 + 54.0 = 174.8)
$$A_r(Cu) = \frac{11\,120.4}{174.8} = \textbf{63.6}\ \textit{[1 mark]}$$
*You can check your answer by seeing if $A_r(Cu)$ is in between 63 and 65 (the lowest and highest relative isotopic masses).*
  b) A sample of copper is a mixture of 2 isotopes in different abundances *[1 mark]*. The relative atomic mass is an average mass of these isotopes which isn't a whole number *[1 mark]*.

2 *You use pretty much the same method here as for question 1 a).*
93.1 × 39 = 3630.9, 0.120 × 40 = 4.8, 6.77 × 41 = 277.57
3630.9 + 4.8 + 277.57 = 3913.27 *[1 mark]*
*This time you divide by 100 because they're percentages.*
$$A_r(K) = \frac{3913.27}{100} = \textbf{39.1}\ \textit{[1 mark]}$$
*Again check your answer's between the lowest and highest relative isotopic masses, 39 and 41. $A_r(K)$ is closer to 39 because most of the sample (93.1 %) is made up of this isotope.*

### Page 9 — More on Relative Mass

1 a)

|         | $^{16}$O | $^{18}$O |
|---------|----------|----------|
| $^{16}$O | $^{16}$O – $^{16}$O: 0.98 × 0.98 = **0.9604** | $^{16}$O – $^{18}$O: 0.98 × 0.02 = **0.0196** |
| $^{18}$O | $^{18}$O – $^{16}$O: 0.02 × 0.98 = **0.0196** | $^{18}$O – $^{18}$O: 0.02 × 0.02 = **0.0004** |

*[2 marks — 2 marks for a correct abundances for all molecules, 1 mark if three correct abundances]*
$^{16}$O – $^{18}$O and $^{18}$O – $^{16}$O are the same, so the relative abundance is 0.0196 + 0.0196 = **0.0392** *[1 mark]*.
  b) Divide each by 0.0004 to get the simplified relative abundances.

| Molecule | $M_r$ | Relative Abundance |
|----------|-------|--------------------|
| $^{16}$O – $^{16}$O | 16 + 16 = **32** | 0.9604 ÷ 0.0004 = **2401** |
| $^{16}$O – $^{18}$O | 16 + 18 = **34** | 0.0392 ÷ 0.0004 = **98** |
| $^{18}$O – $^{18}$O | 18 + 18 = **36** | 0.0004 ÷ 0.0004 = **1** |

*[1 mark for correct relative abundances, 1 mark for correct relative molecular masses]*
So the mass spectrum for the sample of $O_2$ will be:

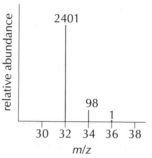

*[1 mark for correctly labelled axes, 1 mark for correctly drawn peaks at correct m/z values, with approximately correct heights]*

2 a) 100% – 94.20% – 0.012% = **5.788%** *[1 mark]*
  b) 39.1 = ((39 × 94.20) + (40 × 0.012) + (X × 5.788)) ÷ 100 *[1 mark]*
39.1 = (3674.28 + (X × 5.788)) ÷ 100
3910 – 3674.28 = X × 5.788.   So, X = 40.726... = **41** *[1 mark]*

3 a) 58 *[1 mark]*
  b) E.g.

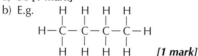

*[1 mark]*

### Page 11 — Electronic Structure

1 a) K atom: $1s^2\ 2s^2\ 2p^6\ 3s^2\ 3p^6\ 4s^1$ or [Ar] $4s^1$ *[1 mark]*
$K^+$ ion: $1s^2\ 2s^2\ 2p^6\ 3s^2\ 3p^6$ or [Ar] *[1 mark]*
  b) $1s^2\ 2s^2\ 2p^4$ *[1 mark]*

2 a) Germanium ($1s^2\ 2s^2\ 2p^6\ 3s^2\ 3p^6\ 3d^{10}\ 4s^2\ 4p^2$ or [Ar] $3d^{10}\ 4s^2\ 4p^2$) *[1 mark]*.
*The 4p sub-shell is partly filled, so it must be a p block element.*
  b) Ar (atom) *[1 mark]*, $K^+$ (positive ion) *[1 mark]*, $Cl^-$ (negative ion) *[1 mark]*.
*You also could have suggested $Ca^{2+}$, $S^{2-}$ or $P^{3-}$.*
  c) $1s^2\ 2s^2\ 2p^6\ 3s^2\ 3p^6\ 3d^{10}\ 4s^1$ *[1 mark]*

### Page 13 — Atomic Emission Spectra

1 a) The movement of electrons/an electron *[1 mark]* from higher to lower energy levels *[1 mark]*.
  b) Line E (because it is at the highest frequency) *[1 mark]*.
  c) Because the energy levels get closer together with increasing energy *[1 mark]*.

2 a) Energy is released/emitted *[1 mark]*.
  b) The lines represent the frequencies of light that are emitted/released when an electron drops from a higher energy level to a lower one *[1 mark]*.
  c) Emission spectra show that specific amounts of energy are emitted when electrons drop down from higher energy levels to lower energy levels *[1 mark]*. In-between amounts of energy are never emitted, which suggests that electrons only exist at very specific energy levels (they're discrete) *[1 mark]*.
  d) E.g. ionisation energy *[1 mark]*

### Page 15 — Ionisation Energies

1 a) $C_{(g)} \rightarrow C^+_{(g)} + e^-$
Correct equation *[1 mark]*. Both state symbols showing gaseous state *[1 mark]*.
  b) First ionisation energy increases as nuclear charge increases *[1 mark]*.
  c) As the nuclear charge increases there is a stronger force of attraction between the nucleus and the electron *[1 mark]* and so more energy is required to remove the electron *[1 mark]*.

# Answers

2 a) Group 3 *[1 mark]*
   There are three electrons removed before the first big jump in energy.
b) The electrons are being removed from an increasingly positive ion *[1 mark]* so there's less repulsion amongst the remaining electrons so they're held more strongly by the nucleus *[1 mark]*.
c) When an electron is removed from a different shell there is a big increase in the energy required (since that shell is closer to the nucleus) *[1 mark]*.
d) There are 3 shells *[1 mark]*.
   You can tell there are 3 shells because there are 2 big jumps in energy. There is always one more shell than big jumps.

## *Page 18 — Periodicity*

1 a) C *[1 mark]*   b) B *[1 mark]*   c) C *[1 mark]*
2 a) Si has a giant covalent lattice structure *[1 mark]* consisting of lots of very strong covalent bonds which require a lot of energy to break *[1 mark]*.
b) Sulfur ($S_8$) has more electrons than phosphorus ($P_4$) *[1 mark]* which results in stronger London forces of attraction between molecules *[1 mark]*.

# *Topic 2 — Bonding and Structure*

## *Page 21 — Ionic Bonding*

1 a) Giant ionic lattice *[1 mark]*.
b) Sodium chloride will have a high melting point *[1 mark]*, because a lot of energy is required to overcome the strong electrostatic attraction between the positive and negative ions *[1 mark]*.
c) Sodium bromide would have a lower melting point than sodium chloride *[1 mark]*. Bromide ions have one more electron shell than chloride ions, so have a larger ionic radius. This means the ions in sodium bromide can't pack as closely together as the ions in sodium chloride *[1 mark]*. Ionic bonding gets weaker as the distance between the ions increases, so the ionic bonding in sodium bromide is weaker than in sodium chloride / less energy is required to break the ionic bonds in sodium bromide than sodium chloride *[1 mark]* (so the ionic melting point is lower).

2 a)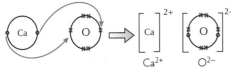

   calcium ion   oxide ion
   *[2 marks — 1 mark for correct electron arrangement, 1 mark for correct charges]*
b) In a solid, ions are held in place by strong ionic bonds *[1 mark]*. When molten, the ions are mobile *[1 mark]* and so carry charge (and hence electricity) through the substance *[1 mark]*.
3 Sodium loses one (outer) electron to form $Na^+$ *[1 mark]*. Fluorine gains one electron to form $F^-$ *[1 mark]*. Electrostatic forces of attraction between oppositely charged ions forms an ionic lattice *[1 mark]*.
4 C *[1 mark]*

## *Page 23 — Covalent Bonding*

1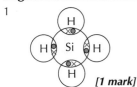
   *[1 mark]*
   Because Si is in the same group as C, it will often form similar compounds.
2 a)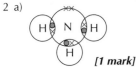
   *[1 mark]*

b)
   *[1 mark]*
c)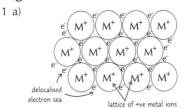
   *[1 mark for all bonds shown correctly, 1 mark for correct charges]*

3 a) An N–N bond is longer than an N=N bond *[1 mark]* as there are four shared electrons in an N=N bond and only two shared electrons in an N–N bond, meaning the electron density between the two nitrogen atoms in the nitrogen double bond is greater than in the nitrogen single bond *[1 mark]*. This increases the strength of the electrostatic attraction between the positive nuclei and the negative electrons in the N=N bond, making the bond shorter *[1 mark]*.
b)
   *[1 mark]*
c) The bond enthalpy of the bond in $N_2$ would be larger than the bond enthalpy of a nitrogen single bond or a nitrogen double bond *[1 mark]*. The bond in $N_2$ is a nitrogen triple bond. There are six shared electrons in this bond, leading to a higher electron density than in N–N or N=N bonds (where there are two and four shared electrons respectively) *[1 mark]*. This means there's a stronger electrostatic attraction between the two nitrogen nuclei and the bonding electrons, so stronger covalent bonding *[1 mark]*.

## *Page 25 — Shapes of Molecules*

1 a) i)
   *[1 mark]*
   shape: trigonal pyramidal *[1 mark]*,
   bond angle: 107° (accept between 106° and 108°) *[1 mark]*.
   ii) F   F
       B   120°
       F   *[1 mark]*
   shape: trigonal planar *[1 mark]*
   bond angle: 120° exactly *[1 mark]*.
b) $BCl_3$ has three electron pairs only around B. *[1 mark]*
   $NCl_3$ has four electron pairs around N *[1 mark]*, including one lone pair. *[1 mark]*
2 Atom A:   shape: trigonal planar,   bond angle: 120° *[1 mark]*
  Atom B:   shape: tetrahedral,   bond angle: 109.5° *[1 mark]*
  Atom C:   shape: non-linear/bent,   bond angle: 104.5° *[1 mark]*

## *Page 27 — Giant Covalent and Metallic Structures*

1 a)
   delocalised electron sea
   lattice of +ve metal ions   *[1 mark]*
   Metallic bonding results from the attraction between positive metal ions and a sea of delocalised electrons between them *[1 mark]*.
b) Calcium ($Ca^{2+}$) has two delocalised electrons per atom, while potassium ($K^+$) has only one delocalised electron per atom. So calcium has more delocalised electrons and therefore stronger metallic bonding *[1 mark]*.

# Answers

2 Silicon dioxide has a giant covalent lattice structure *[1 mark]* so, to melt it, lots of strong covalent bonds must be broken, which requires lots of energy/high temperatures *[1 mark]*.

3 Graphite consists of sheets of carbon atoms, where each carbon atom is bonded to three others *[1 mark]*. This means that each atom has one free electron not involved in bonds, and it is these free electrons that allow graphite to conduct electricity *[1 mark]*.

4 Copper is metallically bonded and so delocalised electrons are free to move (carry electric current) *[1 mark]*. Oxygen and sulfur form copper oxide/sulfide, fixing some electrons (as anions) *[1 mark]*. This prevents them from moving and carrying charge *[1 mark]*.

5 a) Giant covalent *[1 mark]*
   b) Any two from: high melting point / electrical non-conductor (insulator) / insoluble / good thermal conductor. *[1 mark for each]*

## Page 29 — Electronegativity and Polarisation

1 a) The ability of an atom to attract the bonding electrons in a covalent bond *[1 mark]*.
   b) Electronegativity increases across a period and decreases down a group *[1 mark]*.
   c) A *[1 mark]*

2 a) i) 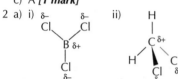 ii)

*[2 marks each — in each part, 1 mark for correct shape, 1 mark for correct partial charges]*

   b) The polar bonds in $BCl_3$ are arranged so that they cancel each other out, so the molecule has no overall dipole *[1 mark]*. $CH_2Cl_2$ does have an overall dipole because the polar bonds are not orientated so they are pointing in opposite directions so they don't cancel each other out *[1 mark]*.

To help you decide if the molecule's polar or not, imagine the atoms are having a tug of war with the electrons. If they're all pulling the same amount in different directions, the electrons aren't going to go anywhere.

## Page 31 — Intermolecular Forces

1 The boiling point of a substance depends on the energy needed to overcome the intermolecular forces between the molecules *[1 mark]*. Pentane is the most linear molecule so it has the greatest surface contact, and so has the strongest London forces. This gives it the highest boiling point *[1 mark]*. The surface contact of 2-methylbutane is less than that of pentane and that of 2,2-dimethylpropane is smaller still, meaning that these substances have weaker London forces and consequently lower boiling points *[1 mark]*.

2 London forces/instantaneous dipole-induced dipole bonds and permanent dipole-permanent dipole bonds *[1 mark]*.

3 NO has a higher boiling point. Both molecules have a similar number of electrons, so the strength of the London forces will be similar *[1 mark]*. NO is a polar molecule, so can also form permanent dipole-permanent dipole bonds. This means there are stronger intermolecular forces between molecules in NO than in $N_2$, which can only form London forces, so NO has a higher boiling point *[1 mark]*.

## Page 33 — Hydrogen Bonding

1 a) Water contains hydrogen covalently bonded to oxygen, so it is able to form hydrogen bonds *[1 mark]*. These hydrogen bonds are stronger than the other types of intermolecular forces, so more energy is needed to break them *[1 mark]*.
   b)

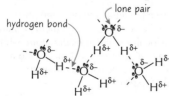

*[2 marks — 1 mark for correctly drawn molecules showing partial charges and lone pairs, 1 mark for at least 3 correctly drawn hydrogen bonds]*

2 a) i) Ammonia will have the higher boiling point *[1 mark]*.
      ii) Water will have the higher boiling point *[1 mark]*.
      iii) Propan-1-ol will have the higher boiling point *[1 mark]*.
   b) The molecules of ammonia, water and propan-1-ol can form hydrogen bonds *[1 mark]*. These are stronger/take more energy to overcome than the intermolecular forces between the molecules of the other compounds *[1 mark]*.

3 Ethane-1,2-diol has stronger intermolecular forces because there are two alcohol groups, twice as many as in ethanol. Therefore ethane-1,2-diol can form twice as many hydrogen bonds as ethanol *[1 mark]*.

## Page 35 — Solubility

1 a) i) Hydrogen bonds *[1 mark]* form between the alcohol and water molecules *[1 mark]*. The (hydrogen) bonds between water molecules are stronger *[1 mark]* than bonds that would form between water and the halogenoalkane molecules *[1 mark]*. For the last two marks, you could also say that the halogenoalkanes do not contain strong enough dipoles to form hydrogen bonds with water.
      ii)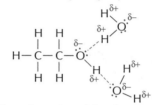

*[2 marks — 1 mark for the two substances with relevant δ+ and δ– marked correctly, 1 mark for showing at least one correctly drawn hydrogen bond between propan-1-ol and a molecule of water]*

   b) $K^+$ ions are attracted to the δ– ends of the water molecules *[1 mark]* and $I^-$ ions are attracted to the δ+ ends *[1 mark]*. This overcomes the ionic bonds in the lattice/the ions are pulled away from the lattice *[1 mark]*, and surrounded by water molecules *[1 mark]*, forming hydrated ions:

*[1 mark]*

2 a) Try to dissolve the substance in water *[1 mark]* and hexane (or other non-polar solvent) *[1 mark]*. If X is non-polar, it is likely to dissolve in hexane, but not in water *[1 mark]*.
   Remember 'like dissolves like' — in other words, substances usually dissolve best in solvents that have similar intermolecular forces.
   b) X and hexane have London forces/instantaneous dipole-induced dipole bonds between their molecules *[1 mark]* and form similar bonds with each other *[1 mark]*. Water has hydrogen bonds *[1 mark]* which are much stronger than the bonds it could form with a non-polar compound *[1 mark]*.

## Page 37 — Predicting Structures and Properties

1 A = ionic *[1 mark]*, B = simple molecular/covalent *[1 mark]*, C = metallic *[1 mark]*, D = giant covalent *[1 mark]*.

2 Iodine is a simple molecular substance *[1 mark]*. To melt or boil iodine, you only need to overcome the weak intermolecular forces holding the molecules together, which doesn't need much energy *[1 mark]*. Graphite is a giant covalent substance *[1 mark]*. Graphite will remain solid unless you can overcome the strong covalent bonds between atoms, which needs a lot of energy *[1 mark]*.

3 B *[1 mark]*

# Answers

## Topic 3 — Redox I

### Page 39 — Oxidation Numbers

1 a) 0   b) +4   c) +6   d) –2   *[4 marks — 1 mark for each]*
2 a) i) +1 *[1 mark]*          ii) –1 *[1 mark]*
  b) +4 *[1 mark]*
  The oxidation number of combined oxygen is –2, so the total charge from the oxygens in $Na_2SO_3$ is $(-2 \times 3) = -6$. Sodium forms ions with a +1 charge, so the total charge from sodium in the compound is $(2 \times +1) = +2$. The contribution to the charge from non-sodium ions is therefore: $-6 + 2 = -4$. The overall charge on the compound is O, so the total charge from sulfur ion/the oxidation number of sulfur must be +4 (since $-4 + 4 = O$).

### Page 41 — Redox Reactions

1 a) Oxidation is the loss of electrons *[1 mark]*.
  b) Oxygen is being reduced *[1 mark]*.   $O_2 + 4e^- \rightarrow 2O^{2-}$ *[1 mark]*
2 a) An oxidising agent accepts electrons and gets reduced *[1 mark]*.
  b) $2In + 3Cl_2 \rightarrow 2InCl_3$ *[2 marks — 1 mark for correct reactants and products, 1 mark for correct balancing]*
  To do this question, you'll have to write out the half-equation for the oxidation of In first. It's $In \rightarrow In^{3+} + 3e^-$.
3 In a disproportionation reaction, an element in a single species is simultaneously oxidised and reduced *[1 mark]*. In the reaction shown, oxygen has an oxidation state of –1 in $H_2O_2$/hydrogen peroxide *[1 mark]*. In the reactants, oxygen has an oxidation state of –2 in $H_2O$ (it's been reduced) and an oxidation state of 0 in $O_2$ (it's been oxidised) *[1 mark]* (so oxygen's been both oxidised and reduced).
4 $VO^{2+} + 2H^+ + e^- \rightarrow V^{3+} + H_2O$ *[1 mark]*
  $Sn^{2+} \rightarrow Sn^{4+} + 2e^-$ *[1 mark]*
  $2VO^{2+} + 4H^+ + Sn^{2+} \rightarrow 2V^{3+} + 2H_2O + Sn^{4+}$ *[1 mark]*

## Topic 4 — Inorganic Chemistry and the Periodic Table

### Page 43 — Group 2

1 a) B *[1 mark]*
  b) Calcium *[1 mark]*. Barium has more electron shells than calcium, meaning that the outer electrons are further away from the nucleus and more shielded by inner shells *[1 mark]*, reducing the strength of the attraction between the outer electrons and the nucleus *[1 mark]*. This makes it easier to remove outer electrons, resulting in barium having a lower combined first and second ionisation energy *[1 mark]*.
  c) $Ca_{(s)} + Cl_{2(g)} \rightarrow CaCl_{2(s)}$ *[1 mark]*
2 a) $Mg(OH)_2 + 2HCl \rightarrow MgCl_2 + 2H_2O$
  *[1 mark for correct reactants and products, and 1 mark if equation correctly balanced]*
  b) $CaO + H_2O \rightarrow Ca^{2+} + 2OH^-$ / $CaO + H_2O \rightarrow Ca(OH)_2$
  *[1 mark for correct reactants and products, plus 1 mark if equation correctly balanced]*

### Page 45 — Group 1 and 2 Compounds

1 a) $CaCO_{3(s)} \rightarrow CaO_{(s)} + CO_{2(g)}$
  *[1 mark for correct equation, and 1 mark for state symbols]*
  b) Barium carbonate is more thermally stable *[1 mark]*. This is because barium has a larger ionic radius than calcium/has a lower charge density than calcium, so it has weaker polarising power *[1 mark]*. The weaker polarising power of the barium ion causes less distortion of the carbonate ion *[1 mark]* (making it more thermally stable).
  You'd also get the marks if you used the reverse argument to explain why $CaCO_3$ is less thermally stable.

2 a) $2NaNO_{3(s)} \rightarrow 2NaNO_{2(s)} + O_{2(g)}$ *[1 mark]*
  b) E.g. $O_2$ gas relights a glowing splint *[1 mark]*.
  c) magnesium nitrate, sodium nitrate, potassium nitrate *[1 mark]* Group 2 nitrates decompose more easily than Group 1 as they have a +2 charge on their cations, compared to the 1+ charge on Group 1 cations. The greater the charge on the cation, the less stable the nitrate compound *[1 mark]*. The further down the group, the more stable the nitrate as the cations increase in size down the group, and the larger the cation, the less distortion to the nitrate anion *[1 mark]*.
3 a) Energy is absorbed and electrons move to higher energy levels. *[1 mark]* Energy is released in the form of coloured light when the electrons fall back to the lower levels *[1 mark]*.
  b) caesium *[1 mark]*

### Page 47 — Halogens

1 a) $Cl_2 + 2Br^- \rightarrow 2Cl^- + Br_2$ *[1 mark]*
  b) The boiling points of the halogens increase down the group *[1 mark]*. There is an increase in electron shells (and therefore electrons) the further down the group you go, and so the London forces also increase down the group *[1 mark]*. Larger London forces make it harder to overcome the intermolecular forces, and so melting and boiling points increase down the group *[1 mark]*.
2 a) (potassium) iodide *[1 mark]*
  b) brown *[1 mark]*

### Page 49 — Reactions of Halogens

1 a) $2OH^- + Br_2 \rightarrow OBr^- + Br^- + H_2O$ *[1 mark]*
  b) A disproportionation reaction *[1 mark]*.
  c) $3Br_2 + 6KOH \rightarrow KBrO_3 + 5KBr + 3H_2O$
  *[1 mark for correct reactants and products, and 1 mark if equation correctly balanced]*

### Page 51 — Reactions of Halides

1 A *[1 mark]*
2 Sodium chloride — misty fumes *[1 mark]*
  $NaCl + H_2SO_4 \rightarrow NaHSO_4 + HCl$ *[1 mark]*
  Sodium bromide — misty fumes *[1 mark]*
  $NaBr + H_2SO_4 \rightarrow NaHSO_4 + HBr$ *[1 mark]*
  $2HBr + H_2SO_4 \rightarrow Br_2 + SO_2 + 2H_2O$ *[1 mark]*
  Orange/brown vapour *[1 mark]*
3 Potassium bromide reacts with sulfuric acid to produce hydrogen bromide, which is seen as misty fumes:
  $KBr + H_2SO_4 \rightarrow KHSO_4 + HBr$ *[1 mark]*
  Bromide ions are a reducing agent, and are strong enough to reduce $H_2SO_4$ as part of a redox reaction:
  $2HBr + H_2SO_4 \rightarrow Br_2 + SO_2 + 2H_2O$ *[1 mark]*.
  Potassium iodide reacts with sulfuric acid in a similar way:
  $KI + H_2SO_4 \rightarrow KHSO_4 + HI$ *[1 mark]*
  $2HI + H_2SO_4 \rightarrow I_2 + SO_{(g)} + 2H_2O$ *[1 mark]*
  But iodide ions are a stronger reducing agent than bromide ions *[1 mark]*, so go onto reduce $SO_2$ to $H_2S$:
  $6HI + SO_2 \rightarrow H_2S + 3I_2 + 2H_2O$ *[1 mark]*

### Page 53 — Tests for Ions

1 Add dilute hydrochloric acid to the solution *[1 mark]* and then test to see whether the gas given off is carbon dioxide by bubbling it through limewater. If the limewater goes cloudy, the solution contains carbonates *[1 mark]*.
2 a) C *[1 mark]*
  b) $Ba^{2+}_{(aq)} + SO_4^{2-}_{(aq)} \rightarrow BaSO_{4(s)}$ *[1 mark for correct equation, 1 mark for correct state symbols]*
3 Add some sodium hydroxide to the solution in a test tube and gently heat the mixture *[1 mark]*. Test the gas produced with a damp piece of red litmus paper. If there's ammonia given off this means there are ammonium ions in the solution. If there's ammonia present, the paper will turn blue *[1 mark]*.

# Answers

## Topic 5 — Formulae, Equations & Amounts of Substances

### Page 55 — The Mole

1   $M$ of $CaSO_4 = 40.1 + 32.1 + (4 \times 16.0) = 136.2$ g mol$^{-1}$

   number of moles $= \frac{34.05}{136.2} =$ **0.2500 moles** *[1 mark]*

2   $M$ of $CH_3COOH = (2 \times 12.0) + (4 \times 1.0) + (2 \times 16.0)$
   $= 60.0$ g mol$^{-1}$

   mass $= 60.0 \times 0.360 =$ **21.6 g** *[1 mark]*

3   $M$ of $HCl = 1.0 + 35.5 = 36.5$ g mol$^{-1}$

   mass $= 0.100 \times 36.5 = 3.65$ g *[1 mark]*

   volume of water in dm$^3 = 100 \div 1000 = 0.100$ dm$^3$

   concentration $= \frac{mass}{volume} = \frac{3.65}{0.100} =$ **36.5 g dm$^{-3}$** *[1 mark]*

4   number of moles $= 0.250 \times \frac{60.0}{1000} = 0.0150$ moles *[1 mark]*

   $M$ of $H_2SO_4 = (2 \times 1.0) + 32.1 + (4 \times 16.0) = 98.1$ g mol$^{-1}$

   mass $= 0.0150 \times 98.1 =$ **1.47 g** *[1 mark]*

5   $M$ of $AgI = 107.9 + 126.9 = 234.8$ g mol$^{-1}$

   number of moles $= \frac{1.01}{234.8} = 0.00430...$ mol *[1 mark]*

   volume of nitric acid in dm$^3 = 15.0 \div 1000 = 0.0150$ dm$^3$

   concentration $= \frac{moles}{volume} = \frac{0.00430...}{0.0150} =$ **0.287 mol dm$^{-3}$** *[1 mark]*

### Page 57 — Empirical and Molecular Formulae

1   The mass 'lost' during the experiment must have been oxygen.
   $2.80 - 2.50 = 0.300$ g oxygen was present in the oxide. *[1 mark]*
   Moles of $Cu = 2.50 \div 63.5 = 0.0394$
   Moles of $O = 0.300 \div 16.0 = 0.0188$ *[1 mark]*
   Dividing both these values by the smaller one:
   Ratio $Cu : O = (0.0394 \div 0.0188) : (0.0188 \div 0.0188)$
   $= 2.09... : 1$ *[1 mark]*
   So, rounding off, empirical formula $= Cu_2O$ *[1 mark]*

2   Assume you've got 100 g of the compound so you can turn the % straight into mass.
   No. of moles of $C = \frac{92.3}{12.0} = 7.69$ moles
   No. of moles of $H = \frac{7.70}{1.00} = 7.70$ moles *[1 mark]*
   Divide both by the smallest number, in this case 7.69.
   So ratio $C : H = 1 : 1$
   So, the empirical formula $= CH$ *[1 mark]*
   The empirical mass $= 12.0 + 1.0 = 13.0$
   No. of empirical units in molecule $= \frac{78.0}{13.0} = 6$
   So the molecular formula $= C_6H_6$ *[1 mark]*

3   The magnesium is burning, so it's reacting with oxygen and the product is magnesium oxide.
   First work out the number of moles of each element.
   No. of moles $Mg = \frac{1.20}{24.0} = 0.0500$ moles
   Mass of O is everything that isn't Mg: $2.00 - 1.20 = 0.800$ g
   No. of moles $O = \frac{0.800}{16.0} = 0.0500$ moles *[1 mark]*
   Ratio $Mg : O = 0.0500 : 0.0500$
   Divide both by the smallest number, in this case 0.0500.
   So ratio $Mg : O = 1 : 1$
   So the empirical formula is **MgO** *[1 mark]*

4   First calculate the no. of moles of each product and then the mass of C and H:
   No. of moles of $CO_2 = \frac{33.0}{44.0} = 0.0750$ moles
   Mass of $C = 0.750 \times 12.0 = 9.00$ g
   No. of moles of $H_2O = \frac{10.8}{18.0} = 0.600$ moles
   0.600 moles $H_2O = 1.20$ moles H
   Mass of $H = 1.20 \times 1.0 = 1.20$ g *[1 mark]*
   Organic acids contain C, H and O, so the rest of the mass must be O.
   Mass of $O = 19.8 - (9.00 + 1.20) = 9.60$ g
   No. of moles of $O = \frac{9.60}{16.0} = 0.600$ moles *[1 mark]*

Mole ratio $= C : H : O = 0.750 : 1.20 : 0.600$
Divide by smallest   $1.25 : 2 : 1$
The carbon part of the ratio isn't a whole number, so you have to multiply them all up until it is. As its fraction is ¼, multiply them all by 4.
So, mole ratio $= C : H : O = 5 : 8 : 4$
Empirical formula $= C_5H_8O_4$ *[1 mark]*
Empirical mass $= (12.0 \times 5) + (1.0 \times 8) + (16.0 \times 4) = 132$ g
This is the same as what we're told the molecular mass is, so the molecular formula is also $C_5H_8O_4$ *[1 mark]*.

### Page 59 — Chemical Equations

1   On the LHS, you need 2 each of K and I, so use 2KI
   This makes the final equation:
   $2KI + Pb(NO_3)_2 \rightarrow PbI_2 + 2KNO_3$ *[1 mark]*
   In this equation, the $NO_3$ group remains unchanged, so it makes balancing much easier if you treat it as one indivisible lump.

2   The equation for the reaction is: $C_2H_4 + HCl \rightarrow C_2H_5Cl$
   $M$ of $C_2H_5Cl = (2 \times 12.0) + (5 \times 1.0) + (1 \times 35.5) = 64.5$ g mol$^{-1}$
   *[1 mark]*
   Number of moles of $C_2H_5Cl = \frac{258}{64.5} = 4.00$ moles *[1 mark]*
   From the equation, 1 mole $C_2H_5Cl$ is made from 1 mole $C_2H_4$ so,
   4 moles $C_2H_5Cl$ is made from 4 moles $C_2H_4$ *[1 mark]*.
   $M$ of $C_2H_4 = (2 \times 12.0) + (4 \times 1.0) = 28.0$ g mol$^{-1}$
   so, the mass of 4 moles $C_2H_4 = 4 \times 28.0 =$ **112 g** *[1 mark]*

3   $Ag^+_{(aq)} + Cl^-_{(aq)} \rightarrow AgCl_{(s)}$ *[2 marks — 1 mark for correct equation, 1 mark for correct state symbols]*
   The question tells you that the reaction is a precipitation reaction, and that magnesium nitrate solution is formed. So the other product, silver chloride, must be the solid precipitate.

### Page 61 — Calculations with Gases

1   Moles of $Cl_2 = \frac{1.28}{35.5 \times 2} = 0.0180...$ moles *[1 mark]*
   Rearranging $pV = nRT$ to find $T$ gives $T = \frac{pV}{nR}$.
   So, $T = \frac{175 \times (98.6 \times 10^{-3})}{0.0180 \times 8.314} =$ **115 K** *[1 mark]*

2   $M$ of $C_3H_8 = (3 \times 12.0) + (8 \times 1.0) = 44.0$ g mol$^{-1}$
   No. of moles of $C_3H_8 = \frac{88}{44.0} = 2.0$ moles *[1 mark]*
   At r.t.p. 1 mole of gas occupies 24 dm$^3$, so 2.0 moles of gas occupies $2.0 \times 24 =$ **48 dm$^3$** *[1 mark]*
   You could also use the equation $pV = nRT$ to answer this question, where at r.t.p, $T = 293$ K, and $p = 101\ 300$ Pa. In this case, your answer would be
   $V = \frac{nRT}{p} = \frac{2.0 \times 8.31 \times 293}{101300} = 0.048$ m$^3 = 48$ dm$^3$.

3   Start by writing the balanced equation for the combustion of butane:
   $C_4H_{10} + 6½O_2 \rightarrow 4CO_2 + 5H_2O$ *[1 mark]*
   So, moles of $O_2$ required $= 3.50 \times 10^{-2} \times 6.5 = 0.2275$ mol
   At room temperature and pressure, 1 mole of gas occupies 24 dm$^3$.
   So $0.2275 \times 24 =$ **5.46 dm$^3$** *[1 mark]*.

4   $MgCO_3 \rightarrow MgO + CO_2$
   1 mole of $MgCO_3$ produces 1 mole of $CO_2$.
   At r.t.p., 6.00 dm$^3$ of $CO_2 = 6.00 \div 24.0 = 0.250$ mol *[1 mark]*.
   So 0.250 mol of $CO_2$ is produced by 0.250 mol of $MgCO_3$.
   $M_r$ of $MgCO_3 = 24.3 + 12.0 + (3 \times 16.0) = 84.3$
   $0.250$ mol of $MgCO_3 = 84.3 \times 0.250 =$ **21.1 g** *[1 mark]*

### Page 63 — Acid-Base Titrations

1   Moles $= \frac{Concentration \times Volume}{1000} = \frac{0.500 \times 200}{1000} = 0.100$ moles
   *[1 mark]*
   Mass $= $ moles $\times$ molar mass
   $= 0.100 \times [(3 \times 1.0) + 14.0 + 32.1 + (16.0 \times 3)]$
   $= 0.100 \times 97.1 =$ **9.71 g** *[1 mark]*

# Answers

**2**  *A maximum of two marks can be awarded for structure and reasoning of the written response:*
  **2 marks:** The answer is constructed logically, and displays clear reasoning and links between points throughout.
  **1 mark:** The answer is mostly logical, with some reasoning and links between points.
  **0 marks:** The answer has no structure and no links between points.
  **Here are some points your answer may include:**
  Indicators change colour when the solution reaches a particular pH to mark an end point. They are used in acid/alkali titrations to mark the end point of the reaction. Indicators used in titrations need to change colour quickly over a very small pH range. A few drops of indicator solution are added to the analyte. The analyte/indicator solution can be placed on a white surface to make a colour change easy to see. Methyl orange and phenolphthalein are both good indicators for titrations as they quickly change colour when the solution turns from alkali to acid. Universal indicator is a poor indicator to use for titrations as its colour changes gradually over a wide pH range.
  *[4 marks — 4 marks if 6 points mentioned covering all areas of the question, 3 marks if 4-5 points covered, 2 marks if 2-3 points covered, 1 mark if 1 point covered]*

## Page 65 — Titration Calculations

**1**  First write down what you know:
  $$CH_3COOH + NaOH \rightarrow CH_3COONa + H_2O$$
  $25.4 \text{ cm}^3 \quad 14.6 \text{ cm}^3$
  $? \quad\quad 0.500 \text{ mol dm}^{-3}$
  No. of moles of NaOH $= \dfrac{0.500 \times 14.6}{1000} = 0.00730$ moles *[1 mark]*

  From the equation, you know 1 mole of NaOH neutralises 1 mole of $CH_3COOH$, so if you've used 0.00730 moles NaOH you must have neutralised 0.00730 moles $CH_3COOH$ *[1 mark]*.

  Concentration of $CH_3COOH = \dfrac{0.00730 \times 1000}{25.4} = \mathbf{0.287 \ mol\,dm^{-3}}$ *[1 mark]*

**2**  First write down what you know again:
  $$CaCO_3 + H_2SO_4 \rightarrow CaSO_4 + H_2O + CO_2$$
  $0.750 \text{ g} \quad 0.250 \text{ mol dm}^{-3}$
  $M$ of $CaCO_3 = 40.1 + 12.0 + (3 \times 16.0) = 100.1 \text{ g mol}^{-1}$ *[1 mark]*
  No. of moles of $CaCO_3 = \dfrac{0.750}{100.1} = 7.49... \times 10^{-3}$ moles *[1 mark]*
  From the equation, 1 mole $CaCO_3$ reacts with 1 mole $H_2SO_4$ so, $7.49... \times 10^{-3}$ moles $CaCO_3$ reacts with $7.49... \times 10^{-3}$ moles $H_2SO_4$ *[1 mark]*.
  Volume needed is $= \dfrac{(7.49... \times 10^{-3}) \times 1000}{0.250} = \mathbf{30.0 \ cm^3}$ *[1 mark]*

**3 a)**  $Ca(OH)_2 + 2HCl \rightarrow CaCl_2 + 2H_2O$ *[1 mark]*
  **b)**  Number of moles of HCl $= \dfrac{0.250 \times 17.1}{1000}$
  $= 4.275 \times 10^{-3}$ moles *[1 mark]*
  From the equation in a), 2 moles HCl reacts with 1 mole $Ca(OH)_2$, so, $4.275 \times 10^{-3}$ moles HCl reacts with $2.1375 \times 10^{-3}$ moles $Ca(OH)_2$ *[1 mark]*.
  So concentration of $Ca(OH)_2$ solution $=$
  $\dfrac{(2.1375 \times 10^{-3}) \times 1000}{25.0} = \mathbf{0.0855 \ mol\,dm^{-3}}$ *[1 mark]*.

## Page 67 — Uncertainty and Errors

**1 a)**  The titre is calculated by subtracting the initial volume from the final volume. Each of these has an uncertainty of 0.05 cm³, so the total uncertainty is 0.1 cm³.
  percentage uncertainty $= (0.1 \div 3.1) \times 100 = \mathbf{3.23\%}$
  *[2 marks — 1 mark for correct use of percentage uncertainty formula, 1 mark for using uncertainty of 0.1 cm³]*
  **b)**  The percentage uncertainty will decrease if the titres are larger *[1 mark]*. Using a less concentrated solution will result in larger titres *[1 mark]*.

**2**  % uncertainty in pipette $= (0.06 \div 25.00) \times 100 = 0.24\%$ *[1 mark]*
  % uncertainty in titre $= (0.1 \div 19.25) \times 100 = 0.519...\%$ *[1 mark]*
  Total % uncertainty $= 0.24 + 0.519... = 0.759...\%$ *[1 mark]*
  So uncertainty of concentration $= 0.759...\%$ of 0.0770
  $= \mathbf{0.00058 \ mol\,dm^{-3}}$ $\mathbf{(5.8 \times 10^{-4} \ mol\,dm^{-3})}$ *[1 mark]*

## Page 69 — Atom Economy and Percentage Yield

**1 a)**  2 is an addition reaction *[1 mark]*
  **b)**  For reaction 1: % atom economy
  $= M_r(C_2H_5Cl) \div [M_r(C_2H_5Cl) + M_r(POCl_3) + M_r(HCl)] \times 100\%$ *[1 mark]*
  $= [(2 \times 12.0) + (5 \times 1.0) + 35.5] \div [(2 \times 12.0) + (5 \times 1.0) + 35.5 + 31.0 + 16.0 + (3 \times 35.5) + 1.0 + 35.5] \times 100\%$
  $= (64.5 \div 254.5) \times 100\% = \mathbf{25.3\%}$ *[1 mark]*
  **c)**  The atom economy is 100% because there is only one product (there are no by-products) *[1 mark]*
**2 a)**  Number of moles = mass ÷ molar mass
  Moles $PCl_3 = 0.275 \div 137.5 = 0.002$ moles
  Chlorine is in excess, so there must be 0.002 moles of product *[1 mark]*. Mass of $PCl_5 = 0.002 \times 208.5 = \mathbf{0.417 \ g}$ *[1 mark]*
  **b)**  percentage yield $= (0.198 \div 0.417) \times 100\% = \mathbf{47.5\%}$ *[1 mark]*
  **c)**  Changing reaction conditions will have no effect on atom economy *[1 mark]*. Since the equation shows that there is only one product, the atom economy will always be 100% *[1 mark]*. *Atom economy is related to the type of reaction — addition, substitution, etc. — not to the quantities of products and reactants.*

# Topic 6 — Organic Chemistry I
## Page 71 — The Basics

**1 a)**

H—C—C—C—C—OH  butan-1-ol
H—C—C—C—C—Br  1-bromobutane
  *[2 marks — 1 mark for each correct structure]*
  **b)**  It tells you that the main functional group (-OH) is attached to the first carbon in the chain *[1 mark]*. The number is necessary because the main functional group could be attached to the first or second carbon/butan-2-ol also exists *[1 mark]*.
**2 a) i)**  1-chloro-2-methylpropane *[1 mark]*
    *Remember to put the substituents in alphabetical order.*
  **ii)**  3-methylbut-1-ene *[1 mark]*
  **iii)**  2,4-dibromo-but-1-ene *[1 mark]*
  **b) i)**  $C_7H_{16}$ *[1 mark]*
  **ii)**  $CH_3CH_2CH(CH_2CH_3)CH_2CH_3$ *[1 mark]*

## Page 73 — Organic Reactions

**1**  C *[1 mark]*
**2 a)**  polymerisation *[1 mark]*
  **b)**  hydrolysis / substitution *[1 mark]*
  **c)**  substitution *[1 mark]*

## Page 75 — Isomerism

**1 a)**  B *[1 mark]*
  **b)**  Isomers that have the same molecular formula but different structural formulae *[1 mark]*.
**2 a)**

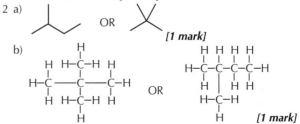
  *[1 mark]*
  **b)**

*[1 mark]*

# Answers

3 a) [ketone structure] *[1 mark]*  [aldehyde structure] *[1 mark]*

b) $CH_3COCH_3$ *[1 mark]* and $CH_3CH_2CHO$ *[1 mark]*

4  D *[1 mark]*

## Page 77 — Alkanes

1 a) Radical substitution *[1 mark]*.

b) $CH_4 + Br_2 \xrightarrow{U.V.} CH_3Br + HBr$  *[1 mark]*

c) $Br\bullet + CH_4 \rightarrow HBr + \bullet CH_3$  *[1 mark]*
$\bullet CH_3 + Br_2 \rightarrow CH_3Br + Br\bullet$  *[1 mark]*

d) i) Two methyl radicals bond together to form an ethane molecule *[1 mark]*. The equation for the reaction is:
$\bullet CH_3 + \bullet CH_3 \rightarrow CH_3CH_3$ *[1 mark]*

ii) termination step *[1 mark]*

e) tetrabromomethane *[1 mark]*

## Page 79 — Crude Oil

1 a) i) E.g. There's greater demand for smaller fractions for things such as motor fuels *[1 mark]*. / There's greater demand for alkenes to make petrochemicals/polymers *[1 mark]*.

ii) E.g. $C_{12}H_{26} \rightarrow C_2H_4 + C_{10}H_{22}$ *[1 mark]*.
There are loads of possible answers — just make sure the C's and H's balance and there's an alkane and an alkene.

b) i) Any two from: Cycloalkanes / arenes / aromatic hydrocarbons / branched alkanes *[2 marks — 1 mark for each]*

ii) They promote efficient combustion/reduce knocking (autoignition) *[1 mark]*.

## Page 81 — Fuels

1 a) $C_5H_{12} + 8O_2 \rightarrow 5CO_2 + 6H_2O$ *[2 marks — 1 mark for reactants and products correct, 1 mark for correct balancing]*

b) The products of incomplete combustion include carbon monoxide gas which is toxic *[1 mark]*. This is because it binds to haemoglobin in the blood, meaning less oxygen can be transported around the body and leading to oxygen deprivation *[1 mark]*.

2 a) Sulfur dioxide and nitrogen oxides ($NO_x$) *[1 mark]*.

b) Catalytic converters convert nitrogen oxides into harmless gases, such as nitrogen and water vapour *[1 mark]*.

3 E.g. Advantage: it's carbon neutral / can be made from waste that would otherwise go to landfill / is renewable *[1 mark]*. Disadvantage: engines would have to be converted to run off biodiesel / growing crops for biodiesel uses land that could otherwise be used to grow food *[1 mark]*.

## Page 82 — Alkenes

1 a) E.g. Both bonds form when two atomic orbitals overlap / when the nuclei of two atoms form electrostatic attractions to a bonding pair of electrons *[1 mark]*.

b) E.g. σ-bonds form when two atomic orbitals overlap directly between two nuclei, whereas π-bonds form when both lobes of two p-orbitals overlap side-on / in σ-bonds, the electron density lies directly between the two nuclei, whereas in π-bonds, the electron density lies above and below the molecular axis / σ-bonds have a higher bond enthalpy than π-bonds *[1 mark]*.

## Page 85 — Stereoisomerism

1 a) [E-pent-2-ene structure]    [Z-pent-2-ene structure]

E-pent-2-ene *[1 mark]*    Z-pent-2-ene *[1 mark]*

b) E/Z isomers occur because atoms can't rotate about C=C double bonds *[1 mark]*. Alkenes contain C=C double bonds and alkanes don't, so alkenes can form E/Z isomers and alkanes can't *[1 mark]*.

2 B *[1 mark]*

---

3 a) i) [structure] E-1-bromo-2-chloroethene *[1 mark]*

[structure] Z-1-bromo-2-chloroethene *[1 mark]*

ii) [structure] E-1-bromo-2-chloroprop-1-ene *[1 mark]*

[structure] Z-1-bromo-2-chloroprop-1-ene *[1 mark]*

b) i) 1-bromo-2-chloroethene *[1 mark]* because there is a hydrogen atom / an identical group attached to the carbons on either side of the double bond *[1 mark]*.

ii) [structure] trans-1-bromo-2-chloroethene *[1 mark]*

[structure] cis-1-bromo-2-chloroethene *[1 mark]*

## Page 87 — Reactions of Alkenes

1 a) Shake the alkene with bromine water, and the solution goes from brown to colourless if a double bond is present *[1 mark]*.

b) Electrophilic addition *[1 mark]*.
E.g. [mechanism diagram]

*[4 marks — 1 mark for correct partial charges on bromine molecule, 1 mark for correct curly arrows showing bromine attacking the C=C double bond and the Br–Br bond breaking heterolytically, 1 mark for structure of intermediate, 1 mark for curly arrow showing attack of Br⁻ on the carbocation]*
This reaction can go via a primary or a secondary carbocation. You'd get the marks for the mechanism for showing it going by either one.

c) [structures]
2-bromobutane *[1 mark]*    1-bromobutane *[1 mark]*
The major product will be 2-bromobutane *[1 mark]* since the formation of this product goes via the more stable carbocation intermediate *[1 mark]*.

## Page 89 — Polymers

1 a) [polymer structure with $C_6H_5$ and H groups] *[1 mark]*

b) [alkene structure with $C_6H_5$ and H groups] *[1 mark]*

2 a) E.g. Saves on landfill / Energy can be used to generate electricity *[1 mark]*.

b) E.g. Toxic gases produced *[1 mark]*. Scrubbers can be used to remove these toxic gases / polymers that might burn to produce toxic gases can be separated out before incineration *[1 mark]*.

# Answers

3   **A maximum of two marks can be awarded for structure and reasoning of the written response:**
   **2 marks:** The answer is constructed logically, and displays clear reasoning and links between points throughout.
   **1 mark:** The answer is mostly logical, with some reasoning and links between points.
   **0 marks:** The answer has no structure and no links between points.
   **Here are some points your answer may include:**
   Chemists could use reactant molecules that are as safe and as environmentally friendly as possible. Chemists should aim to use as few materials as possible in the manufacture process (e.g. limit the use of solvents). Chemists should aim to use renewable raw materials wherever possible. Chemists should minimise energy usage (e.g. by using catalysts) during the manufacturing process. Chemists should minimise the amount of waste products made during the process, especially those which are hazardous to human health or the environment. Polymers should be made with a lifespan that is appropriate for their use. Chemists could create biodegradable polymers which, when disposed of, are less damaging to the environment.
   *[4 marks — 4 marks if 6 points covered, 3 marks if 4-5 points covered, 2 marks if 2-3 points covered, 1 mark if 1 point covered]*

## Page 91 — Halogenoalkanes

1 a) *[1 mark]* 2-iodo-2-methylpropane *[1 mark]*
   b) AgI *[1 mark]*
   c) The tertiary alcohol with formula $C_4H_9Cl$ will be hydrolysed more slowly than 2-methyl-2-iodopropane under the same conditions *[1 mark]*. This is because C–Cl bonds are shorter so have a higher bond enthalpy that C–I bonds *[1 mark]*, and are therefore harder to break than C–I bonds *[1 mark]* (resulting in a slower rate of hydrolysis).

## Page 93 — More on Halogenoalkanes

1 a) $CH_3CHOHCH_3$ *[1 mark]*
   b) i)  ethanolic ammonia *[1 mark]*, warm *[1 mark]*
      ii) Step 1:
      *[2 marks — 1 mark for NH₃ attacking δ+ carbon, 1 mark for C–Br bond breaking]*
      Step 2:
      *[2 marks — 1 mark for correctly drawn intermediate, 1 mark for showing ammonia attacking a positive nitrogen centre]*
   c) $CH_3CHCH_2$ *[1 mark]*

## Page 95 — Alcohols

1 a) primary: e.g. pentan-1-ol *[1 mark]*
   secondary: e.g pentan-2-ol *[1 mark]*
   tertiary: 2-methylbutan-2-ol *[1 mark]*
   b) E.g. React ethanol with sodium bromide (KBr) with a 50% concentrated sulfuric acid catalyst *[1 mark]*.
2 a) Elimination reaction OR dehydration reaction *[1 mark]*.
   b) C *[1 mark]*

## Page 97 — Oxidation of Alcohols

1 a) i)   Propanoic acid ($CH_3CH_2COOH$) *[1 mark]*
      ii)  $CH_3CH_2CH_2OH + [O] \rightarrow CH_3CH_2CHO + H_2O$ *[1 mark]*
           $CH_3CH_2CHO + [O] \rightarrow CH_3CH_2COOH$ *[1 mark]*
      iii) Distillation. This is so aldehyde is removed immediately as it forms *[1 mark]*.
      *If you don't get the aldehyde out quick-smart, it'll be a carboxylic acid before you know it.*
   b) i) *[1 mark]*
      ii) 2-methylpropan-2-ol is a tertiary alcohol *[1 mark]*.
2   D *[1 mark]*
3   React 2-methylpropan-1-ol ($CH_3CH(CH_3)CH_2OH$) *[1 mark]* with a controlled amount of acidified potassium dichromate(VI) and heat gently in distillation apparatus to distil off the aldehyde *[1 mark]*.

## Page 99 — Organic Techniques

1 a) i)   Reflux is continuous boiling/evaporation and condensation *[1 mark]*. It's done to prevent loss of volatile liquids while heating *[1 mark]*.
      ii)  Unreacted hexan-1-ol *[1 mark]*
      iii) Pour the reaction mixture into a separating funnel and add water *[1 mark]*. Shake the funnel and allow the layers to settle *[1 mark]*. To separate the layers, open the tap to run the lower layer out of the separating funnel into a container. Then, collect the upper layer in a separate container *[1 mark]*.
   b) i)  The alkene product may dehydrate again to form a diene *[1 mark]*.
      ii) Carry out the experiment in a distillation apparatus *[1 mark]* so the singly dehydrated product is removed immediately from the reaction mixture and doesn't react a second time *[1 mark]*.

ANSWERS

# Answers

## Topic 7 — Modern Analytical Techniques I

### Page 101 — Mass Spectrometry

1 a) 44 *[1 mark]*
   b) X has a mass of 15. It is probably a methyl group/$CH_3^+$ *[1 mark]*.
      Y has a mass of 29. It is probably an ethyl group/$C_2H_5^+$ *[1 mark]*.
   c)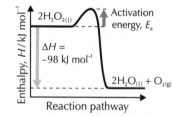
   d) If the compound was an alcohol, you would expect a peak with
      $m/z$ ratio of 17, caused by the OH fragment *[1 mark]*.

2 a) 56 *[1 mark]*
   b) $CH_3CHCH^+$ *[1 mark]*
   c) E.g. $m/z$ = 15 *[1 mark]*, $CH_3^+$ *[1 mark]* or
      $m/z$ = 28 *[1 mark]*, $CH_3CH^+$ *[1 mark]*.

3

H H OH
| | |
H—C—C—C—H
| | |
H H H     *[1 mark]*, propan-1-ol *[1 mark]*

The mass spectrum could be for one of 2 isomers — propan-1-ol
or propan-2-ol. The spectrum of propan-1-ol would produce a
peak at $m/z$ = 31, due to the fragment $CH_2OH^+$ *[1 mark]*. This
would be absent from the spectrum of propan-2-ol *[1 mark]*
(therefore the unknown alcohol is propan-1-ol).

### Page 103 — Infrared Spectroscopy

1 a) A *[1 mark]*
   b) There is a broad peak in the region of 3300-2500 $cm^{-1}$,
      corresponding to an O–H stretch in a carboxylic acid *[1 mark]*.
      There is also a strong peak in the region of 1725-1700 $cm^{-1}$,
      corresponding to a C=O stretch in a carboxylic acid *[1 mark]*.

2 a) A: O–H group in a carboxylic acid *[1 mark]*.
      B: C=O as in an aldehyde, ketone or carboxylic acid *[1 mark]*.
   b) The spectrum suggests that the compound is a carboxylic acid, so
      it must be propanoic acid *[1 mark]* ($CH_3CH_2COOH$) *[1 mark]*.

## Topic 8 — Energetics I

### Page 105 — Enthalpy Changes

1

*[1 mark for having reactants lower in energy than products.
1 mark for labelling activation energy correctly. 1 mark for
labelling ΔH correctly, with arrow pointing downwards]*
For an exothermic reaction, the ΔH arrow points downwards, but for an
endothermic reaction it points upwards. The activation energy arrow always
points upwards though.

2 a) $CH_3OH_{(l)} + 1\frac{1}{2}O_{2(g)} \rightarrow CO_{2(g)} + 2H_2O_{(l)}$ *[1 mark]*
      Make sure that only 1 mole of $CH_3OH$ is combusted, as it says in the
      definition for $\Delta_cH^\circ$.
   b) $C_{(s)} + 2H_{2(g)} + \frac{1}{2}O_{2(g)} \rightarrow CH_3OH_{(l)}$ *[1 mark]*
   c) Only 1 mole of $C_3H_8$ should be shown according to the definition
      of $\Delta_cH^\circ$ *[1 mark]*.
      You really need to know the definitions of the standard enthalpy changes off
      by heart. There are loads of nit-picky little details they could ask you
      questions about.

3 a) $C_{(s)} + O_{2(g)} \rightarrow CO_{2(g)}$ *[1 mark]*
   b) It has the same value because it is the same reaction *[1 mark]*.
   c) 1 tonne = 1 000 000 g
      1 mole of carbon is 12.0 g
      so 1 tonne is 1 000 000 ÷ 12.0 = 83 333... moles *[1 mark]*
      1 mole releases 393.5 kJ
      so 1 tonne will release 83 333... × 393.5 = **32 800 000 kJ**
      ($32.8 \times 10^7$ kJ) *[1 mark]*
      The final answer is rounded to 3 significant figures because the number with
      the fewest significant figures in the whole calculation is 12.O.

### Page 107 — More on Enthalpy Changes

1 $\Delta T = 25.8 - 19.0 = 6.80\ °C = 6.80\ K$
   $m = 25.0 + 25.0 = 50.0\ cm^3$ of solution,
   which has a mass of 50.0 g.
   Assume density to be 1.OO $g\ cm^{-3}$.
   Heat produced by reaction = $mc\Delta T$
   $= 50.0 \times 4.18 \times 6.80 = 1421.2\ J$ *[1 mark]*
   No. of moles of HCl = $1 \times (25.0 \div 1000) = 0.0250$
   No. of moles of NaOH = $1 \times (25.0 \div 1000) = 0.0250$
   Therefore, no. of moles of water = 0.0250 *[1 mark]*
   Producing 0.0250 mol of water takes 1421.2 J of heat, therefore
   producing 1 mol of water takes 1421.2 ÷ 0.0250 = 56 848 J
   $\approx 56.8\ kJ$ (3 s.f.)
   So the enthalpy change is **–56.8 kJ mol⁻¹** *[1 mark]*
   You need the minus sign because it's exothermic.

2 No. of moles of $CuSO_4 = 0.200 \times (50.0 \div 1000) = 0.0100$ mol
   From the equation, 1 mole of $CuSO_4$ reacts with 1 mole of Zn.
   So, 0.0100 mol of $CuSO_4$ reacts with 0.0100 mol of Zn *[1 mark]*.
   Heat produced by reaction = $mc\Delta T$
   $= 50.0 \times 4.18 \times 2.00 = 418\ J$ *[1 mark]*
   0.0100 mol of zinc produces 418 J of heat, therefore 1 mol of
   zinc produces 418 ÷ 0.0100 = 41 800 J = 41.8 kJ
   So the enthalpy change is **–41.8 kJ mol⁻¹** *[1 mark]*.
   You need the minus sign because it's exothermic.
   It'd be dead easy to work out the heat produced by the reaction, breathe
   a sigh of relief and sail on to the next question. But you need to find out
   the enthalpy change when 1 mole of zinc reacts. It's always a good idea to
   reread the question and check you've actually answered it.

### Page 109 — Hess's Law

1 $\Delta_rH^\circ$ = sum of $\Delta_fH^\circ$(products) – sum of $\Delta_fH^\circ$(reactants)
   *[1 mark]*
   $\Delta_rH^\circ = [0 + (3 \times -602)] - [-1676 + 0]$
   $\Delta_rH^\circ = $ **–130 kJ mol⁻¹** *[1 mark]*
   Don't forget the units. It's a daft way to lose marks.

2 $\Delta_fH^\circ = \Delta_cH^\circ$(glucose) – $2 \times \Delta_cH^\circ$(ethanol) *[1 mark]*
   $\Delta_fH^\circ = [-2820] - [(2 \times -1367)]$
   $\Delta_fH^\circ = $ **–86 kJ mol⁻¹** *[1 mark]*

### Page 111 — Bond Enthalpy

1 Sum of bond enthalpies of reactants = $(4 \times 435) + (2 \times 498)$
   $= 2736\ kJ\ mol^{-1}$
   Sum of bond enthalpies of products = $(2 \times 805) + (4 \times 464)$
   $= 3466\ kJ\ mol^{-1}$ *[1 mark]*
   Enthalpy change of reaction = 2736 + (–3466)
   $= $ **–730 kJ mol⁻¹** *[1 mark]*

2 Sum of bond enthalpies of reactants = $(\frac{1}{2} \times 498) + 436$
   $= 685\ kJ\ mol^{-1}$
   Sum of bond enthalpies of products = $(2 \times 460)$
   $= 920\ kJ\ mol^{-1}$
   Enthalpy change of formation = 685 – 920
   $= $ **–235 kJ mol⁻¹** *[1 mark]*

# Answers

3 a) Sum of bond enthalpies of reactants = (4 × 435) + 243
 = 1983 kJ mol⁻¹
 Sum of bond enthalpies of products = (3 × 397) + 432 + $E$(C–Cl)
 = 1623 + $E$(C–Cl) kJ mol⁻¹ *[1 mark]*
 –101 = 1983 – (1623 + $E$(C–Cl))
 $E$(C–Cl) = 1983 – 1623 + 101 = **461 kJ mol⁻¹** *[1 mark]*
 b) The values differ because the data book value of C–Cl is an
 average of C–Cl bond energies in many molecules, while
 461 kJ mol⁻¹ is the C–Cl bond energy in chloromethane *[1 mark]*.

## *Topic 9 — Kinetics I*

### *Page 113 — Collision Theory*

1 Increasing the pressure will increase the rate of reaction *[1 mark]*
 because there will be more particles in a given volume, so they
 will collide more frequently and therefore are more likely to react
 *[1 mark]*.
2 The particles in a liquid move freely and all of them are able
 to collide with the solid particles *[1 mark]*. Particles in solids
 just vibrate about fixed positions, so only those on the touching
 surfaces between the two solids will be able to react *[1 mark]*.
3 a) X *[1 mark]*
 The X curve shows the same total number of molecules as the 25 °C
 curve, but more of them have lower energy.
 b) The shape of the curve shows fewer molecules have the required
 activation energy *[1 mark]*.

### *Page 115 — Reaction Rates*

1 E.g.

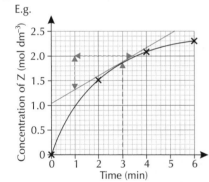

*[1 mark for tangent drawn at 3 mins]*
rate of reaction = gradient of tangent at 3 mins
gradient = change in $y$ ÷ change in $x$
e.g. = (2.0 – 1.3) ÷ (3.4 – 1.0)
 = **0.29 (± 0.06) mol dm⁻³ min⁻¹**
*[1 mark for answer within margin of error. 1 mark for units]*
Different people will draw slightly different tangents and pick different spots
on the tangent so there's a margin of error in this answer.
0.29 (± 0.06) mol dm⁻³ min⁻¹ means any answer between
0.35 mol dm⁻³ min⁻¹ and 0.23 mol dm⁻³ min⁻¹ is worth the mark.

### *Page 117 — Catalysts*

1 a) A *[1 mark]*
 A catalyst only lowers activation energy. It doesn't affect the enthalpy
 change.
 b) The catalyst lowers the activation energy *[1 mark]*, meaning
 there are more particles with enough energy to react when
 they collide *[1 mark]*. So, in a certain amount of time, more
 particles react *[1 mark]*.
 c) The vanadium(V) oxide catalyst is heterogenous because it's in
 a different physical state to the reactants *[1 mark]*.

## *Topic 10 — Equilibrium I*

### *Page 119 — Dynamic Equilibrium*

1 a) At dynamic equilibrium, the rate of the forwards and backwards
 reactions are the same *[1 mark]* and the concentrations of the
 reactants and the products are constant *[1 mark]*.
 b) $K_c = \dfrac{[NH_3]^2}{[N_2][H_2]^3}$ *[1 mark]*
2 The reaction is heterogeneous so pure liquids / water should
 be excluded from the expression *[1 mark]*. The reactants and
 products are also the wrong way round / the reactants should be
 on the bottom of the expression and the products should be on
 the top *[1 mark]*.
3 B *[1 mark]*

### *Page 121 — Le Chatelier's Principle*

1 a) i) There's no change as there's the same number of molecules/
 moles of gas on each side of the equation *[1 mark]*.
 ii) Reducing temperature removes heat. The equilibrium
 shifts in the exothermic direction to release heat, so the
 position of equilibrium shifts left *[1 mark]*.
 iii) Removing nitrogen monoxide reduces its concentration.
 The equilibrium position shifts right to try and increase the
 nitrogen monoxide concentration again *[1 mark]*.
2 For an exothermic reaction, a low temperature means a high yield
 *[1 mark]*. But a low temperature also means a slow reaction rate,
 so moderate temperatures are chosen as a compromise *[1 mark]*.

## *Practical Skills*

### *Page 123 — Planning Experiments*

1 Using litmus paper is not a particularly accurate method of
 measuring pH / not very sensitive equipment *[1 mark]*. It would
 be better to use a pH meter *[1 mark]*.

### *Page 125 — Practical Techniques*

1 a) The student measured the level of the liquid from the top of the
 meniscus, when he should have measured it from the bottom
 *[1 mark]*.
 b) B *[1 mark]*.

### *Page 127 — Presenting Results*

1 a) mean volume = $\dfrac{7.30 + 7.25 + 7.25}{3}$ = 7.26666... cm³
 = **0.00727 dm³ or 7.27 × 10⁻³ dm³** (3 s.f.) *[1 mark]*
 b) 0.50 ÷ 1000 = **0.00050 mol cm⁻³ or 5.0 × 10⁻⁴ mol cm⁻³**
 *[1 mark]*

### *Page 129 — Analysing Results*

1 a) 15 °C and 25 °C *[1 mark]*.
 b) Positive correlation *[1 mark]*.
 c) C *[1 mark]*

### *Page 131 — Evaluating Experiments*

1 a) The volumetric flask reads to the nearest 0.5 cm³, so the
 uncertainty is ±0.25 cm³.
 percentage error = $\dfrac{uncertainty}{reading} \times 100 = \dfrac{0.25}{25} \times 100$ = **1.0 %** *[1 mark]*
 b) E.g. The student should add the thermometer to the citric acid
 solution and allow it to stabilise before adding the sodium
 bicarbonate to give an accurate value for the initial temperature
 *[1 mark]*. The student should then measure the temperature
 change until the solution stops reacting to give a valid result for
 the temperature change of the entire reaction *[1 mark]*.

# Index